N.W. Bishop

INK

ON

PAPER

INK
ON
PAPER

A HANDBOOK OF THE GRAPHIC ARTS

Edmund C. Arnold

Chairman, Graphic Arts Department
School of Journalism, Syracuse University
and
Editor, *Linotype News*

HARPER & ROW, PUBLISHERS
NEW YORK AND EVANSTON

To Francis R. VanAllen and Mattie Gay Crump,

who first exposed me to printer's ink—

from which, fortunately, I never recovered.

Contents

1 WRITTEN LANGUAGE, The Commonplace Miracle   1

2 THE LATIN ALPHABET, Our Most Valuable Tool   9

3 PRINTING TYPES, Form Follows the Tool   20

4 PRINTERS' TERMS, The Jargon of the Craft   31

5 SETTING TYPE, Composition by Man and Machine   42

6 COPYFITTING, Equalizing Type and Space   65

7 PROOFREADING, To Err Is Human   74

8 LAYOUT, Patterns to Please the Reading Eye   89

9 BASIC LAYOUTS, Books and Letterheads   129

10 LETTERPRESS, The Classic Printing Method   143

11 PRINTING PLATES, Putting Pictures on Paper   154

12 COLOR, Communicating by the Spectrum   192

13 COLOR PRINTING, The Rainbow on the Page   200

14 INTAGLIO, Legacy from the Armorer   212

15 OFFSET LITHOGRAPHY, Oil and Water Don't Mix   218

16 THE FINE ARTS, The Craftsman as an Artist   228

17 COLD TYPE, Setting Type Photographically   237

18 PAPER, The Wrapping of Culture   246

19 INK, The Lifeblood of Printing   258

20 THE BINDERY, Packaging the Written Word   263

21 PLANNING PRINTING, Economics and the Budget   277

GLOSSARY   290

INDEX   315

INK

ON

PAPER

Written Language

THE COMMONPLACE MIRACLE

The level and life of civilizations depend on how easily and permanently they can duplicate written messages.

Man made a tremendous stride when he developed a spoken language. Although gestures could convey much information and emotion —warnings, defiance, directions, and commendation—manual conversation ended at darkness or when communicators were out of sight.

Spoken language extended communication and made it more precise. Still, perpetuation of knowledge depended on memory; dissemination was confined to earshot. Besides, words change meanings; spoken language can become gibberish in a few generations.

Written language was the only solution to these problems and man began writing in many ways. Twigs broken to form pointers were "writing." So were blazes on tree trunks. Cave men painted pictures on the walls of their shelters to communicate as much as to decorate. Warriors decorated shields to record history as well as to intimidate opponents.

But twigs and trunks became humus; men followed their herds away from caves; shields were hacked or captured. The writing was not permanent enough. Worse, it was less precise than spoken words; only broad ideas could be thus recorded. Such "writing" was far more *mnemonic*—a crutch for memory—than definitive.

1

When man finally found precision and permanence for his languag
he recognized a man-made miracle. *Devanagari*—the name of the San
skrit alphabet—means "pertaining to the city of the gods." That mo
permanent of Egyptian writing—*hieroglyphics*—was "sacred stone wri
ing." Cultures from Mayan to Assyrian called their writing a gift (
the gods.

Men tried many tools and materials for writing. A sharp stick an
a smooth beach could hold a message until the next tide or tempest;
sharp stick and a tablet of wax lasted far longer. A broad tropical lea
held a scratched message for days; a clay brick, "written" on with im
pressing wedges, has lasted for six thousand years.

Man wrote on birchbark, shells, hides, and papyrus. He wrote with
juices of berries, trees, sea creatures, and even himself, his blood. But
no writing was easier—or much more permanent—than that of ink on
paper.

Printing is a form of writing that lubricates all the wheels of modern
living. Plenitude of printing is the hallmark of advanced civilization.
It is one of the major ways in which such civilization came about.

Development of a written language brought demands for extra
copies; "scribes" are mentioned in the earliest records, and much of
their work was copying. When a pharaoh promulgated a decree,
instead of circulating a single letter through the provinces, he had
duplicates made for simultaneous distribution. The man who had written down axioms of a religious leader wanted a copy for each of his
sons. Missionaries wanted to pass sacred words quickly to many
peoples and regions.

When time and labor were cheap, a platoon of scribes could be assigned to making copies. Religious men devoted their lives to copying
and recopying the Bible and theological works. But even with that low
overhead, books were priced only within the range of the rich.

The hunger for permanence of knowledge that spurred development
of written language prodded the search for easy, inexpensive methods
to make stored knowledge and new discoveries available to many men
at once. The Renaissance was a natural corollary of the invention of
printing as we know it today.

Printing had its origins in the Orient. As early as A.D. 770, Empress
Shotoku of Japan, a devout Buddhist, had a million prayer-charms
printed from wood blocks.

By A.D. 950 the first paper money was being printed in the Szechuen

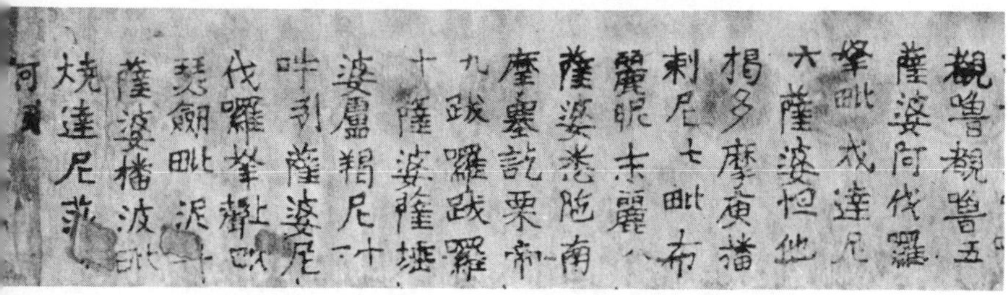

Fig. 1. World's oldest printed matter is this Buddhist prayer-charm printed in Japan in 770. From collection of, and through courtesy of, Dr. Richard C. Rudolph, chairman of Oriental languages department, University of California at Los Angeles.

province of China (and the earliest known counterfeiting was recorded here in A.D. 1068). This useful art—printing, not counterfeiting—migrated to Europe, probably via the ubiquitous Marco Polo. At least wood-block printing was known on the Continent shortly after his return from the East.

But it awaited Johann Gensfleisch Gutenberg to launch the modern craft of printing with his invention of movable type, about A.D. 1450. Although no one had enough sense of history to keep precise records of this milestone, even the ignorant peasantry sensed that here was an awesome power. The association with the supernatural that ancient cultures had ascribed to their writing was immediately accorded to the new art of printing. Instead of linking it with benevolent deities, however, the public believed that printers had acquired their profound power from Satanic sources. Even the ink-stained apprentice boy was called *the printer's devil.*

If printing was not black magic, it certainly spread like it. In less than a generation the new craft had blanketed Europe—recorded dates for printing include: Germany, no later than 1454; Italy, 1465; Switzerland, 1468; France, two years later; Holland, 1473; Austria-Hungary, that same year; Spain, 1474; England, 1476; Denmark, 1482; Sweden, a year later and Portugal, 1487.

The first printing press in North America was operated by Spaniards in Mexico City, almost a century before the Pilgrims disembarked at Plymouth Rock.

There is evidence suggesting that a Dutchman named Coster printed from movable type before Gutenberg did. This controversy waxes as hot as the one concerning Shakespeare *vs.* Bacon, or Columbus and Leif

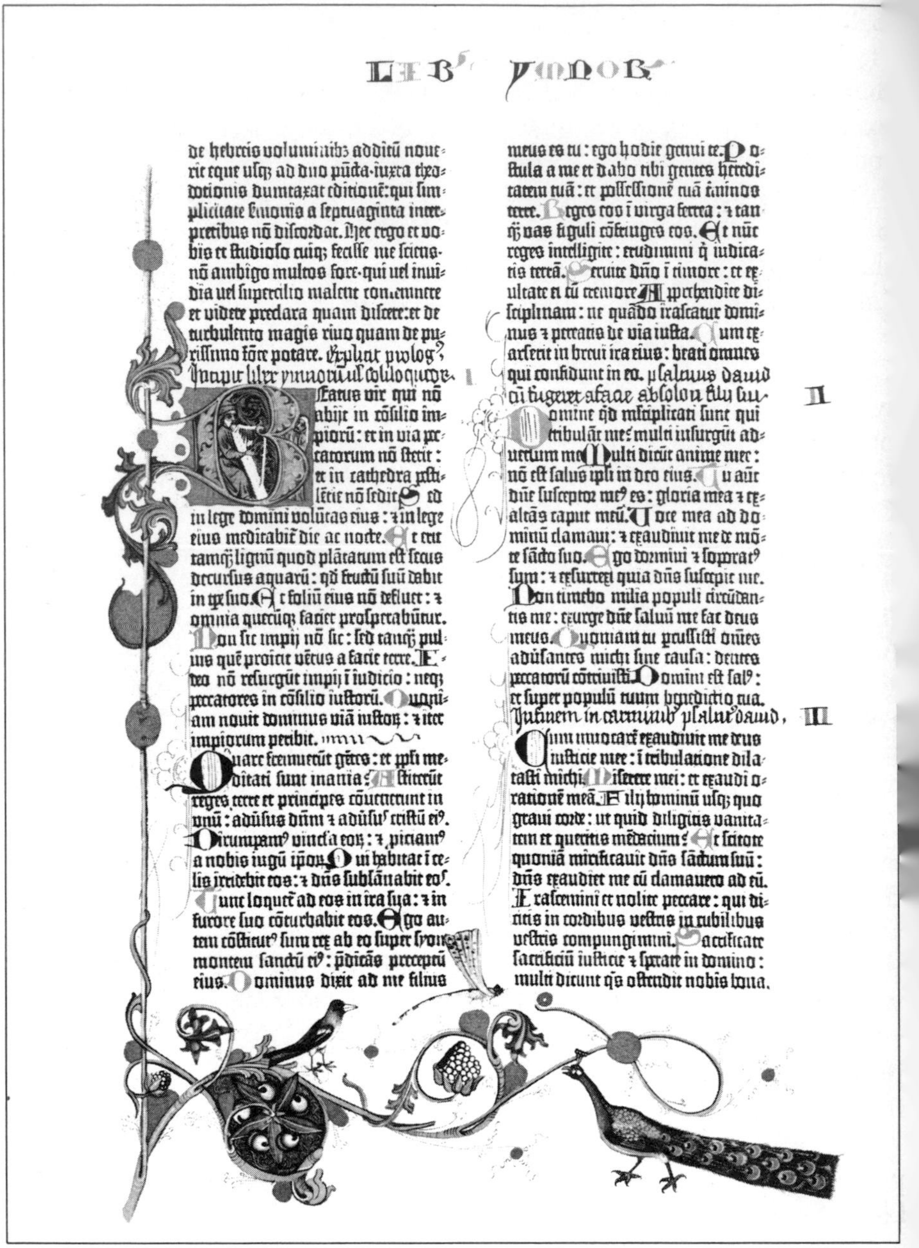

Fig. 2. Page from Gutenberg Bible. Initials were done by hand in colored inks. Decorations are brilliant, enlivened by gold leaf.

Ericson. But history books are rarely rewritten, even less so popular belief. No matter what Coster did, Gutenberg deserves the title of "father of modern printing" because he was the first to replace the manuscript with the printed book. Whether or not he drew upon earlier experiments really does not matter; his invention is the one we still use today with surprisingly little improvement or change.

To mark again the close tie between printing and religion, the first products of Gutenberg's press were for the Church. Either a hymnal, the Mainz Psalter, or the famed 42-line Gutenberg Bible was the first "modern printing"; the Bible remains the most-often printed work.

Men of the cloth used printing as a most effective tool to propagate Christianity. As they spread the Gospel, they dispelled illiteracy. Men who read become educated, and educated men seek freedom. So the printing press has always been a weapon for liberty; our own Colonial forebears rallied the land by means of pamphlets and debated its new Constitution through printed pages.

Handsome as Gutenberg's Bible was, and is—its paper is as white and its ink as black as the day they first married—he felt the need to embellish it. Painstakingly, artists drew in initials and ornamented them with brilliant miniature paintings.

The same artistry was demanded of men who cut punches for making type molds. Later craftsmen engraved delicate metal plates for printing illustrations and decorations right along with the type.

Other artists hand-tooled gorgeous bindings for printed books.

Today whole schools of fine artists devote most of their talents to creating work for presses to reproduce, in books, in magazines, in all the myriad forms of advertising.

Photoengravers developed a new craft to supply voracious presses; the growth of photography itself has been greatest since it allied itself with printing.

Artists found a new medium as they arranged type in esthetically pleasing patterns. Administrators found need for their talent in specifying how type should be set and the business of printing conducted.

Typesetters and pressmen are among the oldest race of craftsmen; probably only carpenters can trace their vocational ancestry back as far and unchanged.

At hundreds of jobs "people with ink on their fingers" make up that vast complex of activity we call "the graphic arts."

The graphic arts are all the skills, talents, and experience required to make permanent and multiple records of written communication

The stonecarver who "wrote" panegyrics to the Ptolemies was not a graphic artsman; he made only one "copy." The lad who indites his affection for a young female may repeat the same phrase on my sidewall as he did on the side of your garage. But he fails to qualify; his message, like his emotion, is not permanent.

But there are thousands upon thousands who can claim ink on their fingers. For graphic arts is a most important segment of a developed economy.

According to 1959 figures, total annual sales volume for the "printing and publishing industry" was $11.4 billion, making it the eighth largest industry in the United States. It had 853,300 employees in 40,200 companies. But this does not accurately report the grand total of the graphic arts. Many small, often one-man, businesses are not included, and countless people whose work is totally or in part in the graphic arts are listed under other Census Bureau categories; so is their product.

Many employees of supplying firms, such as papermakers, machinery manufacturers and ink makers—not to mention the huge photography industry—must be considered as graphic arts personnel.

The United States Department of Labor predicts that the printing and publishing industry—and hence its suppliers, too—will enjoy continued growth "as a result of population growth and the expansion of the American economy as well as the tendency toward relatively greater use of printed material for information, advertising and various industrial and commercial purposes."

Bound so loosely, many members of the clan do not even recognize their kinship. Men who make paper, mix ink, edit books, design business forms, draw cartoons, remelt stereotype plates, shoot pictures, or type mimeograph stencils are all professionals in the graphic arts.

Amateurs are even more numerous: housewives who are tapped to produce the membership roster for their Ladies Aid Society; men who order printing of company letterheads or tickets for their lodge's annual dinner dance; farmers who write copy for auction sale handbills; families who design or color or fold or even print their Christmas greetings; hobbyists who operate a basement hand press; Sunday artists who make etchings or dry points.

This book is written for everyone who works for—or is served by—printing presses. No single book can cover this vast field in depth.

Fig. 3. Ancient printing press. Form is being inked by balls as printed sheet is removed. Typesetters in background.

Daniel B. Updike, for instance, wrote two volumes, containing 611 pages, on printing types alone—and there has been a whole generation of type designers since them.

This book might be subtitled "Printing for Non-Printers." Yet "printers" might find something interesting—and even useful—in these pages. The pressman might learn to advantage from the problems of the engraver. The compositor may delight in the affinity of his craft to that of the glamour photographer.

Primarily, this book is directed to those removed, even if only by a thin partition, from the actual mechanics of printing: executives who plan and purchase printing for business; newspapermen who dummy editions for the composing room; artists who prepare copy for the engraver—slapstick cartoons, technical diagrams, or oils for magazine covers. It is for the amateur: book collectors, Cub Scout publicity chairmen, or vestrymen who plan a scroll for their pastor's testimonial dinner.

Most of all, it is for the young people from whom graphic arts must replenish and expand talents and skills. In an economy that lives on paper and ink, such expansion is almost without limit. Graphic arts can offer careers with monetary attraction, but they also provide other satisfactions far more rewarding.

The graphic artsman knows the thrill of creation. Here is a career that electric brains and vacuum tubes can never threaten; creativity is still man's monopoly.

The graphic artsman knows the deep satisfaction of discipline. Part of this is inherent in the rigidity of the metal with which he eventuall works. That "type isn't made of rubber" is an early lesson; but he feel no more constriction from type that can be neither stretched no squeezed than the poet does from the inflexible fourteen lines of sonnet.

The graphic artsman learns the value of time. Deadlines are sterr taskmasters; they are judicially constant.

The final satisfaction is the realization that the graphic artsman i: making a substantial and permanent contribution to his society. Al though he must sometimes use his talents to sell uplift bras, no one car deny that by advertising automatic washers and electric ovens he ha: helped to extend and enhance the life span of women freed from drudgery. Although he sometimes draws the improbable characters in a comic book, he also illustrates the exciting texts from which our children learn much more about our world than their parents did at a comparable age.

Granted that our press gives forum to demagogues, it also preserves our freedom by alerting the citizenry in time for defenses to be raised against encroachments and educates the people so that grave decisions can be made from knowledge instead of prejudice.

And the graphic arts, today as from their inception, are the evangelists for all our religions.

Printing is called "the art preservative of all arts." Whether it be the fading *Last Supper* of Leonardo da Vinci, the oratory of Churchill, the Beatitudes, or $E = mc^2$, every art and every knowledge of mankind, whether already venerated or still gestating in someone's mind, will be preserved by the printer and graphic artsman.

The world of graphic arts is an exciting one, a world given genuine affection from those who labor in it. Many supplementary readings are suggested in these pages, which serve to flesh out the broad strokes of this single volume and enable detailed study of any aspect that most concerns the reader. In each of these suggested books there is one common characteristic: The author truly loves his work.

SUGGESTED READINGS

Laird, Charlton. *The Miracle of Language.* Cleveland, Ohio: The World Publishing Company, 1953.
Pei, Mario. *The Story of Language.* Philadelphia: J. B. Lippincott Co., 1949.

2

The Latin Alphabet

OUR MOST VALUABLE TOOL

If printing began in China, at least 800 years before it came to Europe, and if the Koreans cast bronze type as early as A.D. 1403, why did Western civilization forge ahead of these nations whose culture was well developed when our Anglo-Saxon ancestors were still adorning themselves with blue paint?

The answer is: the Latin alphabet.

Requisites for a good written language are permanence and convenience. China's and Korea's, though permanent as those of the West, are nowhere near as convenient. Even a hasty survey illustrates the flexibility and convenience of our alphabet over that of Oriental *ideograms.*

Man's oldest known "writing" was by the Reindeer Men, between 35,000 and 15,000 B.C., pictures they drew on the walls of deep caves in France and Spain. These could be classified as simple declarative sentences: "This is a mammoth." Then pictures became more explanatory, tribesmen stalking the quarry, making the kill, feasting on the trophy. For people familiar with the subject matter, such picture stories were quite complete communications, just as a series of sketches might narrate a baseball game to a knowledgeable fan.

Later, the writer found that he need not draw a complete picture; he could simplify an object into a symbol just as recognizable to the

9

"reader." See how much more easily he could write "man" with the symbol *b* than with the picture *a:*

American Indians, Chinese, Egyptians, Scandinavians, and northern Europeans all created simplified pictures combined into lucid messages: *symbol writing*.

But language must include abstract as well as concrete concepts. It is easy to picture *Man kills caribou;* how do we write *Man loves freedom?*

At first, man wrote abstract terms by combining existing symbols for the concrete. The symbol of a tangible *sun* with seven little marks under it became the intangible *week*. A charming symbol was made by combining the sign for *woman* with that for *son* to designate *love*.

Writing progressed to a device familiar to our children: the *rebus*.

We can take a series of pictures and put them together like this:

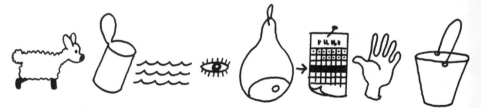

As picture writing this is gibberish. But when we name the objects aloud, we have "read" a sentence: *You can see I am weak and pale.* (Puns, such as those on *ham* and *hand*, were common in the earliest rebuses.)

When man discovered this method, he made a huge leap toward the ideal written language. He was learning that if there is a method of writing sounds it is possible to combine sound-pictures into words just as spoken sounds are combined. The *can* and *ewe* of our rebus can combine into *canoe*.

The step now was to convert the rebus pictures into sound-symbols; it is easier to write *I* than to draw a picture of an eye.

Logical as this step is, it took generations and centuries for man to accomplish it.

a)
picture

(b)
symbol
(hieroglyphic)

transition

(hieratic)

Fig. 4. Transition from realistic picture to written symbol.

There is no definite time to which we can point and say, "Here our alphabet came into being." Most of its history is deductive and thus open to rebuttal. But to find the origin of the alphabet becomes a fascinating detective story with clues abounding.

We know our alphabet came from the shores of the Mediterranean and is an amalgam of many systems that developed simultaneously and probably quite independently.

The Egyptians had gone through all the steps. In that process, a realistic picture of a leaf, Figure 4, (a) was simplified into a symbol (b) and became the sign for the *l* sound. But the Egyptians never completed a sufficiently workable alphabet, though they made substantial contributions to our system of writing.

The closest we can come to the actual beginning of our alphabet is a tiny country, Phoenicia, now part of Syria. Phoenicians were traders, too busy at commerce to produce literature or art. But they did produce an alphabet, purely as a business tool. They needed a system for keeping ledgers and writing business messages with a minimum of fuss or bother. Engrossed with profit and loss statements, they had neither the time nor the artistic yearnings to produce the beautiful drawings that made the Egyptian written language. Phoenicians stripped sound pictures of everything extraneous so that they could write rapidly.

Undoubtedly, the Phoenicians started with pictures. It seems reasonable to assume that the butcher drew a picture of an ox in his ledger, like this:

Later, because businessmen are always pressed for time, he simplified that drawing into:

Eventually this symbol came to represent, not an ox, but a sound.
We still use the same symbol (although turned around 180 degrees)
for the very same sound.

The Phoenician word for ox was *aleph*. This was later translated into
the Greek *alpha* and remains in our language as two-thirds of *alphabet*.
The other third is from a picture of a house, *beth*, simplified into our *B*.

All the characters in this early alphabet were simplified drawings of
common objects as Figure 5 indicates.

The Phoenicians developed 19 such letters. Many came from Egypt,
some undoubtedly from farther east where the Assyrians, Babylonians,
and Hittites were developing their *cuneiform* writing about the same
time, pressing small wedges into clay tablets. Although they never advanced beyond the ideogram stage, they probably showed the Phoenicians how to simplify symbols to the bone.

It is interesting to note that two Phoenician alphabets developed at
the same time—and only 20 miles apart. Tyre and Sidon, cities of Biblical fame, each created its own collection of symbols, although both
clearly sprang from a common origin and shared many individual
letters.

Between Tyre, the greatest commercial city of its era, and Mycene
and Tiryns, brightest cities in the splendid peninsula of Greece, trade
was lively. The Greeks, aflame with intellectual curiosity, saw in the
Phoenicians' alphabet a useful tool for preserving the knowledge they
sought so eagerly and respected so highly. By the ninth century B.C.
the Greeks had taken the Phoenician alphabet—then about 300 years
old—and transformed it into their own.

Total transformation took hundreds of years. By 403 B.C. the Greek
alphabet had been polished up and was officially adopted by Athens.
Letters had crystallized into definite, unchanging forms.

That was a major contribution of the Greeks. Until that time, there
was as much variation in letter forms as there is in individual hand-

Pictures into Sounds

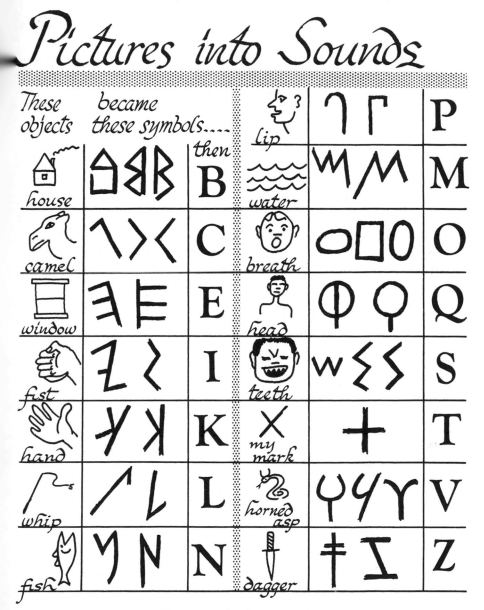

Fig. 5. All letters used today were once pictures.

writing today; even more, for you and I, no matter how scrawling our handwriting, have a common, accepted form upon which to base our script.

Contributing to the rugged individualism of early letter forms was the casual way in which the early scribes wrote. Some wrote left-to-right, as we do now; others wrote right-to-left; some wrote up and down. Still others wrote both ways, changing direction at the start of each new line, like this:

THIS IS THE WAY THE
ƎH ИƎHW ꙅИЯUT XO
PLOWS A FIELD.

This system was called *boustrophedon*—"ox-turning," the way an ox turns as it plows a field. Boustrophedon didn't do anything to an *M, O,* or *W* but it created two forms of *R, B,* and all non-symmetrical letters. About 600 B.C. the ox no longer turned; by common agreement Greek writing was now done left-to-right.

Greeks also contributed vowels. Like present-day Hebrew and Arabic, the Phoenician alphabet consisted only of consonants. (We still do that with abbreviations such as *bldg.* and *St.*) In a simple language, the reader could easily decide which vowel was needed; as vocabulary grew, confusion was compounded. *Fr* could mean *for, four,* or *far.* Many scholars believe that major discrepancies in the Bible may have sprung from the freedom permitted the translator from ancient Hebrew when he was forced to insert vowels. *Written in our alphabet, this is a simple sentence.* Without vowels, it would be: *Wrttn n r lphbt, ths s smpl sntnc.* If not dangerously confusing, it is hardly conducive to unmistakable and rapid reading.

The Greeks took several Phoenician consonants for which they had no need and converted them into vowels, then added several of their own. Eventually many characters were dropped as unnecessary and the Greek alphabet solidified at 24 letters.

Although these letters look just like the ones that the Greeks still use today (Plato and Aristotle could read today's *Athens Daily Acropolis*) there are a few striking differences. Old letters were all capitals; there were no paragraphs; there was no punctuation—as a matter of fact, there was no space between words.

ALLTHESEAIDSTOSWIFTANDEASYREADINGWEREYET
TOBEDEVELOPEDANDFORMOSTOFTHEMWEAREINDEBTED
TOTHEROMANS.

The Romans and the Greeks were developing our modern alphabet simultaneously.

The first kings of Rome were Etruscans. Their country, Etruria—north of Rome—had borrowed the Greek alphabet only about a century after the Greeks had helped themselves to Phoenicia's.

Long before the wolf boys founded Rome, Greece had built magnificent colony-cities on the toe of the Italian boot. So, by the time Rome grew into a state, it was surrounded by users of the Greek alphabet. Romans never wasted much time creating anything they could take; now they simply took the Greek alphabet and subjected it to the same refining and expansion given to the Phoenician alphabet by Athens.

Half our present Latin alphabet moved unchanged from Greek: A, B, E, Z, H, I, K, M, N, O, T, X, and Y.

Eight letters were revised: C, G, L, S, P, R, D, and V. The Greek *gamma*, for instance, looks like a *T* with the left part of the crosspiece missing; it came from a picture of an ox goad. The Romans rounded off the right angle, curved the bottom, and made it into a semicircle, a *C*. Later, to distinguish between the crisp sound of *C* and a more guttural variation, they put a distinguishing mark on the letter and used it to denote the sound of *G*.

The Greeks had created the *F* and *Q*, then abandoned them. Romans rescued these letters from the junk pile and put them back into use. Now they had the 23 letters that were all they needed to write Latin.

All this had happened by about 2,700 years ago, a very brief interval in the time of the world. But the alphabet as we know it is even newer. We added the last letter as recently as 500 years ago and abandoned a form of one within the lifetime of our nation.

The Romans used *V* as a vowel and a consonant. (We still put on airs and use it in *PVBLIC LIBRARY* on too many facades.) But, about a thousand years ago, the vowel *V* was rounded off to become *U*—Number 24—and *VV*, with a special sound all their own, were tied together into *W*—Number 25.

Our newest letter, only about five centuries old, is *J*. This was derived from *I*, which had been used as both vowel and consonant. Its most important use was as the initial in the name of the Savior. Medi-

eval scribes, feeling that the sacred name deserved typographic dis-
tinction, embellished the *I* when it appeared at the start of *Iesus*.
Eventually it was given a sweeping loop and became our *J*, whether as
part of a holy name or as a consonant in any word. There is no *J* in the
Authorized Version of the Bible, printed in 1611. It was not until the
nineteenth century that *J* was firmly in our alphabet.

So today our Latin alphabet consists of 26 letters, from *A* to *Z*. (Although commonly known as the Roman alphabet, its designation is
more properly *Latin*. This avoids confusion between the alphabet itself and the Roman letterform which we shall soon consider.)

But why is it *A to Z?* It is not *alpha to omega,* as in the Biblical
phrase, because omega was left unclaimed by the Romans. But why
not alpha to chi, *X*, the last Greek letter the Romans used? Why is zeta,
Z, the sixth Greek letter but the Roman twenty-sixth?

The Romans had picked up zeta, then decided it was superfluous.
When later they decided that Z was pretty useful after all and returned
it to the alphabet, *F* had moved into sixth position and all the others
had climbed a notch, too. The only place for Z was at the end of the
line. (But in the California job case, from which a printer handsets type
today, *J* and *U* are the Johnny-come-latelies—after Z.)

The last deletion from our Latin alphabet was the long *s* which
looked like an Italic *f* without the crosspiece. This form was used
within a word, never at the end, rarely at the beginning. It began ob-
solescence about the start of the nineteenth century when type founders
no longer manufactured it; printers, however, continued using it until
their cases were depleted and we can detect no definite end to its use.

As Christianity spread, its sacred writings came into constantly
greater demand. These were copied by hand by scribes who devoted
their whole lives to this labor. As they became intimately familiar with
the forms of letters, they learned to make them with the least effort.

If you were to write and rewrite many times a simple sentence in
all capitals, you too would modify the letter forms. Instead of using
three separate strokes to make an *A*, you would soon make the left
stroke and crossbar without lifting your pen. Then you would round
off the top corner, in the interest of speed, and soon the result would
be very much like the lowercase *a*. Soon you would tie letters together
to avoid wasting time by lifting the pen; and eventually you would
have a new letterform—"handwriting."

That is just what happened. Over the centuries the original capital

His MAJESTY's moſt Gracious SPEECH
to both Houſes of Parliament, on
Thurſday *October* 11. 1722.

My Lords and Gentlemen,

I Am ſorry to find my ſelf obliged, at the Opening of this Parliament, to acquaint you, That
a dangerous Conſpiracy has been for ſome time formed, and is ſtill carrying on againſt my Perſon and
Government, in Favour of a Popiſh Pretender.

The Diſcoveries I have made here, the Informati-
ons I have received from my Miniſters abroad, and
the Intelligences I have had from the Powers in Al-
liance with me, and indeed from moſt parts of Europe, have given me moſt ample and current Proofs
of this wicked Deſign.

The Conſpirators have, by their Emiſſaries, made
the ſtrongeſt Inſtances for Aſſiſtance from Foreign
Powers, but were diſſappointed in their Expectations:

Fig. 6. The long *s* was used in Benjamin Franklin's New-England *Courant,* of 1723.

letters were retained to start sentences or proper names; these were called *majuscules,* "a little larger." The newer and smaller letters became formalized and were named *minuscules;* we call them *lowercase* because of their position in old type cases.

The first true minuscules were developed at Tours, France, by Alcuin, a famed scholar from England. He designed the *Caroline* alphabet, named for his patron Charlemagne, under whose direction Alcuin re-edited and rewrote the classical Greek and Roman literature that had been lost or poorly copied in the Dark Ages. All this was done somewhere between A.D. 781 and 810, the most definitive dates in the history of our alphabet.

By that time the practice was well established that words should be separated. A slash/was/used/by/some/scribes; others.used.a.period. or.a-dash-as-separation; finally the words were separated only by white space.

Punctuation, like Topsy, just grew. Sometimes it was almost part of the words themselves; punctuation marks were placed where there happened to be room for them, in the bowl of an *a* or the vertex of a *v* or *w* or over or under any letter. Not until printing was invented did punctuation become regular and specific.

Our alphabet became crystallized with the advent of metal type. Attempts to change it have been desultory and ignored. The printing presses that have perpetuated the alphabet have also disseminated it so widely that it is virtually impossible to make any changes in it. Such changes can be made only when an alphabet is plastic, being changed at least a little by every person who writes it, and without a formal standard as common reference. Once committed to unyielding metal, the alphabet is as permanent as anything man has created.

New alphabets are still being created. Many a spoken language is today being transformed into written language. These alphabets, almost all based on the Latin, are being created by men who have the total knowledge of all the earth's alphabets and thus can by scientific methods achieve in a short time what our ancestors labored over so long by trial-and-error.

A comparatively new, and most interesting, written language is that of the Cherokee Indians. It was created by a genius, their chief Sequoyah.

The red man created in a dozen years what the white man had taken centuries to do. He developed a *syllabary*, and in 1828 began printing a daily newspaper, *The Phoenix*, at New Echota, now Georgia, to record the events of the highly developed civilization of the Cherokees. A syllabary uses a sign for an entire syllable. While it requires more

Fig. 7. Daily newspaper set in Cherokee syllabary devised by Sequoyah.

characters—86 in Cherokee, for instance—than an alphabet, words can be written with far fewer letters.

Today over 850 languages and dialects can be printed. Most of them use variations of the Latin alphabet; most of them are newer, in written form, than the Linotype which sets them—and that is only 75 years old.

SUGGESTED READINGS

Denman, Frank. *The Shaping of Our Alphabet.* New York: Alfred A. Knopf, Inc., 1955.

Ogg, Oscar. *The 26 Letters.* New York: Thomas Y. Crowell Company, 1948.

Nesbitt, Alexander. *Lettering: The History and Technique of Lettering as Design.* Englewood Cliffs, N.J.: Prentice-Hall, Inc., 1957.

3

Printing Types

FORM FOLLOWS THE TOOL

The influence of the tool is so great on our alphabet that it creates the basic categories into which we divide all forms of the Latin alphabet.

Our alphabet took its classical, permanent form from the tools used to create it. Although we usually think of these beautiful characters being created by the stonecutter's chisel across splendid Roman arches and facades, it was the painter's brush that determined their basic shapes.

Before the carver began to incise his ineradicable lines, he wanted to make sure that all the letters would fit in the given space. It would be more than embarrassing if he carved a 50-foot panegyric to Caesar across some vaulting arch and then found out there wasn't quite enough room for the last R in the emperor's name. So first he painted the letters onto the stone so changes could be made easily before cutting began.

It was the paint brush that created the distinguishing shape of the classical Roman letters. That brush was broad and thin, similar to the ones we use today to paint a house. When you painted a vertical stroke, such as the two on an *H*, the broad side of the brush made a wide line. When you painted the horizontal crossbar on the *H*, the brush drew a narrow line, only as wide as the thickness of the brush. When a brush like this draws an O, it paints with its thin edge at the very top; on the

Friend Tour

Fig. 8. Roman type: Old Style at left; Modern at right.

curve the line thickens to the full width of the brush; then the line thins to its narrowest at the bottom, swells to another maximum and finally thins down to its starting width.

This thinning and swelling of curved strokes is the primary distinguishing mark of the Roman alphabet. Equally important are the *serifs*, the form created by the stonecarver's tool.

After the carver had incised a straight stroke—again let's look at the *H*—he had to finish off the ends. This he would do, naturally, by cutting across the main stroke. It is difficult to start such a horizontal stroke at the exact corner of the vertical one. Rather than risk a slip of the chisel that could spoil the whole letter, the carver started a little outside the main stroke and let it go across and a little beyond on the other side. To avoid a fragile point, he then rounded off the serif, that little finishing stroke, into the main stroke.

This solution satisfied not only the needs of the stonecutter, but the artistic eye of the beholder. It became an integral part of the classic alphabet and today the serif is the second distinguishing feature of the Roman letterform.

The finest example of Roman is the letters carved into the great Trajan Column, erected in Rome about A.D. 113. Although scholars and artists have, almost ever since, attempted to reduce these characters to mathematical formulas, none has succeeded in bettering the work of the original craftsmen.

As Roman legions spread across Europe, their alphabet went with them. In Germany and the Low Countries, scribes' tools also influenced letterforms. They used quill pens that lacked the flexibility of the brush to sweep in graceful curves. They could write straight lines smoothly; on curves the two points of the nib overlapped and the pen spluttered and splashed. The solution was to abandon curved lines and create circles or arcs with a series of straight lines.

The result is the letterform called *Text* (because it was used primarily for the text of holy writings), or *Black Letter* (for obvious reasons), or, most commonly if inaccurately, *Old English.*

a b c d e î m n o p r u

Specializing Makes

Frankenmuth News

Fig. 9. Text or Black Letter. Top line is Gutenberg's characters. Lower line is Goudy's shaded version.

It is ironic that this offspring should be used as movable type before its classical Roman parent. A German, Johann Gutenberg, invented that type and it is only natural that he should duplicate the letterforms he was most familiar with.

It did not take long before printing moved back into the birthplace of our alphabet. There, in Venice, one Aldus Manutius set up a print shop and, as most printers of that age, designed and cast his own type. Like Gutenberg, Manutius based his type design on the letters most familiar to him. These were not the classical Trajan letters but the written hand of Italy. Its marked characteristic was its slant to the northeast that right-handed people naturally impart to *roundhand* or *cursive* writing.

Aldus used his new type to set inexpensive books which were as popular as their twentieth-century counterparts, the ubiquitous pocketbook sold in every drugstore and bus depot today. His type zoomed

A Good Printer

Is Superior To

nationally adv=

Closely Placed

its neighbor to

Fig. 10. Italic type. Note finials on Old Style, top, and Modern, right. Some serifs are used in specimen at lower left.

into popularity. Called *Aldine* in his own country, the type was known as *Italic* to the rest of Europe and to us today.

As printing flourished, type reflected the culture of each country. In the Victorian or Gay Nineties era, type was as overdecorated as the houses and clothes people lived in. Bustles, ruffles, and whalebone disguised the female form almost beyond recognition; flowers, cherubs, animals, and ribbons gussied up the alphabet nearly to illegibility.

When, after World War I, creative people rebelled against all reminders of the gaudy era, they began stripping gingerbread off furniture and architecture. "Functional" became the watchword. Architecture became functional, unadorned planes of concrete and steel in sleek rectangular boxes. Furniture lost antimacassars and overstuffing; now it was antiseptic and chromium.

At the famed Bauhaus, where this revolt began, the Latin alphabet came up for disapproving scrutiny, too. Just as they had stripped buildings and their contents of all ornamentation, Bauhaus designers tore the furbelows off the ABC's, not only the tasteless gaudies but the beautiful serifs as well, and reduced the pleasantly swelling and thinning strokes to a uniform, monotonal stroke. To this new letter form they gave the French title *Sans Serif*, "without serifs."

Serifless letters were not new. In an earlier version, such letters had resembled those that kindergarten pupils cut out of colored paper. Strokes were monotonal, but the corners were squared and the letterform was anything but beautiful. In fact, it was their noticeable lack of charm that gave them their name. The ugliest connotation that the educated European could attribute to anything was to associate it with the barbaric Goths. So this crude letterform was named *Gothic*. Europeans still call these letters *Grotesk*.

Fig. 11. Sans Serif: Perpendicular, top; Oblique, bottom. Note acute terminals on E.

TYPE faces are stand

TYPE faces are standard   ABCDEFGHIJKL
ABCDEFGHIJKL

The modern method of sp

Fig. 12. Gothics. Bottom line in calligraphic style shows influence of lettering pen.

Among the many nineteenth-century variations on the Roman theme were the *Square Serifs*. Here the discreet serifs of Trajan's letters were exaggerated to the same or even heavier weight of the basic monotonal strokes that made the letter.

Printer's lore says that these Square Serifs were used by Napoleon for communication during his military campaign in Egypt. Messages were written on large boards, held high atop a sand dune, and read from a distance by telescope. There the messages were rewritten and held up for reading by the next relay station. Supposedly, Square Serifs were used for such messages.

Whether for that reason, or because anything pertaining to Egypt was most fashionable in that age, this style of letter was known as *Egyptian.* (Some authorities, with logic, believe the name came from the resemblance of the slab serifs to the strong horizontal lines of Egyptian architecture.) It is interesting to note that the trade names for the best-known American Square Serifs bow to the legend; they are called *Memphis, Cairo,* and *Karnak.* A famous French Square is *Ramses* and in England, *Scarab.*

In Europe this style is also called *Antique,* the name by which the first Square Serif was shown in a specimen book by Vincent Figgins in 1815.

A version of the Squares, in which serifs outweigh main strokes, is associated in American minds with the great showman, P. T. Barnum.

Glance

Fig. 13. Square Serif.

To specialize is

Modern Design

Fig. 14. Script letters, top, are joined. Cursives, bottom, have form of written hand but are not connected.

One version bears his name; another, *Playbill*.

Just as Gutenberg and Manutius used written hands as the bases for their type, so later designers turned to handwriting when they created *Script* or *Cursive* faces. The names—*scriptum* is Latin for "writing," *cursus* means "running"—describe the flowing manner in which handwriting runs from one letter to the other. The only slight difference between the two: Script letters are tied together, the Cursives are separated, although sometimes so narrowly that it is not easily apparent.

Ornamentation fills a basic human need and our alphabet is still often decorated although rarely as flamboyantly as those faces which brought the Bauhaus rebellion.

The most common forms of ornamentation are: *Shaded* letters, in which a white line is tooled into the black stroke close to one side, or in which a regular pattern decorates the strokes; *Inline,* where the white stroke runs at the center of the black; *Shadowed,* where any extra stroke runs outside the letter as if it were casting a shadow, and *Outline,* as its name implies.

Sometimes more than one of these ornaments is used on a single letter. *Beton* in Figure 15, for instance, is a shadowed outline. *Prisma* has three inlines, *Umbra* has only the shadow with the eye being invited to create the basic form.

Many Ornamented faces might logically be classified in one of the other races. *Saphir* is obviously a Modern, and *Hadrian* an Old Style, Roman. But the Ornamented category—also called *Novelties*—is a useful *Miscellaneous* file for faces otherwise hard to classify.

We classify type for the same reason the botanist classifies plants, to

Fig. 15. Ornamented or Novelty letters.

make it easier to study and discuss them. A tomato is a tomato whether it is called a fruit or a vegetable. So type is good or poor whether it is Modern, Old Style, or Transitional. Classifications are useful if accepted as a convenience and not as a strait jacket.

Types can be classified and subdivided as minutely as the botanist groups his specimens. For our needs, only basic categories are necessary.

Type is first classified by *race*: Roman, Text, San Serif, Square Serifs, Script, and Ornamented.

Roman is subdivided into *Old Style, Transitional,* and *Modern.* It is the only race with such major subdivisions.

In Old Style Romans, the widest portions of an O are at 2 and 8 o'clock and all bowls are on an axis that tilts to the left a little. The difference between thick and thin is not pronounced; serifs are *bracketed* into the stem.

A contemporary of Benjamin Franklin, patron saint of American printers, created one of the subdivisions. Giambatista Bodoni, a Parmesan printer, drew his Roman letters with thin and sharp serifs, showing the influence of the engraving tools of the punch cutter. His O— and other bowls—he made on a perpendicular axis with the thinnest portions at 12 and 6 o'clock and the widest at 3 and 9. The difference between thick and thin strokes is marked.

People gave the new type the accolade of each generation: "It's modern!" To this day Bodoni's type is not only a Modern Roman but *the* Modern Roman.

Romans that combine characteristics of Modern and Old Style are called Transitional. There are many specific hallmarks in each of these three subdivisions but only those discussed here are significant to the average graphic arts observer. Remember that the date of the design of a face does not necessarily indicate its category; Bodoni cut his Modern in 1788 and Goudy his Old Style in the 1930's.

The auxiliary to the alphabet, the Arabic numerals, also have Old Style and Modern versions. *Modern numbers* align on the base line; in Old Style, the 3, 4, 5, 7, and 9 drop below the baseline. In this illustration:

1234567890   1234567890

the numbers on the left are Old Style, those at the right, Modern. Old Style or Transitional Romans have both versions in a standard font.

Not all the historic developments of type design make a separate race. Italic was originally a race of its own and in older books is so referred to. But in recent years, the term Italic has become corrupted to refer to any letters that slant to the right. Today there are "Italic" forms of the Sans and the Squares although the purists properly refer to them as *Obliques*. This is a definitive term but not a popular one. This book will use "Italic" only to designate the classic letterform and that form is placed in the Roman race. Always remember the dual use of the term and, if there is any doubt, ask whether "Italic" refers to form or angle. Italics, too, have Old Style and Modern versions.

"Roman" is also misused by some people to refer to *perpendicular* letters. This book will use Roman only for a race or a form. Thus, we shall say Oblique (rather than Italic) Square Serifs, or Perpendicular (not Roman) Sans, even if many printers use the incorrect adjectives.

Between the original square-letter Gothics and the Sans Serifs there was once a marked difference. But the Gothics have been so refined that now the distinguishing features are often almost imperceptible and we group both letterforms into the single "without-serifs" race. That the Sans are generally more attractive is a criterion that depends too much on personal taste. The only concrete difference is that the Gothics are not always entirely monotonal. Sometimes there is a difference in the weight of Gothic strokes; especially where the bowl meets the stem, the curved stroke may be *pinched*. If there is a difference in the weight of any strokes, the letter is a Gothic.

The slight difference between the Scripts and the Cursives has already been pointed out. These logically form one race, too.

Type races are subdivided into *families*. These are known by their trade names. Some are called after their designers: Bodoni and Goudy are notable. Others recall national characteristics: Karnak, Scotch, Caledonia. Some names have been adopted without too obvious reasons: Spartan, Electra, Stymie.

Each family includes varying numbers of *series*. A series bears the family name, either alone or, usually, with one or more adjectives that describe the basic variations of a type face. These include *slant*—perpendicular or oblique; *weight*—such as *Heavy, Book, Extra Bold,* etc.; *width*—normal or *fullface, Condensed,* and *Extended*.

Each series consists of all the *sizes* of that one particular face. Spartan Medium, for instance, has 11 sizes, from 6-point through 36-point.

The smallest subdivision is the *font*. This consists of capital and

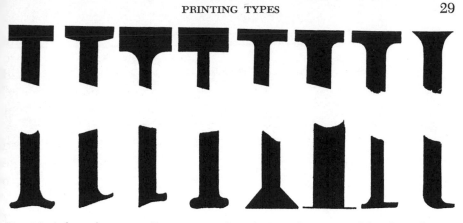

Fig. 16. A few of many serif treatments that distinguish races and families of type.

lowercase letters, punctuation marks and symbols of one size of a series. (This book is set in Caledonia 11-point. All the Roman characters and supplemental material such as &, *, #, $, !, etc., make one font. Italics used here come from another font.)

One of the most widely used families was Cheltenham, the first one cut for both mechanical and hand setting. By race, Cheltenham is a Roman; by subdivision, a Transitional.

Its series are many: Cheltenham (the original fullface version), Cheltenham Wide, Condensed, and Extra Condensed (variations in width), and Medium and Bold weights. Often there are combinations of more than one variation, so that series names include Cheltenham Medium Condensed and Extra Condensed Italic.

The number of different characters in a font varies with the face and its use. A California job case has 89 spaces. These contain capital and lowercase alphabets, eight punctuation marks, five *f* and the *æ* and *œ* ligatures, 10 numbers, dollar and pound signs, and ampersand. The other receptacles contain spacing from em quads to 5-em spaces.

The standard Linotype has 90 channels for characters and spacing other than the spacebands.

There are many special characters to augment a given font or take the place of little used characters. These might be fractions beyond those commonly used, symbols for scientific composition, footnote marks, or commercial signs, such as the lb. logo and @.

The number of pieces of type or matrices per font also varies. In America, or for setting English, the *e* is the most frequent character and its receptacle is the largest in the job case so the compositor has an adequate supply. In a standard font of Linotype matrices, there are 20 *e* matrices.

Because of less frequent use, there are only five *z* matrices in a line-caster font and only a small space is left for *z* in the job case.

In older days type was sold by weight. A pound of 6-point contained far more pieces than a pound of 36. The number of pieces in a standard font still varies by the size of the type. Type is no longer sold by weight, but the compositor who sets a paragraph of body type still needs more pieces to work with than the one who sets larger sizes as headlines. Title faces, with no lowercase, are adequate in fonts of even smaller numbers of pieces.

Foundry-type fonts are designated by the number of lowercase *a*'s they contain. The standard for 36-point Caslon Oldstyle is a *7-a* font—seven *a*'s, five *A*'s, and all other characters in proper ratio. In 6-point Caslon the standard is a *65-a* font. Thus a font will vary from as many as 200 pieces of type to 1,500, plus necessary quads and spaces.

Decorative faces, such as those used only for initials, may be fonted with as few as three *A*'s.

The United States Patent Office will not grant a patent for a new type face; there are so many variations of the Latin alphabet that nothing truly new is possible in official eyes. While this attitude condones unconscionable pirating of truly creative type designs, it does reflect a truth. There are so many forms of our alphabet that a person could spend his whole life in studying and classifying them.

Whether a person wants to immerse himself in the subject or learn only basic facts, the study of type is fascinating. The typophile finds as much pleasure in browsing through a specimen book as the artist does in visiting the Louvre.

SUGGESTED READINGS

Hlasta, Stanley C. *Printing Types and How to Use Them.* New Brunswick, N.J.: Rutgers University Press, 1950.

Updike, D. B. *Printing Types.* 2 vols. Cambridge, Mass.: Harvard University Press, 1951.

Zapf, Hermann. *Manuale Typographicum.* New York: Museum Books, 1959.

4

Printers' Terms

THE JARGON OF THE CRAFT

A craft that goes back 500 years without any drastic change in tools or methods is bound to acquire a highly specialized jargon. The printer's is no exception. Not only has his craft an extensive language, but each shop has terms uniquely its own.

The glossary at the end of this book, sizable as it is, does not include all the phrases familiar to the printer. (Some are too salty for inclusion.) Terms will be explained as they crop up in discussion. Many of them are used so infrequently that there is no need to dwell on them. This chapter will discuss the more common ones.

A basic problem is the ambiguity of many terms and a tendency to use the same one for several incompatible meanings. The public finds the very term "graphic arts" confusing because fine artists use those words to describe a subdivision of their art, *printmaking,* while the printer's definition is the one given in the first chapter of this book.

There are sporadic attempts to give the great field of communicative graphic arts the name of *graphics.* But popular usage changes with no more alacrity than that of a glacier. We can probably canonize Coster as the patron saint of printers or Marlowe as the author of *Hamlet* long before "graphics" becomes universally accepted.

There is no single word that refers to all practitioners of the graphic arts. *Graphic artist* is inappropriate as a name for the many *craftsmen*

31

in the field; *graphic artsman* has a contrived sound. So, in this book, the specific name of the performer of a specific task will be used.

It must be pointed out that in many instances one person will perform a whole series of assignments, sometimes two or more simultaneously. A man may be a *designer* and a *type specifier* at the same time. An advertising manager may function in the role of the "author" even as he is a proofreader, referring the latter's queries to himself as the person responsible for content, even if he has not written the copy himself.

But until an acceptable substitute for graphic artist/artsman is coined, the reader must be content with names of the parts, rather than the whole, of the industry's personnel.

Printer, itself, is a name claimed by many craftsmen: The *compositor* sets type; the *make-up man* (or *stoneman*) combines typographic elements into larger units, an advertisement, a page, or a *signature* (a group of pages). They work in a *composing room*. In a newspaper plant, it is divided into the *ad alley* and the *news line*. In a *job shop*, which does commercial composition or printing, the basic division is between machine and hand composition.

The hand compositor works before a shallow tray, a *California job case*. Each case contains one font and is subdivided into small rectangles, each containing one character. In older days, he used two cases; one held capitals, beneath it was one of small letters. Today we still refer to *uppercase* or *lowercase* for majuscules or minuscules.

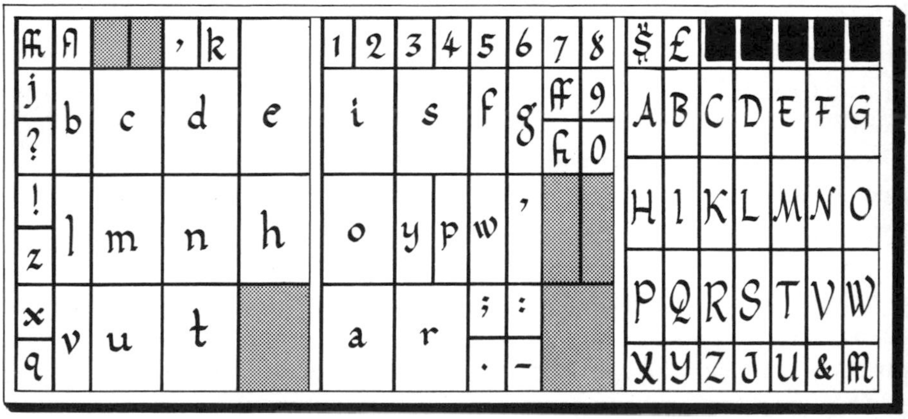

Fig. 17. California job case provides compartments sized to frequency of letter's use. Dark spaces, upper right, hold special characters; shaded ones hold spacing.

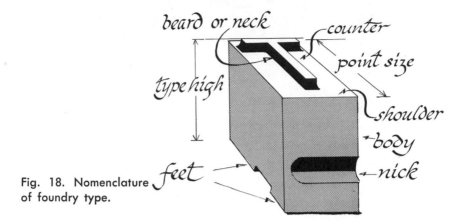

Fig. 18. Nomenclature of foundry type.

Type is set by hand in a *composing stick* (a shallow, three-sided tray), and is later placed in a similar but far longer tray, called a *galley*, and stored on the *bank*.

The make-up man's work surface is the *stone*. Formerly it was actually a slab of smooth stone; today it is a metal surface. Here the type and any headlines, illustrations, or rules needed are assembled into a *form*. Later the form is placed in a metal frame, a *chase*, which holds it firmly, while printing, by means of iron wedges, *quoins*.

A single piece of type contributes many entries to the printer's lexicon: The main mass is called the *body;* it stands on *feet*, separated by the *groove*. The top plane of the body is the *shoulder* from which projects the printing surface, the *face*. The side of this projection is the *beard*. The depressed area between the raised lines of the face is a *counter*. *Nicks* are grooves in one side of the body, varying in number and placement to identify it as from an individual font.

Some faces, notably classical Italics, project over the side of the body. The projecting elements are called *kerns* and are supported by the shoulder of adjacent characters. *Kerned letters* are apt to break off during handling or printing and therefore are not popular with frugal printers.

Spacing, at the start of a paragraph, between words or at the end of a short *widow* line, is created by *quads*. The *em* or *mutton quad* is a square of the point size. Thus, in a 14-point font the em will be 14 points high (as are all the characters) and 14 points wide.

The *en* or *nut quad* is half as wide; in a 14-point font the en is 14 points high and 7 points wide. Smaller spacing material are the one-third, one-fourth, and one-fifth of an em. By shortening their names to

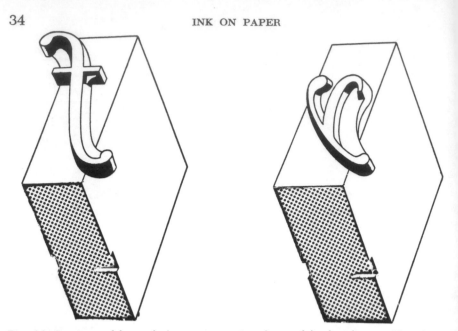

Fig. 19. Portions of kerned characters project beyond body of type. Kern is supported by shoulders of adjacent characters.

em spaces, the printer saves breath but creates confusion. A 3-em quad, in 14-point, is 14 points high and 52 points (3 × 14) wide; but a *3-em space* is 14 points high and only one-third of 14 points—4⅔ points—wide.

Thin spaces of brass or copper, in ½- and 1-point, are used in more meticulous composition and in some instances the compositor even uses tissue paper for exactly right spacing.

Horizontal spacing—between lines or other printing elements—is created by *ledds,* metal strips 2 points tall, or *slugs,* which are 6 points tall. (To prevent confusion, this book uses the phonetic form *"ledd"* instead of the common *lead.*) *Reglets,* of wood or metal, are 12 points. Larger spacing material is called *furniture.*

There are also 1- and 3-point ledds and slugs from 4- through 12-point. Unless otherwise designated, a ledd is 2 points, a slug is 6.

The printer scorns inches; he has his own linear measurement, the *American point system.* This he might well cherish; it had a long, hard birth.

When metal type was first cast for sale, each foundry used its own measurements; a customer would thus be committed to a single source of supply to avoid the nuisance of making disparate type fit into a

abcdefghijklmnopqrstuv
wxyz .-,,:;'?!& '''" fffifflffifffl
ABCDEFGHIJKLMNOP
QRST UVWXYZ
$1234567890

Fig. 20. Characters in standard font of foundry type.

smooth line or form.

It was not until 1737—after almost 200 years of measurement anarchy—that a French printer, Fournier, devised a standard for type measurement. His smallest unit was the point. Sensible as it was, the system was resisted and it took a royal decree by King Louis XV, who was intensely interested in printing, to make founders conform.

Later another famous French printing family, the Didots, modified Fournier's point to make it conform to the French inch and that system is still in use in Europe. A Didot point is .0148 inches. Its most common unit is the *cicero* and type is measured by *corps*. Twelve corps equal a cicero.

English printers adopted the point system; it came to America and, in 1886, was standardized here as the American point system. This brought a uniformity that made it possible for printers to use type and spacing material from any source. If the reader is confused by the following table of measures, he can thank his stars this book wasn't written in 1886.

The American *point* is .01384 inches, close enough to $\frac{1}{72}$ for all practical purposes. Twelve points equal a *pica*, the common unit of horizontal measurement. Thus, 6 picas (72 points) equal one inch.

Printers almost invariably use em and pica interchangeably. A 12-

point em, of course, is 1 pica wide and 1 pica tall. But it must be remem-
bered that an em is a unit of area, a pica is a lineal measurement.

The em is commonly used as a measure for composition. Obviously
a compositor who sets a 30-pica line of 36-point type would have to
handle only about 26 pieces of type; to set the same length line in
agate (5½ point), he would need more than a hundred characters. Ems
give a measurement that eliminates such discrepancies. In a 30-pica
line (360 points) there are only 10 36-point ems (360 ÷ 36). In the
same length of line there are 65.4 agate (5½-point) ems.

To determine the amount of composition, convert line length into
points and divide by the point-size of the type used. This gives ems per
line. Multiply by the number of lines for total production.

The same anarchy that eventually demanded the point system also
applied to the height of a piece of type, from the plane on which it
stood to the printing surface. This was more annoying than differences
in other measurements, for type not high enough to meet the paper
at exactly the same point as its neighbors just did not print at all; one
only a trifle taller than the rest of the form would punch into the paper.

This vital measurement was finally standardized at .918 inches. This
is the *height-to-paper* or *type-high* that is used in the United States,
Canada, England, and most of Latin America. But because the rest of
the world still uses other type-high standards, from .928 to .991, foreign and American type cannot be mixed in the same form without
excessive adjustment.

Until the point system came into use, type sizes were indicated by
name. *Agate* (5½ point) is the only size still designated by name. Its
primary use is in classified ads, so, should such ads be set in 6-point, the
printer—never a linguistic purist—blithely calls that agate, too!

Smallest size was *diamond* (4½-point). *Minion* (7-point) and *brevier*
(8-point) were popular sizes. Pica (12-point) gave its name to our
measuring system. *Long primer* was 10-point, *great primer*, 18-point.
Canon (48-point) was the largest.

In many ways this nomenclature was as good as our point system for
designating type size. For so much confusion exists today that Bulmer
9-point is actually smaller in printing area than 8-point Corona.

Actually, "8-point type" has only a vague reference to the typographical size. It refers only to the measurement of the rectangular body upon
which the printing face rests.

Before we can explore this paradox, let us look at the nomenclature of the type character itself. *Primary letters* are those such as *a, o, m,* and *x*. Theirs is the *x-height* of that particular font. Those which have projections upward are called *ascenders—d, f, h, k, l,* and *t*—as are the "necks" themselves. *Descenders* refer not only to the downward projections but to the letters that own them—*j, p, q*.

Vertical strokes are *stems*; curved ones make *bowls*. Bottom alignment of primary letters is the *baseline;* at their top is the *mean line* or *x-line*.

Thin lines of Roman letters are *hairlines,* even if they are far thicker than the term commonly connotes.

Diagonal strokes meet at the *apex* of such letters as *A* and at the *vertex* of *V*. So *M* and *W* have both vertex and apex.

When outside strokes of the *M* are not vertical but spread outward, they form a *splayed* letter.

Although the *g*, as a letter, is a descender, its lower loop is called the *tail* (*Q* and *y* also have tails). From the upper loop projects the *claw*, (the *r* also has a claw) and connecting the loops of the *g* is the *link* or *neck*. *Loops* are owned by the *e* and some forms of *k*.

Arms are the short strokes, horizontal or upward, from the stem of *Y, K,* and *T*. The *cross* of the *t, A,* and *H* and the bottom of the loop of *e* are the *bar*. But on *t* and *f*, the short line is the *cross-stroke*.

Serifs are the small finishing lines on the ends of main strokes of a Roman letter. Those on arms are descriptively called *beaks*. The serif-like projection from the short stem on some forms of *G* is the *spur* and *G*'s cross stroke is sometimes called the *beard* (not to be confused with the same term that is synonymous with the neck of a piece of type.)

In most Italics and some Romans, instead of a serif, a hook or sharp curve finishes a stroke in a *finial*. When a letter contains a sweeping, decorative stroke, such as a flourishing tail on *R* or *Q*, both the letter and the stroke are a *swash*.

Those strokes which do not carry a serif or finial are *terminals*. These can be sliced into *acute* or *grave* terminals or they may end in a *ball* such as on certain *c*'s or *a*'s.

By their individual form, certain combinations of letters tend to tie themselves together. These are *ligatures,* most common of which are those with combinations of *f* such as *fi, fl, ff, ffi,* and *ffl*. These are cast on a single body or from a single linecaster matrix.

Logotypes carry more than one letter—often a trademark—on a single body. Logoed letters are not tied together; the *Qu* combination is

Fig. 21. Nomenclature of type design.

the most common.

In the process of standardizing height-to-paper and the point system, a standard *lining system* was also adopted to great relief of printers. Until that time, the baseline of a type face came only where the whim of the designer placed it. If it came 3 points from the lower edge of the body, the printing face would not align with one whose baseline ran, say, 4 points from the bottom. This meant that the printer who had to go to another font to set a word in Greek—in a textbook, for instance—found that word sat higher or lower than the words in Latin letters.

In *standard lining*, all type of one point size will align at the bottom

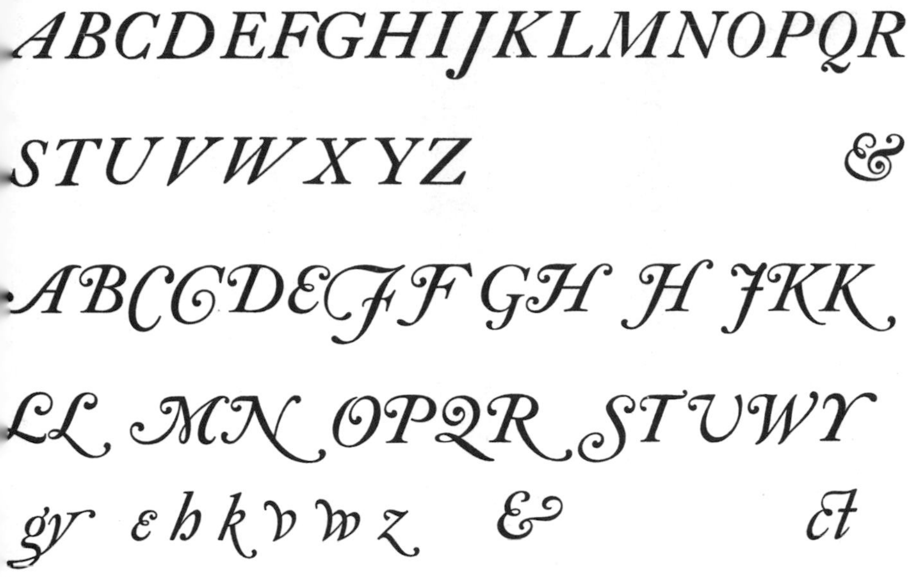

ABCDEFGHIJKLMNOPQR

STUVWXYZ &

ABCCDEFFGHJKK

LL MN OPQR STUWY

gy ε h k v w z & ct

Fig. 22. Old Style Italic, top, compared to Swash characters of same font.

with all other characters of that size, no matter what their design or source.

Some letterforms, usually cursive or swash, have unusually long descenders and thus require more shoulder at the bottom to accommodate these elongated "tails." These are designed for *art lining*. Here the baseline is higher than in standard lining. Art-lining characters will align with all other art lining of the same point size and can be made to align with the standard by using only regular spacing materials.

An alphabet with only capitals needs no room for descenders; its baseline can come close to the edge of the body. Because all-caps are used most frequently for titles, *title lining* is used for such fonts. Again, all title-lining faces of the same size will align, and standard spacing can make them align with standard or art.

Now, finally, it can be understood why "point size" only vaguely defines the actual size of a type face.

The designer, assigned to do an 18-point face, must first set a vertical dimension of 18 points for the body of the type. Then he must establish the baseline. From here on, he is as free as a bird. He can have tall or short primary letters to accommodate long or short ascenders and descenders. If he decides to have long ascenders and descenders, he must make the bowls—and primary letters—smaller; for the length of

Fig. 23. Comparison of three common lining systems.

the projections is limited by the over-all 18-point dimensions of the body. Conversely, if projections are kept short, the bowls and primaries can be taller.

So, instead of using the indefinite point size, typographers tend to size a type by its x-height and also by whether its round letters are nearly circular or more oval.

It is difficult to determine the size of type by measuring a printed character. We must remember to measure from the top of the ascenders to the bottom of the descenders and then add the shoulder. In the case of *display type*, from 14-point up, this is easy. But the difference in *body type*, through 12-point, can be slight. It takes a keen eye to differentiate between 5½- and 6-point type, for instance.

Most type used today is of metal. *Foundry type* is cast by type founders, each character, except ligatures, on a separate body. Type *slugs* are manufactured in the composing room; they are complete lines of type. *Monotype type* is cast by the machine that gives it its name, one character at a time but automatically assembled into lines.

Metal type normally goes to 96-point and, cast sideways on the body, to 144-point. Type larger than that is made of wood.

All metal type is known collectively as *hot metal*, in contrast to *cold type*, which is produced photographically.

But be it hot or cold, the terminology of type and of the men who use it is a language comparatively easy to learn. And, as with all foreign languages, its mastery enables you to work better in the area where it is used.

SUGGESTED READINGS

Hymes, David G. *Production in Advertising*. New York: Henry Holt & Co., Inc., 1958.

Jahn, Hugo. *The Dictionary of Graphic Arts Terms*. Boston: United Typothetae of America, 1932.

Stevenson, George A. *Graphic Arts Handbook and Production Manual*. Torrance, Calif.: Pen & Pencil, 1961.

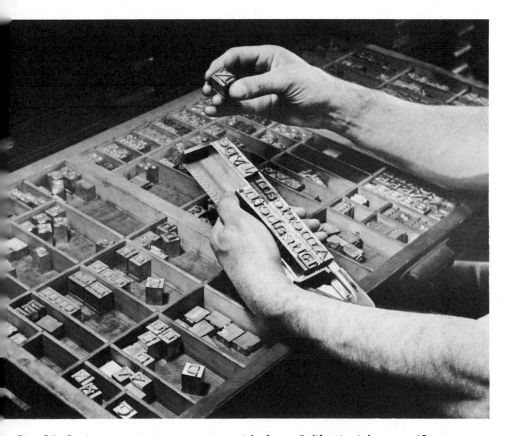

Fig. 24. Setting type into composing stick from California job case. (Courtesy American Type Founders)

5

Setting Type

COMPOSITION BY MAN AND MACHINE

The modern printer still *sticks* or *pegs* type in the same way that Gutenberg set his first book. On his stick—once actually a wooden receptacle, now a finely tooled metal one—he sets the movable right side to the width of his line. Into it he places a slug of the same length. Then he picks each character from the job case with his right hand. He need not look for the proper compartment any more than a typist must search for the proper key. As he grasps the type, and his skilled fingers detect the nick, he turns it to the proper position. In the stick, the thumb of the left hand, which holds the stick, keeps the type standing properly. Letter by letter, the type is sticked. Quads or spaces create white space where required.

When the line is filled, or almost filled, the compositor reads it for errors. Type reads from left to right, just as the written or printed words will, but it is upside down and, of course, in mirror form. But the printer reads it as easily as we read printing.

Now he must *justify* it: bring the right-hand margin even with the side of the stick, and with all succeeding lines. This he does by adding more space between words, or by decreasing it to make room for another word or syllable in the line. Justification not only takes time, proper spacing requires great skill.

The *comp* then places a ledd under the first line and sets the second.

When a *stickful* of type has been set, an inch or two, it is dumped into a galley.

One of the greatest calamities that can befall a compositor is to *pi the type*. Pi (pronounced "pie"), as a verb, means to mix up the type by allowing it to fall, either off its feet or out of the stick or galley. As a noun, pi is the mess that results from such a misfortune or clumsiness. Especially in smaller type sizes, where each piece rests on feet much smaller than its height, pi-ing is a constant danger.

Although a skilled compositor, a *swift,* can set type at a surprising speed, it is still a most inefficient operation. For he works one-handed; the left hand just holds the stick and keeps the type standing.

Probably not long after Gutenberg's day ways were sought to speed the process; one comp hung his stick from his neck so he could peg type with both hands. But it was the industrial revolution and the mechanization of many tasks, from sewing to cleaning cotton bolls, that brought the greatest demand for mechanizing typesetting.

Think of the newspaper you read today. If it is an average one, it has over a quarter-million individual characters and spaces. To set all of these by hand would require a crew of compositors far too large to house in an efficiently sized room. The increasing number of newspaper pages and their need for a fast method for composition spurred the search by inventors throughout the civilized world.

By 1880 over 40 such machines had been patented. The earliest ones stored each type character in a receptacle from which one piece was released by touching a corresponding key. But, once the line was filled, justification still had to be done by hand. This machine was just an extension of an earlier system whereby several compositors set type, then sent their lines to one man who justified the product of several comps.

Neither of these systems solved a vexing concomitant to hand composition, namely, *distribution*. After a handset job is printed, each piece of type and each quad, space, ledd, or slug must be returned to its proper receptacle so that it can be used again. While this distribution takes far less time than setting, it is totally unproductive labor.

The first typesetting machine that met at least minimal standards was the *Unitype,* which appeared in 1870. From a series of vertical containers, pieces of type would drop when a corresponding key was depressed. Justification was still a hand operation. By using the nicks in the type, as notches are used to match a key to a lock, type was automatically distributed back into the proper receptacles. Elementary as it was, the Unitype could do the work of four hand compositors.

Another notable machine was the *Paige Compositor*. Its fame came not from its performance, which was disappointing, but from its major financial backer, Mark Twain. The only existing machine of this kind now reposes in the Mark Twain Museum in Hartford, Conn. Before it was written off as a failure, it had consumed most of the author's considerable fortune and had forced him to spend his declining years, not in leisure he deserved, but on the arduous lecture circuit.

Solving the typesetting problem wrote a new name into the annals of the graphic arts: Ottmar Mergenthaler.

A German like Gutenberg, he also shares a distinguished rank in history; his invention has been called one of the 10 greatest of all time.

He came to America as a young man, and soon after his arrival met a court reporter, James O. Clephane, who sought a quick method of converting shorthand into multiple written copies. After several disheartening failures, which saw feasible laboratory devices fail in practice, Mergenthaler advanced on his own, backed by a group of newspaper publishers.

His machine was first demonstrated on July 3, 1886, in the composing room of the *New York Tribune,* which Horace Greeley had brought to fame and which was then edited by Whitelaw Reid, a giant in American journalism and organizer of the syndicate which financed the inventor.

The key to Mergenthaler's success was the *circulating matrix.* Basically, the operation of that 1886 machine was the same as that of today's refined and speeded-up machines.

A shallow rhomboid-shaped container is divided into 90 vertical channels, each containing *matrices* for one character.

This *matrix* is a piece of brass, bearing in one side the mold for the given character. When the operator presses a key, the corresponding matrix is released and drops onto a belt that carries it into an assembling area. Successively, each proper matrix is released until enough are assembled to fill a line.

Justification is achieved by *spacebands* between words. These bands are an ingenious combination of two wedges. When they are pushed upward, they expand so that the line is exactly filled.

Now the line is moved over in front of a *pot* containing molten metal. A metal frame forms four sides of a box, the matrices the fifth, and the

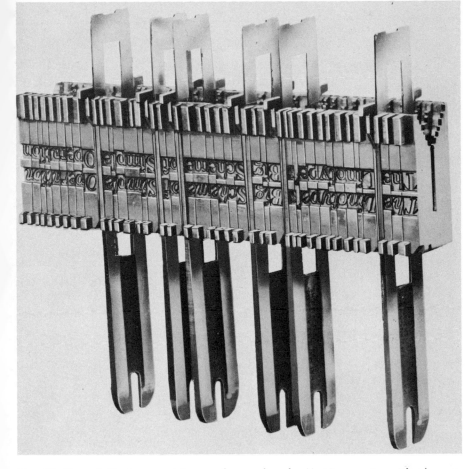

Fig. 25. Line of Linotype matrices and spacebands. Matrices cast upside down to create necessary mirror image on the slug. Note wedges of spacebands which are expanded by upward pressure.

mouthpiece of the pot, the sixth. When the molten metal is forced into the "box," the result is a rectangular piece of metal bearing on one side the line of relief characters cast from the matrices. This is the "line of type" that gives the machine its name.

The *type metal* is an alloy of lead, tin, and antimony. It has the unusual characteristic of expanding when it cools. This assures that metal will be forced into the smallest cavities of the matrix and will cast a perfect mirror image of the matrix.

When the line has been cast, it drops into a shallow tray, the galley.

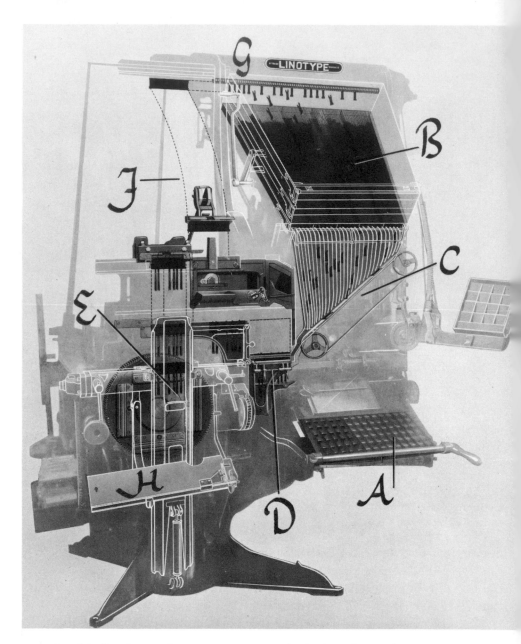

Fig. 26. Circulation of matrices. Action on the keyboard (A) releases matrices from magazine (B). Mats drop by gravity (C), are carried to D where operator can see them. They move to E where slug is cast. Matrices are raised (F) to distributor bar (G) where they drop into proper channels. Slug drops in galley, H.

The machine can cast up to 14 newspaper-column lines per minute.

After casting, matrices are lifted to the top of the machine and pushed back over the magazine. They are supported on a triangular, grooved *distributor bar,* and hang from the teeth that are arranged in a characteristic triangular pattern at the top of the matrix. Grooves in the bar are keyed to the tooth combination just as a key matches notches in a lock. When the matrix is directly above its proper channel, it is released and drops down for immediate reuse.

The number of matrices per channel depends on the frequency with which that letter appears in English sentences, as noted in Chapter 3. The operator never has to wait for matrices; he sets one line while the preceding one is being cast. A swift operator can *hang the elevator,* assemble lines faster than the machine can cast them.

The advantages of the *Linotype* are obvious. Each line of type is brand-new with perfect printing surfaces. There is no distribution problem; after the type has been used, it is simply remelted and fresh type cast from it. Keyboarding is much faster than sticking type by hand; justification is automatic. Slugs are much easier to handle than individual pieces of type, and danger of pi-ing is minimized.

Although printers at first resisted the new machine because they feared it would destroy their jobs, the Linotype was so popular that within 10 years it had gone into use as far away as Hawaii, as well as in Europe. Compositors found their fears baseless; instead of destroying jobs, the Linotype created jobs. It gave an impetus that boomed the graphic arts industry; efficient typesetting lowered costs and increased demand.

When Mergenthaler's basic patents expired, a new machine, the *Intertype,* was put on the market. Basically, there is no difference between these two machines; they are the only two American *keyboarded linecasters* on the market today, although similar machines are manufactured in Europe. Linotype has almost become a generic name.

Most Linotype and Intertype matrices through 24-point are *duplexed;* they have two individual molds on each piece of brass. The most common duplex is Roman with Italic, or *fullface*—the normal weight—with boldface. In a few instances two entirely different faces or sizes are duplexed. Twenty-four-point Spartan Black Condensed is duplexed with 18-point Spartan Heavy, for instance.

Standard machines cast a maximum 30-pica line, although there are some 42-pica machines for specialized composition. Measures wider

Fig. 27. Linotype slugs in galley on machine.

than that must be set in two *butted lines*. There is a danger, however slight, that such lines will not butt tightly or that they will not align precisely. For these reasons, as well as the fact that it takes more time to set a line in two portions, it is wise to avoid butted lines.

When a line is extremely narrow, or when there are not enough spacebands to expand far enough to make the line tight, the operator must insert blank spacing by hand between the letters of a word. This not only takes valuable time, it makes reading difficult.

Another American linecaster is the *Ludlow*. It does not have a keyboard; matrices are assembled by hand.

Although Ludlow casts type from 8- through 144-point, its major use is for larger sizes. Ludlow matrices are kept in a case roughly similar to the California case but with only a few matrices of each character. They are shaped so that the operator can easily gather several in his hand before placing them in a special stick. Spacing is created by blank matrices; justification and centering are performed automatically by the stick. The assembled line is placed into the casting device where the rest of the process is automatic. Matrices are distributed by hand after each line is cast.

Though there are several hand operations, the Ludlow has many advantages. Type is in convenient slug form and is always new. Operation is far speedier than setting foundry type. Italic matrices are slanted so that the letters fit tightly, without kerning.

Ludlow slugs are T-shaped. The body forms the stem; the type, the cross bar. Low slugs, *underpinning,* support the overhanging portion of the face.

Although the maximum line cast by the Ludlow is 22½ picas, lines can be butted with no apparent break.

A companion to the Ludlow is the *Elrod Caster,* which produces strip material: ledds, slugs, rules, underpinning for Ludlow slugs, and bases for engravings and stereotypes.

The Elrod produces a continuous strip of material from 1- through 36-point thickness. Molten metal is constantly fed into the mold, where it is cast, solidified under pressure, and ejected at one end, while molding continues at the other. The machine can also be set to cut off the strips at any given length.

A year after Mergenthaler brought out his first Linotype, another inventor, Tolbert Lanston, received a patent for the *Monotype.* Its principal features have undergone major changes since then to make it an important machine. Instead of setting a whole line of type as a slug, the Monotype casts individual characters and assembles them in a justified line up to 60 picas wide.

Two separate machines make up the Monotype system. The operator works at a keyboard similar to, but larger than, that on a typewriter. This produces a roll of paper into which has been punched coded holes; it looks very much like the rolls for player pianos.

This *controller paper* actuates the second unit, the casting machine. Actual casting is done from matrices in a small *matrix case,* about the size of a man's hand. In body sizes, there are 225 matrices in the case, about two-and-a-half times more characters than are available in a Linotype magazine.

The matrix case is positioned over the casting mold. Holes in the controller paper direct a complex of springs that move the case so that the proper matrix is directly over the mold. Metal is forced into the matrix to form the character. The cast is cooled immediately by water and pushed into a galley until a whole line has then been assembled.

Justification is automatic. All characters in a Monotype font are designed in increments of one-eighteenth of an em. Quads necessary to justify the line are also made in such increments. As the operator punches keys, a gauge shows him how much space is left in the line. When the line is wide enough to justify, the operator is told by the gauge how wide the quads must be, and he presses the proper key to encode that information into the paper.

This information, obviously, comes after that which calls for individual characters. But the casting machine must have this data at the time it must cast the first quad. So the paper is simply fed into the machine backward. The machine first reads the justification information, then it casts the last letter of the line, the second last, and so on. When it reaches its first quad, the information is already there, permitting the blank to be cast at the proper width. It does not matter, of course, in which order the line is cast, from the beginning or end, so long as the characters are positioned properly in relation to each other.

Advantages of Monotype composition are obvious. The operator has many characters available to him; this is especially useful in setting a textbook, for example, where words in non-Latin alphabets must be interpolated or where many scientific symbols are used. The casting machine is fast—150 casts per minute; thus, the output of several keyboard operators may be fed into the caster. Or controller rolls may be punched at distant points for casting by a centrally located machine. Rolls may be stored for casting at more convenient times, perhaps on the night shift. They can be stored for recasting much later. Keyboarding and casting can be done entirely independently of the other operation.

Corrections are easy. Instead of having to recast a whole line to correct one wrong letter, as with the Linotype, a Monotype error can be corrected by simply changing that single letter.

The ability to change a single character is especially valuable in the case of tabulated figures, a stock market table, or a tariff schedule, which change frequently but only partially. Figures can be changed without resetting the entire line. Because such tabular setting is a time-consuming process, Monotype's flexibility is especially desirable.

The Monotype can also be used to produce strip material.

Like the linecasters, Monotype produces material for *non-distribution* use. This means that after the type has been printed, it is not distributed but remelted. In a newspaper plant, for instance, after the edition has been printed, only a few elements are saved from a page form, the nameplate on the front page or an ad on an inside page which will be rerun later. Then the whole page is pushed off the edge of the stone into a wheeled container and hauled to the remelt pot.

The Monotype *Giant Caster* produces individual type characters, which are stored in California job cases and are set just like foundry type, by hand. The *Monotype-Thompson Caster* also makes type for hand sticking. Both are, in effect, small type foundries and give the advantages of new type for every job as well as those of non-distribution of used material.

The same needs of newspapers that encouraged the invention of the Linotype later brought the invention of the *Teletypesetter, TTS*. Although the first commercially successful TTS was introduced as far back as 1928, the device really came into its own only in the period immediately after World War II and its use is still growing.

The TTS is an attachment to the Linotype or Intertype. It is a tape-operated machine that translates coded information. It uses perforated tape, similar to that of the Monotype but only about a quarter as wide. This tape may be punched locally on a unit very similar to an electric typewriter, or may be transmitted by wire from distant points.

News services had long used *Teletypewriters* to transmit copy. An operator types the story at a central news bureau. Each key action is translated into a series of electrical impulses, which are carried by telegraph or telephone wires, or even radio waves, to a distant newspaper office. There the impulses actuate a typewriter, which simultaneously reproduces the original typing. These same impulses perforate tape in the news office even as they produce typescript.

The coded tape is fed into the TTS operating unit on the linecaster where its information is translated into mechanical movements which, in effect, duplicate the action of an operator's fingers on the keyboard to set type.

Advantages are many, in addition to those of tape already discussed for the Monotype. A single operator in New York City, let us say, can punch tape that is simultaneously reperforated in newspapers throughout the country. There, typesetting is virtually automatic. One man, the *monitor,* can service up to four or five linecasters. He feeds tape, removes filled galleys of type, keeps the metal pot filled and corrects any minor mechanical difficulties. The substantial savings of TTS have enabled many a small newspaper to remain operative since World War II. Not only does this method save that time which is never plentiful in news operations, it has enabled many a publisher to overcome the pressing lack of Linotype operators which seems to be chronic in America.

Electro-Typesetting, ETS, is a newer variation of tape-operation. Although it uses electronic, rather than mechanical, power, and by-passes the conventional keyboard to operate directly upon the matrix-release mechanism, its similarity to TTS is far greater than its disparity.

As this book goes to press, the Linotype company has just announced its own *Linomatic Tape System, LTS,* consisting of a perforator and operating unit. Among features to increase speed and efficiency is the ability to mix, entirely automatically, matrices from two different fonts.

Composition by tape is most frequently used by newspapers, but it is becoming increasingly popular for books and commercial typesetting. Union restrictions have prevented its maximum utilization but leaders in the craft believe that, like the original mechanization of typesetting by the Linotype, wider use of automatic tape composition will prove to be a stimulus to the already important growth of the industry.

SELECTION AND USE OF TYPE

The function of type is solely to convey information, easily, quickly, and clearly. No matter by what method it is set, there are well defined principles that assure maximum functionalism.

Two characteristics of type are often misunderstood because the terms are used interchangeably—and incorrectly. *Readability* is that characteristic which makes it easy and pleasant to read large masses of type. The pages of a book or columns of newspapers must be set in readable type. *Legibility* is that characteristic which brings a few words off the page and into the comprehension of the reader as rapidly and unmistakably as possible. The word STOP on a highway sign is an excellent example of legibility, but graphic artsmen are most concerned with this quality in headlines, title pages, chapter headings, etc.

Roman types have the highest readability; Sans Serifs, the highest legibility.

Sometimes it is easy to confuse the function of type in a specific use. In telephone directories, stock market quotations, and classified advertising pages we see Sans Serifs used well. Here are large masses of type and the immediate conclusion of many people is that here we must use a face of high readability. Yet, despite the many lines of type, the reader is interested in only a few: a single name and phone number, two or three stocks, those want ads under a single heading.

The typographer has three choices that make for readability: the face itself, the line length, the spacing within and between lines.

The selection of a type face is not always easy; there are literally thousands of fonts to choose from. What, then, are the characteristics the specifier should seek in a face?

Readable type is *big on the slug*. This is another way of saying that it should have a large x-height. It has already been observed that point sizes are not an unwavering unit of measurement. If the designer devotes much of the available area to ascenders and descenders, the bowls and primary letters must be small. Yet it is these letters that determine the size of a font of type as far as the reader's eye is concerned. So type specifiers seek those faces in which the x-height is the largest possible for a given point size.

A good type face should be *invisible*. The reader should easily grasp entire words and phrases without being aware of the individual letter forms. That precludes obtrusive letter designs; eccentric curves or serifs call so much attention to themselves that the reader is distracted.

The type must have a *pleasant texture*. As the letters are woven into a fabric of words, the over-all tonal value must be dark enough so the eye need not strain, yet not so heavy that it irritates. The only way to determine the texture is to scrutinize type, not by individual letters or a line or two, but in large blocks, as most type specimen books show.

Type should have *proper proportions*. The printer says: "You can see a pumpkin better than a goose egg." He means that a full, round O is easier to read than one that has been squeezed into an oval. Faces always lose readability in condensation. So, although there are times when small amounts of Condensed type can be used effectively, if choice is possible, a fullface type should be selected.

Other proportions contribute to the basic design of the letters that effect texture and invisibility. Whether a face is "beautiful" or not varies with the eye and taste of the beholder, whether that face belongs to type or a human female. In the final analysis, every type specifier must rely on his own judgment. It may be of help, though, to note the selection of body type for the Fifty Books of the Year, the annual selection by the American Institute of Graphic Arts of the best books produced in the United States. In the 34 years since 1925, Baskerville set 152 winners; Janson, 115; Granjon, 112; Caledonia, 94, and Caslon Old Face, 87. It should be noted that Caledonia achieved its success in only 18 of those years—it wasn't cut until 1940.

The type face must be *appropriate*. There is a definite, if hard to define, flavor to even the most unobtrusive type design. So the appropriately named Primer or Schoolbook have a natural affinity to textbook composition. Many faces have strong feminine or masculine connotations. Type must be appropriate to the paper on which, and to the process by which, it will be printed. Rough papers love Old Style Romans and other rugged faces; high-finish papers treat Modern Romans and lighter faces in a most kindly fashion. Newspaper ads should be set in faces that have been designed to withstand the distortions of stereotyping; for gravure, faces must have sturdy bodies lest their hairlines disappear in screening.

Copy set in all capitals is difficult to read. This is because we "read" only the top portion of letters in normally rapid reading. The top silhouette of lowercase letters is distinctive and easy to distinguish; that of all-caps is basically a rectangle with few variations to make word recognition easy. Capitals can be used for titles and very short headlines but all-cap matter should be kept at a minimum.

One of the few flat statements that can be made about type is this: Text, Script, Cursive, and ornamental initials can never be used in all-capitals. In most cases the result is not even a pleasing design element. In all cases, it is the nadir of illegibility.

Printers attribute low readability to Italics although this is not necessarily a concomitant of the Italic form. Indeed, suspicion has arisen that it was the desire to avoid using Italic with its fragile kerns that gave birth to this disparagement. If an Italic is designed to meet the specifications we have just discussed, its readability is acceptable. Most Italics are too light for effective readability in masses but this lightness is useful when a typographic accent is sought.

When Rudolph Ruzicka designed Electra, he recognized that in many books, and other composition, there is a need to set large quantities of copy in an accent face. So he made Electra Italic as an Oblique Roman that retained the readability of the perpendicular letterform. Later he added Electra Cursive, which is a true Italic; another example of the rugged independence of typographic nomenclature!

Typographic harmony must be sought whenever type is mixed.

Rarely is it necessary to mix body types; the perpendicular, oblique and boldface readily available are almost always adequate to achieve the necessary differences. Sometimes a different font must be selected, of course, if words in a foreign language or mathematical or scientific symbols must be interspersed into the copy. In this case, the main factor is one of texture and color.

The choice of display type used with text sizes is important. If the body type is 10-point or smaller, any headletter will blend reasonably well. Thus we find newspapers using Roman or Sans headlines with equal effectiveness. A *headline schedule,* the complete assortment of all headline forms used by a newspaper, is most effective if it is entirely within one race and preferably within one family. To have to shift mental gears between Bodoni and Metro slows down reading as much as gear-shifting slows down driving.

This same harmony should be sought in all printing, advertising, books, letterheads, etc. Keep all display lines in one family.

Occasionally an *accent face* is desired. In the case of newspapers, the accent is used for *kicker heads,* small ones that ride above a main head as here, where *Doctors Plead* is the kicker:

Doctors Plead

Children Bitten by Dog Sought in Rabies Scare

This accent is best when it is an exaggerated form of the basic headletter. In our example, Spartan Extra Black is used with Spartan Bold. Ultra Bodoni or Poster Bodoni—they are the same Extra Heavy version—or Companile or Onyx, the Condensed, are excellent accents for a Bodoni schedule.

In other printing, the accent face may also be from the same family or from an entirely different race. Whatever the accent, it should be used sparingly. The speaker who accents every word communicates as poorly as he who mumbles in a monotone.

When body type is 12-point or larger, display type should harmonize very closely or contrast markedly. In many families, there is an adequate size range so that body and display can be set in the same family.

But if the two kinds of type are chosen from a major subdivision of a single race, harmony is usually assured. Sans Serif wears well with most body types. Headlines from other races should be chosen to harmonize by weight, either approximating the tonal value of text type or varying as extremely as possible. This cannot be reduced to formula; the designer must train his eye to make proper selection.

Initials, although they help form text words, must be considered as display. They must match exactly or vary greatly. Initials are useful to add typographic color to large masses of body type which might otherwise be as gray and unappetizing as a big bowl of cold oatmeal. Many fonts of initials are available. Their size is indicated by points or by the number of lines of text type they occupy: thus, a 3-line initial.

Initials are used in two ways. The *inset initial* occupies a space cut out of the top left corner of a paragraph. Ideally it should align at the top with the x-line of the text and at the bottom with the baseline of the smaller letters. This is often difficult to achieve without spacing the adjacent text lines at a distance which is not desirable for succeeding lines. Inset initials pose problems in mechanical typesetting; under pressure of stereotyping, they frequently break.

Rising initials align with the baseline of, and rise above, accompanying text type. This is easy to achieve and, mechanically, the best way to use initials. The white space that they "build in" above the first line of text is useful in adding "fresh air" to the page.

Initials align at the left with body type. But those such as *T, A, V,* and *W* often have to be moved farther to the left so the alignment is on the mass of the letter, the stem of the *T,* for instance, rather than on the left edge of the lighter cross stroke.

When the initial is enclosed in an ornamental frame, it is almost always inset. It usually aligns at the top and bottom of the frame. But where ornamentation is light, as in Dutch Initials, for instance, alignment is made on the initial itself, not the ornamental elements.

The length of a line—or *measure*—of type has major bearing on its readability. Oldtime printers established a formula which modern researchers have validated: *The optimum line length is 1.5 times the lowercase alphabet length.*

We cannot always set type at the optimum measure. But we should never set it less than 25 per cent narrower or more than 50 per cent wider than the optimum.

A less exact formula is adequate in many instances: *The optimum line length is twice the point size of the type,* with the answer in picas. Thus, an 8-point type would have a 16-pica optimum, 12 picas as minimum and 24 picas as maximum measures.

Body type set on keyboarded linecasters should not be set wider than 30 picas to avoid butted slugs.

Headlines should have a maximum of 32 or 33 characters and spaces per line. A greater number reduces legibility.

Display type is customarily read line by line and should be written so that each line is reasonably self-contained. Breaking closely knit phrases breaks the normal rhythm or stride of reading. Headlines such as these:

NEW BONNETS FOR LITTLE
GIRLS' EASTER PARADE

or

ASTRONAUTS' TRIP TO
MOON EXPECTED SOON

demonstrably result in a jarring disruption of reading as the eye reads the first line, embarks upon the second, realizes that a phrase has been split, then goes back to the first line to pick up the adjective or preposition and carries it down to the next line where it makes sense.

The loss in time is not significant. But the break in *reading rhythm* is. As long as the eye can move along at a normal stride and pace, reading is adequately easy. But anything that breaks the rhythm irritates the eye. *Eye fatigue* is often the determining factor in how much of a printed message the reader will consume. When the eye gets tired—even though its owner is not specifically aware of it—he will quit reading. While the delay or annoyance of a single misuse is almost too slight to measure, the accumulative effect is considerable and serious.

Spacing, as much as any single factor, influences reading rhythm. Interlineal spacing, ledding, must be designated for all composition. Inadequate ledding makes it difficult for the eye to read a line of type without distraction from those above and below. Too much ledding makes type "fall apart"; the eye must search for the start of each line instead of moving flowingly to that point from the end of the preceding one.

Descenders help determine adequate interlineal spacing. Where descenders are long, they create more white space between lines of primary letters than when short descenders are used. Up to 8-point type,

Fig. 28. Decorative initials. Inset initial, lower left; rising initial, lower right.

a half point of ledding is usually preferred. From 8- through 12-point a whole point of ledding is usually the best. It is wise to accumulate samples of type with various ledding so that you can see the effect of interlineal spacing on masses of the body type. Ledding is a major determinant of texture.

Display type, too, must be kept close enough so that the eye moves smoothly from line to line. For headlines, type shoulders usually afford optimum spacing. If any spacing other than this is required, it is usually indicated on the dummy and supplied by the makeup man.

Justification of columns by *ledding out* is almost always done by the makeup man without consultation with the designer. But this should not be taken for granted; unobtrusive as it is, ledding contributes greatly to the harmony of a page.

Extra ledding should be done from the top of a page or column. If type must be stretched out to an extreme, extra space—usually a slug—may be dropped above the start of each paragraph. But if the column is just two or three lines short, 2-point ledds should be dropped between lines of the first paragraph. Should ledding have to be done in more than one paragraph, it is wise to drop, not two, but four points of space between the first and second paragraphs.

Under no circumstances may ledding be done from the bottom. This is an abominable practice in many newspapers. It saves the makeup man a few seconds, but the result is horrible. After the reader has read many lines spaced normally and then comes upon the last five or six lines with extra ledding, the effect is that of a bagpipe that is slowly expiring with disquieting grunts and groans.

The spacing between words is equally important to readability. Word spacing should never be wider than the division necessary to separate words. For machine composition, the typesetter should be instructed to use *narrow spacebands*; there are five different band widths. In hand setting, a quarter-em space is best. Word spacing will vary, of course, to justify the line. But in all cases, extreme word spacing that causes "rivers" of white to run down the column should be avoided.

It was customary to drop an em quad after a period on the theory that the pause between sentences is longer than between words and must be so indicated spatially. But the signal is the punctuation mark, not the space. So modern practice is to use normal word spacing after a period. Copy set all-caps usually requires an en quad between words.

Except in extreme cases, *letterspacing* should be avoided in body type unless justification is absolutely impossible by any other means. Often all-cap words must be letterspaced to create the optical effect of equal spacing, especially in display sizes. In the following example, the top word is spaced normally. Yet the I and N look much closer together than the T and Y. So, in the second line, extra spacing has been added to make all letters look in proper relation to adjacent ones. Because this

LINOTYPE

LINOTYPE

technique is used to create an optical effect, it is also called *optical spacing*. When letterspacing is used, word spacing must increase proportionately.

Condensed letters should never be letterspaced. Their capitals are so designed that they will fit properly with normal spacing. It negates the only excuse for Condensed letters when they are stretched out to occupy more space.

Paragraph indention is usually one em. Sometimes no indent is used at all, a blank line above the start of the paragraph serving as the indicator. This is effective but does carry the danger that this space will inadvertently be omitted. The result is confusion, however slight, which adversely affects readership.

Some designers like to use *paragraph starters*. Instead of the normal indent, the paragraph begins with a paragraph mark, one of the standard symbols in many fonts, such as these:

¶ ¶ ¶ ► (g ¶ (
(¶ ¶ ◄ (¶ ¶ (
(¶ ¶ ¶ ¶ ¶ (¶
(¶ ¶ ¶ ¶ ¶ (¶

or a *bullet* (a large period), arrow, triangle, or some decorative element may be used. This technique is especially effective for listing a number of items, either alone or with explanatory text.

The end of a paragraph often creates a *widow line*. Some designers consider any line not completely filled as a widow. Others keep the term only for those less than a quarter filled.

Widows are particularly annoying to book designers. Pages that begin or end with a widow have a ragged look as opposed to the neat rectangle formed by full lines. In good books, type is manipulated to avoid placing widows at the top or bottom of pages.

Widows can be remedied by deleting or adding a word or two of copy. In some cases this is justifiable. But it is presumptuous of the designer to ask an author to change his copy just to make it fit into an arbitrary shape. Well-written copy suffers when it is edited by the mathematics of copyfitting rather than by its sense or style. Contemporary designers accept this and are far less concerned with widows than the past generation was.

But there are times when widows should be eliminated, even by drastic means. If the eye must travel a long distance from the end of Column 1 to the start of Column 2, it justifiably feels imposed upon if, having made the long trek, it finds only a word, or even a syllable, at the head of the succeeding column.

Some, usually older, designers get quite exercised if more than two successive lines end in hyphens or punctuation marks. Surely it is annoying to the eye if many hyphens or points pile up on each other, or if too many successive lines begin with a capital. The effect is one of tabulation and does hamper reading rhythm. Whether a designer should set an arbitrary number of lines which can begin or end repetitively is a matter of argument; it is probably better to solve each problem as it arises rather than to attempt to create a formula.

If any matter is inserted into a block of body type, space surrounding it is important. Tables, figures, cut-in notes, or pictures are often dropped into type. In all cases, these should definitely be more or less than half the measure of body type; never should the column be divided evenly. Space above, below and at the side of such inserts should be equal and it should be appreciably greater than word spacing. If the insert is of irregular shape, such spacing must give the effect of being equal all around even though, mathematically, this is impossible. If the outline is very intricate, it is best to leave a rectangle of white upon which to place the picture.

Tabulations follow specific rules which need not be dwelled on here; every good typesetter is well aware of them. We might note, however, that in most fonts, numbers are all of equal width so that vertical columns are automatically achieved whether the numbers be a narrow 1 or a wide 5.

One form of tabulation which is entirely in the hands of the typographic designer is the coupon—an excellent device—which is used so much in advertising. Coupons defeat their own purpose if adequate space has not been left, both vertically and horizontally, for the respondent to write his name and address with ease. At least a pica of white space, and preferably 14 points, should be the minimum height of such blanks. The typical city needs at least 5 picas; a state, 2, and a street address, 8, to allow comfortable space for writing.

Another tabulation specification that the designer must make concerns the *leaders*. These are the line of dots or dashes that connect a tabulated item at the start of a line with other data, so:

Automobile registrations 8,796

Few designers realize that there is any difference in leaders. Yet the Linotype specimen book lists over 20 styles. They are either periods or hyphens, varying from two to six characters per em. Two-unit patterns are entirely adequate to lead the eye across the page and they assure sharp, clean printing.

Equally unknown is the fact that fractions are available in several styles. With many fonts, fractions are cut in either 1-en or 1-em widths. The line dividing the two numbers may be horizontal or diagonal. *Piece fractions* have the superior figure and the lower half of the slash on one matrix, the rest of the slash and the inferior figure on another, so that any fraction may be created. Most fonts have only the simple, widely used fractions ½ to ⅞. But *universal fractions* can be used for such composition that requires a wider range. Universal fractions in Roman run through $63\!/\!64$. For Sans Serif faces universal fractions have *single-numerator fractions* from ⅛ through $9\!/\!64$. Independent superior figures can be added before the numerator to give a complete range through sixty-fourths. Beyond that, fractions are created by using regular numbers divided by a slash.

Universal fractions, in 6- through 12-point, blend without disturbance into any body type. But in display sizes, fractions are a nuisance. Many printers use any fractions in the proper size that they have on hand with no regard for typographic harmony. (The % is another mark misused this way because many display fonts do not have this character.) It is better to use regular numerals and the slash and to spell out per cent—or abbreviate to *pct.*—rather than use a disharmonious character in conspicuous sizes.

If many—indeed, any—fractions must be used, it is wise to consider their availability in the regular font.

This same foresight is valuable when specifying type for copy that requires many footnotes. In Caledonia, used in this book, footnote signs include the asterisk *, dagger †, double dagger ‡, section mark § and paragraph mark ¶. These will handle the most intricate annotations. Most such marks are universal in design and can be transferred from one font to another. But attention to details as minute as this is the mark of a good typographer.

All principles of spacing may be summed up: Type carries a message; it must have room to do its job. We would not expect an orator to convey an effective message in a telephone booth; we cannot expect type to carry a message unless it has elbow room.

UNLIKE
THE SHORT-
TAILED SHREW*

*Smaller than a mouse, this ● is the most nervous and irascible of all mammals. Some are so high-strung that a sudden sound will cause them to leap into the air, fall in a dead faint, or even drop dead! They also shriek when enraged, which is very often. Unlike the Short-Tailed Shrew, Economy Lithograph is a monument of calm. If the pressures become unbearable, a few wives may be beaten with an old matrice, but there is never an intemperate word to a customer. Some customers claim that by dealing with Economy they save enough in Miltowns alone to pay for a small printing job each year. If you think this is just advertising chatter, start keeping track of your tranquillizer consumption. Then switch to Economy and marvel at the difference. ¨ECONOMY LITHOGRAPH CO., 101 So. La Brea, Los Angeles WE-8-2511.

USA ★

Monthly News & Current History

It is a year for new magazines! TV, sex, hot-rods, body-building, crime, even the most circumscribed interests now command whole publications. This is about a different new magazine, one whose range is broad -- ideas, people, events, and our survival as a nation. It is called USA 1 and you are invited herein to preview a first issue before being billed .... and then, if you like Volume I, Number 1, to benefit from CHARTER SUBSCRIPTION PRIVILEGES

Fig. 29. Type set in forms other than rectangles. "Shrew" courtesy Economy Lithography Co.; "flower pot," in hand lettering, courtesy New York Times; device, courtesy USA 1 magazine.

If you make it your constant motto that TYPE WAS MADE TO BE READ, you need not memorize formal axioms. Common sense will tell when type is forced to work under conditions that make its job impossible.

Type is not a decorative element. Fads come, too often, and go, too slowly, in typography. With the regularity of locusts, new styles hatch that use type only to create patterns—and ignore or kill readability. This is acceptable in designing patterns for shower curtains; it is anathema to conveying information.

While headline type is most commonly perverted to the use of design, body type also falls victim. Type is most easily read in neat rectangles. It should not be set into diamonds and circles or to create the shape of vases or Christmas trees or crosses. The design created may be pleasant, but if the readability of type has been diminished even slightly, the typographer is as guilty—or foolish—as the man who uses a finely tempered straight-edge razor to cut linoleum or digs a fence-post hole with a soup spoon instead of a shovel.

Anyone who embarks on the task of communicating has voluntarily assumed an obligation to communicate clearly. The typographic designer must make communication his primary objective. Only by knowing his tools and using them with skill, respect, and honesty can he hope to achieve this difficult task.

SUGGESTED READINGS

Abel, Oscar R., and Straw, Windsor A. Mechanism of the Linotype and Intertype. New York: John de Graff, Inc., 1950.

A Composition Manual. Philadelphia: Printing Industries of America, 1953.

Elements of Composition. Unit I of the ITU Lessons in Printing. Indianapolis, Ind.: International Typographic Union, 1950.

Orcutt, William Dana, and Bartlett, Edward E. Manual of Linotype Composition. New York: Mergenthaler Linotype Co., 1923.

6

Copyfitting

EQUALIZING TYPE AND SPACE

How much space will the President's Message take in the annual report?

I've got this much room for captions in this picture layout. How many words will it take to fill it exactly?

What is the biggest size type in which I can set this booklet and keep it in 16 pages?

Problems like this are common and constant. Their solution is simple. For *copyfitting*—establishing area ratios between typescript and type— is not the bugbear it is commonly considered. This calumny springs from the cumbersome systems that are being slowly discarded; they will not even be mentioned here. Why should they be, when a simple and highly accurate one is available? It's the *character-per-pica system*.

The best way to learn it is to set up a problem, then work it out while reading this explanation.

PROBLEM: A manuscript for a book on gardening consists of 217 pages of typescript, 29 lines to the page, and 62 characters in an average line.

This will be set in 10-point Caledonia, ledded 1 point, in 25-pica lines. Pages will be 36 picas deep.

How many illustrations can we have while keeping the book to 192 pages?

The key to any copyfitting problem is the manuscript; it makes a difference if the compositor has a single sheet of copy or if he is handed the manuscript of *Gone With the Wind.* So the first step is to evaluate the manuscript—*ms.*

The typesetter is concerned with the total number of *characters in the ms* rather than the number of words, even if the latter is the most popular editorial measurement. Five hundred words of *Look, Tom, look. The dog is here!* in a children's book would occupy far less space than 500 multisyllabic jawbreakers of a scientist writing about parthenogenesis or nuclear physics.

First, determine the length of the average typescript line, either by actually counting the characters or measuring it. *Pica* type, the larger of the two common typewriter faces, measures 10 characters per horizontal inch. *Elite,* the smaller face, measures 12 characters per inch.

Then determine the number of lines per average page. This too, can be done by counting; the usual page has about 30 lines so this is not a formidable task. Or you can measure: Double-space (on which most editors insist) runs 3 lines per vertical inch. Single space has 6 lines and triple-space (rarely used), 2 lines per inch.

Multiplying the number of lines by the characters per line gives *characters per ms page.* This, multiplied by the number of pages, gives the total *characters in the manuscript:* (29 lines $\times$ 62 characters $\times$ 217 pages $=$ 390,166): the first required information.

If a more accurate count is required, draw a faint pencil line within the right margin of the typewritten page. Then count the characters by which each line falls short or exceeds this mark, noting them as $+$ or $-$ in the margin.

Multiplying the number of lines by the number of characters to the penciled limit, then adding the pluses and minuses, gives the precise number of characters.

Note that the first line in a paragraph is counted to include the blank spaces of the indention at the left. On average copy, count the short lines that end a paragraph as a complete manuscript line; this will average out with similar short lines in the typeset job.

Counting manuscript characters is predicated on the fact that each typewritten character receives the same space horizontally. While this is true on standard typewriters, it does not apply to newer models which use proportionate spacing. So it is wise to have manuscripts typed on standard machines.

Undoubtedly there is a formula which will compensate for variations in typewritten characters just as it does for those in type metal. It will take time to derive such a formula, for it must be proved by applying it to a great many specimens of typescript, just as did the experts from Mergenthaler Linotype Company who devised the *cpp formula* for type.

Now the copyfitter follows the steps that the typesetter must perform.

The first thing a compositor must know as he embarks upon a job is, "What type face do I set this in?" Then he must know the *measure,* the length of the type line.

Face and line are vital factors. A block of copy set in 24-point type will occupy more space than the identical copy in 6-point; the longer the line, the more characters in it.

Another determining factor is the width of the individual charac-

Alphabet Lengths — Characters by Picas

								241	1.45
								250	1.4
								260	1.35
								270	1.3
73	4.35	91	3.55	118	2.85	162	2.15	260	1.35
75	4.25	93	3.5	120	2.8	166	2.1	270	1.3
76	4.20	94	3.45	122	2.75	170	2.05	280	1.25
77	4.15	96	3.4	124	2.7	175	2.	295	1.2
79	4.05	98	3.35	127	2.65	180	1.95	310	1.15
80	4.	100	3.3	129	2.6	185	1.9	325	1.1
81	3.95	102	3.25	132	2.55	190	1.85	340	1.05
82	3.9	104	3.2	135	2.5	195	1.8	360	1.
83	3.85	106	3.15	138	2.45	200	1.75	380	.95
84	3.8	108	3.1	142	2.4	206	1.7	400	.9
86	3.75	110	3.05	146	2.35	212	1.65	425	.85
87	3.7	112	3.	150	2.3	218	1.6	450	.8
88	3.65	114	2.95	154	2.25	225	1.55	475	.75
90	3.6	116	2.9	158	2.2	233	1.5	500	.7

Fig. 30. Conversion chart showing characters per pica when lowercase-alphabet length is known.

ters. A face with fat, round *o*'s and *a*'s and widespread *M*'s and *W*'s will fill more space than a face of the same point-size whose *o*'s are goose eggs and whose *M*'s are squeezed-together columns.

This *set-width* factor determines the number of *characters per pica* that any given face will fill. This information is usually given in the type specimen book with which the estimator works. As this factor, *cpp*, is a function of the *lowercase alphabet length, lca*, it may be determined by a simple conversion chart such as Figure 30. Any face with an lca of 104 points, for instance, has 3.2 characters per pica.

It must be kept in mind that the estimator needs the cpp for the specific face with which he works. Linotype Baskerville 6-point, as an example, has 3.8 characters per pica, while the same face as cut by American Type Founders counts 4.96. This is a spread of some 30 per cent and even in a short novel would make a sizable difference in the number of pages of type.

In the given problem, setting is in 10-point Caledonia. Its lowercase alphabet length is 130, and its cpp 2.55.

This Caledonia will be set 25 picas wide. Thus, multiplying characters per pica (cpp) times the number of picas in the line—2.55 × 25— gives 63.75 *characters per average line of type* (cpl).

Remember that this 63.75 is an average. While we cannot have .75 characters dangling at the end of each line, there will be some lines that run heavily to *l*'s and *i*'s, narrow characters, and perhaps have a total of 65, or even more. Others may contain only 60 or 61, should they have more *m*'s and *W*'s than usual. This average has been determined for the Latin alphabet used in the English language.

Now the Linotype operator begins hitting keys. Each time he has hit 63.75 of them he has produced a line of type. Dividing 63.75 into the total manuscript characters, 390,166, shows that when he's exhausted the manuscript, he will have produced 6,120 and a fraction lines of type.

This fraction must be counted as a whole line. Whether type fills all 25 picas, 24 of them or only 10 or 11, it is a whole line of metal; the quads at the end of a line occupy as much area as do letters.

Now, how many pages will all these lines of type occupy? That depends, of course, on the depth of each page and how thick each line is. Specifications tell that the pages will be 36 picas deep and that each line will be the depth of the type, 10 points, plus one point of ledding— 11 points.

Vertical measurements should always be converted to points because that is the unit by which the thickness of a line of type is measured. Because the width of a line is measured in picas, horizontal measurements are always converted to picas.

The 36-pica page equals 432 points. Divide 11 points (the depth of one line) into the depth of the page. Answer: 39³⁄₁₁ lines. As we cannot print the top ³⁄₁₁ of a line, drop this fraction. If 39 lines make one page, 6,121 lines—by simple division—make 156.9 pages. Subtracting that figure from the total of 192 pages proposed for this book shows that there will be 35.1 pages to devote to charts, diagrams, and photos.

If the original question posed had been "How many pages will this copy make?" the answer would not be 156.9 pages, for there can be no fraction of a page. If there is as much as a single line to be printed, there must be a whole page of paper to print it on.

So the copyfitter would answer: "This copy makes 157 pages; but the last page will be four lines short." He adds the qualifier especially in case there are only a very few lines on the last page. It may be that, by eliminating widows, the compositor can gain those few lines and perhaps save not only that page but a whole signature, which is discussed in Chapter 20.

To recap the copyfitting process:
1. Determine the characters in the manuscript.
2. Determine the characters per average line of type, cpl (cpp ×
no. picas per line).
3. Determine the number of lines of type.
4. Determine the number of lines per page.
5. Determine the number of pages.

Note that in Step 2, fractions of a character are retained, because the estimator is working with averages for a great number of lines and, the greater the number, the closer the average comes to actuality.

In Steps 3 and 5, fractions are rounded off to the next higher number because, in metal or on paper, a fraction of a line or of a page occupies as much space as if it were completely filled.

In Step 4, round off to the lower number of lines per page because you cannot print just that fraction of a line.

Once the simple steps outlined here are mastered, any copy-estimating problem can easily be solved.

A typical problem is: "I have room in this ad for a block of copy 2½ inches wide and 3 inches deep. How many words do I have to write to fill it exactly?"

In this case you cannot first take Step 1, determining characters in the manuscript. It must be the last step, the answer you seek.

So move to Step 2, finding cpl. Characters per pica depends on the face. It is decided to set this in 8-point Bodoni; its cpp is 2.85. The line will be 2½ inches long, so convert it into picas—2½ × 6 equals 15 picas —and determine that there will be 42.75 characters per average type line.

How many lines will fit into this copy block? Three inches is 216 points deep. If the type is set solid, each line will occupy 8 points and 27 lines will fit into the area. Each line contains 42.75 characters and so 27 × 42.75 tells us the total characters to write—1,154.25. Drop the .25 character; you cannot typewrite part of a letter.

But the question was, "How many words?" As has already been noted, "words" is a poor unit of measurement. But because many copy-writers insist on this answer, a "word" has arbitrarily been defined as five characters. In this problem the answer would be given both as 230 words—dropping the last four characters because a fraction of a word is not possible—and as 1,154 characters, for a more accurate measure-ment.

Suppose the type will be set with 1 point of ledding. Then each line is 9 points deep. Dividing 216 points by 9 points gives 24 lines; now you need 24 × 42.75, or 1,026 characters, to fill.

If type is ledded 2 points, each line will be 10 points thick. Ten divided into 216 points is 21.6 lines. In this case, drop the fraction as there cannot be just the top .6 of a line in print. Nor can the other .4 of a line extend beyond the specified copy block; there just isn't room for it.

All problems of copyfitting body type are variations of the two worked out here.

The important thing to remember, in copyfitting, is to visualize the actual steps that are taken in the composing room. Do not con-sider this as an abstract mathematical problem. When you visualize Linotype slugs fitting into a chase, common sense will save you from making common errors, such as moving a decimal and deciding there will be 422 characters in a line. You recognize at once that a line of that many characters will not fit on the page of any book ever seen.

Unusually short lines—less than 20 characters—will often require letter spacing or extra word spacing; so the number of printing characters may be fewer than cpp × line length will show. Unusually long lines may contain more characters than the formula determines. Such extremes in length reduce readability and should be avoided. When this is not possible, it is wise to have the compositor set about a third of a galley so you can determine the degree of accuracy of your estimate before the job proceeds to a point where any necessary revision in plans becomes too costly.

The problem of fitting display type into a given area (or determining the maximum characters that will fit into a layout) is much simpler. You are working with smaller numbers and can actually measure the space of a word.

Assume that you have the headline for an ad: *It's Paint-up Time!* The layout indicates that 28 picas is the maximum line length that can be used.

You want to set this in the largest Caslon that will fit, so turn to the type specimen page showing this face (Fig. 31). Specimen books commonly repeat the same phrase for each showing. Now type the *key phrase* and, immediately under it, the headline:

Have The Chronicle-Telegram, The
It's Paint-Up Time

You know that your head will occupy approximately as much space as *Have The Chronicle*.

Measure the length of that phrase in 24-point; it occupies 20 picas. In 30-point, it is 24 picas long; in 36, it is 30 picas. To keep it within the 28-pica maximum, you have to use 30-point.

In the specimen book illustrated—and in many others—pica increments are underprinted in green. If there is no grid, we simply measure with a pica rule.

This method assumes that all letters, numbers, and punctuation points are exactly the same width, and that all capitals are exactly twice as wide as any lowercase letter. Although this is not so, for most purposes wide and narrow letters will average out in almost any given line, and if there are many wide letters, allow more space for them.

The same approximation may be used for body type, when accuracy within a line or two is adequate. Find a block of type set in the face and size you desire. Measure it off at the line length you need. Type

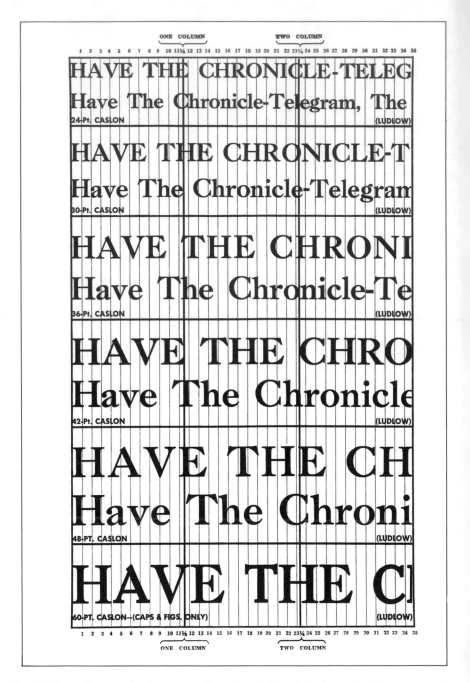

Fig. 31. Page from typical type specimen book. In original, vertical lines, one pica apart, are printed in green. [Courtesy *Elyria* (Ohio) *Chronicle-Telegram*]

three or four consecutive lines. Determine the average characters per line and set your typewriter righthand margin at that number. Then, keeping always under that maximum, type the number of lines needed to fill your space.

When a more accurate fit is required for display type, the newspaper headline writer's *unit count system* should be used. He gives a value to each character: Most lowercase letters, numbers, and spaces count 1; m and w count 1½; punctuation, i, and l count ½; M and W, 2½; I, 1; all other capitals, 2.

So our headline counts;

1	1	½	1	1	2	1	½	1	1	1	2	1	1	2	½	1½	1	½	
I	t	'	s	P	a	i	n	t	-	U	p	T	i	m	e	!			

$= 20½$ units

Using the same system, count out 20½ units on the sample line in the key phrase; the head will occupy 24 picas in 30-point Caslon Bold.

In this case there is an ample margin—4 picas—for variation in letter widths. But in any case, and using any method, it is always best to write headlines a little short. It is simple to distribute extra spacing to fill out a line; often it is impossible to decrease spacing enough to squeeze type into a tight fit, or, at least, without damaging readability seriously. The practice of eliminating word spacing entirely to make a line fit—a practice of slovenly newspapers or advertisers—can never be condoned.

If these two methods indicate that the head will just fit, with no margin at all, the infallible check is to tick off the width of each letter on a strip of paper and determine the length of the whole head. This requires a specimen which has ABC in addition to, or instead of, a key phrase.

Accurate copyfitting is essential in all phases of converting words into type. It is easy to delete a few words in the manuscript to fit available space; once copy is in type, it may mean resetting many lines in order to make a proper fit. This is costly in cash and time and the results often show the pressure of deadlines under which such condensation is done.

Arithmetic must be precise. A minor error in addition may cause an unforeseen additional press run or result in wasted, blank pages. Prove every arithmetical answer.

It will pay handsome dividends to any designer to master copyfitting; he will use it as often as he uses multiplication tables.

7

Proofreading

TO ERR IS HUMAN

Typesetters are instructed to "follow the copy . . . out the window."

The *proofreader* insists that copy be followed implicitly. It is his important job to make sure that the printed word reproduces exactly the words of the manuscript. Should it have to be followed out the window, he will question the author about the accuracy of a statement or the use of a word. But basically the proofreader leaves to the author all responsibility other than that of cleansing the printed work of any compositor's errors.

This is a ceaseless task; to err is human and compositors are human. Add certain characteristics of typesetting machines and the opportunity for error is staggering.

Checking for accuracy begins long before the typesetter sees the manuscript. The author himself and several skilled readers examine the manuscript meticulously, to correct or query errors of fact, or grammar and construction, and of typewriting. (This is *copyreading*, which we shall not discuss in this volume, but which has been explained in many admirable books including those listed in the bibliography at the end of this chapter.)

The typesetter makes the first *proofreading* check. Each time he sets a line of type, whether by hand or machine, he looks at the type, matrices or hard copy to correct any mechanical errors which he or the

74

machine may have made. We shall examine procedure with hot-metal machines although cold type follows the same general steps.

When a galley of type has been set it is *proved*—or *proofed*—by printing from it on a simple hand press. The proof is pulled on long narrow sheets of paper whose size and shape roughly duplicate that of the galley which gives the name *galley proofs.*

This proof is read and corrections ordered. After they are made, a revised proof is pulled. This *first revise* is read as carefully as the first proof; special care is given to the corrections, lest new errors be made while original ones are remedied. There may be second or third revises and on some jobs the revises may run to two numbers, not to correct errors but to achieve close to perfect spacing and word division.

After a form has been made up, it may be proofed on the same press used for galley proofs. If the form is too large to fit into this small press, a *stone* or *beaten* proof may be taken. The form, resting on the composing stone, is inked with a hand *brayer*. A piece of paper, sometimes dampened, is placed over the form. A *planer*, a flat block of wood with a large, flat handle, is placed on the paper and pounded with a mallet. The planer is moved so that all the type is thus impressed upon the paper. The resulting proof is crude but adequate.

Even after the form has been locked into the regular press, the first impressions, *page proofs,* are read once more. Although corrections are expensive at this stage, they still are made if necessary.

Proofreading is usually done by two-man teams. The *proofreader* works with the proof; the *copyholder* has the original manuscript. As they take turns reading from the material in front of them, the proofreader marks corrections on the proof.

Sometimes in the composing room, and most frequently by the printing customer, proofs are read by one man who concentrates on the proof and only occasionally compares it to the manuscript. This is called *horsing.*

Corrections are made by two methods, the *guideline system* and the *book system.* In the first, the error is corrected by circling it and running a line from the error to the margin where the correction is written. This method is invitation for confusion. Especially with a *dirty proof,* one containing many errors or changes, the guidelines may cross each other or may obliterate other errors.

In the book system, two marks are used for each error. One, at the scene of the crime, points out the error. The other, on exactly the

Position

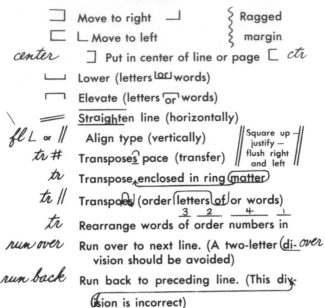

⌐	Move to right ⌐ { Ragged
⌐	∟ Move to left { margin
center	⌐ Put in center of line or page ⌐ *ctr*
	⌐⌐ Lower (letters ⌐or⌐ words)
	⌐⌐ Elevate (letters ⌐or⌐ words)
\ =	Straighten line (horizontally)
fl ∟ or //	Align type (vertically)
tr #	Transposes pace (transfer)
tr	Transpose, enclosed in ring (matter)
tr //	Transpose (order letters of or words)
tr	Rearrange words of order numbers in
run over	Run over to next line. (A two-letter (di- *over* vision should be avoided)
run back	Run back to preceding line. (This division is incorrect)

Square up — justify — flush right and left

Spacing

solid	Means "not leaded" (Pron. "ledded")
leaded	Additional space between lines
lead	Insert lead between lines
₂ ld	Take out lead or) *tr lead*
⌣	Close up entirely; take out space
#⃓	Close up partly; leave some space
⌄ or ⌣	Less space between words
√√√	Equalize space between words
thin #	Thin space where indicated *hair #*
l/s	LETTER-SPACE
#	Insert space (or more space)
space out	More space between words
en quad	½-em (nut) space or indention
☐	Em quad (mutton) space or indention
☐☐☐	Insert number of em quadrats shown

Fig. 32. Proofreader's marks. (Courtesy Mergenthaler Linotype Company, copyright holder)

Size and Style of Type

wf   Wrong font (size or style of type)
        Repeat stop mark for each additional identical error in same line

lc   Lower Case Letter

lc   Set in LOWER CASE or LOWER CASE

caps   Capital letter

        SET IN capitals

u + lc   Lower Case with Initial Caps

sm. caps   SET IN small capitals

caps + s.c.   SMALL CAPITALS WITH INITIAL CAPS

rom.   Set in roman (or regular) type

ital   Set in *italic* (or oblique) type

L.F.   Set in lightface type

bf   Set in **boldface** type

bf ital   ***Bold italic***

    Superior letter or figure[b]

    Inferior letter or figure[2]

A marginal correction of lower case matter should NOT be written in CAPITALS

Punctuation

⊙   Period or "full point."
        Periods and commas ALWAYS go inside quotes

or   Comma   or   Colon

    Semicolon

or   Apostrophe or 'single quote'

or   Quotation marks "quotes"

    Question mark or "query"

    Exclamation point or "bang!"

or   Hyphen   or   En dash

or   One-em dash   Two-em dash

(/)   Parentheses (parens; curves; fingernails)

[/]   Brackets (crotchets)   } Brace

Paragraphing

¶   Begin a paragraph

no ¶   No paragraph.

run in   Run in or run on

2 ¶   Indent the number of em quads shown

flush ¶   No paragraph indention

Insertion and Deletion

OUT   Insert matter omitted; refer to copy
see copy   (Mark copy Out, see proof, galley 0)

the / l   Insert marginal additions

ℓ or ℓ   Dele — take out (delete) (Orig. δ)

ℓ   Delete and close up

stet   Let it stand — (all matter above dots)

Miscellaneous

e /   Correct letter or word marked

e/⊗ k/⊗ or X   Replace broken or imperfect type

⭕   Reverse (upside-down type or cut)

⊥ or ⊤   Push down space or lead that prints

SP   Spell out (20 gr.) (Also used conversely)

G?   Question of grammar

F?   Question of fact

2u au: or ?   Query to author *2u ?*

2u Ed   Query to editor *2u Ed*

A ring around a marginal correction indicates
that it is not the typesetter's error. All queries
should be ringed

OK w/c
or OK a/c   OK "with corrections"   Correct and print; no
     or "as corrected"   revised proof wanted

⌐   Mark-off or break; start new line

End   End of copy: #   or 30   or *End*

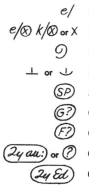

same horizontal line but out in the margin, instructs the typesetter how to correct the fault. The book system is the most efficient one and the only one to be discussed here.

Each composing room has its own variations on the basic system. But mastery of the elementary method will enable any proofreader to be unmistakably understood by the printer or to accommodate himself to any minor variations he may meet.

Proofreaders have a kind of shorthand, symbols that can be quickly written in a form impossible to misunderstand. These symbols are shown in Figure 32. Let us consider those most frequently used.

The most distinctive mark is the *delete* sign. This is an ancient version of the lowercase *d*, its final stroke looping off to the right of the ascender. Because this symbol is written rapidly, it varies as much as any handwritten character does. Care should be taken to write it the same way each time. The delete, as the name expresses, is used to take out unwanted letters, words, phrases, or whole sections of type.

Another frequently used sign is that indicating a *transposition*. This error is often that of the typesetting machine, especially those that are badly worn or not kept perfectly clean. If a matrix, drawn from a channel at the far right of the magazine, is delayed as it drops and is transported to the assembler at the far left, a character from a left-hand channel may drop or enter the assembler first, although its key was struck after that of the tardy matrix. So the word *milk* might appear as *mikl*. To correct this, the transposition mark—something like an S lying on its side—circles the two elements to be transposed and the mark *tr* in the margin tells the printer to reverse the order of letters or words so marked.

The symbol *wf* is frequently seen; it means *wrong font*. This indicates that a matrix or piece of type of the wrong size or style has been used inadvertently.

A mark like an upside-down *T* represents a finger pushing down a slug or spacing material that has worked up high enough to print. A symbol like a square-bottomed *U* depicts a finger pushing type into proper position—left, right, up or down—depending upon the direction of the *U*. The sign that calls for inserting space is the old tick-tack-toe diagram. A pair of parentheses ( ), lying on their sides, joins two separated elements that should be moved together. This mark is used in conjunction with the delete when a superfluous letter—like an extra *e* in *leetter*—is to be removed and the *le* moved tight up to the *t*.

A small open square calls for an em quad. If more quads are needed, a square is drawn for each one or, in a single square, the required number is written.

A hyphen is indicated by two short, parallel lines like the equal sign. A dash is a longer line, with a serif at each end. Its length is indicated by writing a number above the dash and *en* or *em* under it. A paragraph is marked either with an L-shaped mark or with a mark like a reverse P with two vertical strokes.

If a line or a character is upside down, the mark is like a loose 9, as a finger would make didactic by describing clockwise motion.

Most of the other marks are self-explanatory. A few are exaggerated to avoid misunderstanding. A period, for instance, is circled so it is not overlooked. A comma is indicated by a heavy dot with a tail, something like a 9 with the bowl blacked in.

When the author has made what appears to be an obvious error—calling Lincoln our first President, for instance—the proofreader will ask the author about it by writing *Qu?*, for *query*, or just a question mark with a circle around it. This circle is most necessary; an uncircled question mark instructs the compositor to insert a *?*.

Any editor of a military publication that was printed in a foreign shop by craftsmen who did not speak English can recount embarrassing instances when the printer would "correct" an error by setting the proofreader's marks:

The Armwfy said that all non-coms 2/em with the exception of lcCorporals—would draw extra combat pay.

Unfortunately, less obvious but just as disconcerting errors are made in domestic composing rooms, too, especially if proofreading marks are not absolutely clear.

Comma symbols are usually tented with a *caret*, an inverted V. This distinguishes them from the same symbol used for apostrophes or quotation marks, which are written between the arms of a normal V.

The check mark that calls for *equalize spacing* is often confusing. If the compositor has put too much or too little space between two words, the proofreader inserts the check mark between those words and repeats a single check in the margin. But if the space is irregular throughout the entire line, he places a check at each word space and puts three check marks in the margin. This tells the typesetter that spacing is incorrect between all, or at least most, of the words and that the whole line needs reworking.

Marginal correction marks can be written in either the right or left margin as long as they are level with the line. When more than one symbol must be used in one line, they are written in the order in which the errors occur and separated from each other by a diagonal *slash* /.

Marks at the point of the error vary.

When a letter is deleted, it is crossed out by a vertical stroke. If the letters on either side are to be brought together, the sideways brackets are used, too.

Words to be deleted are crossed out by a horizontal stroke. When several lines are to be taken out, the top and bottom lines are crossed out horizontally and these two lines are joined by a large X crossing out the intervening matter.

When a letter must be replaced, either because it is the wrong one or the type is broken, that letter is circled.

Insertions, including that of spacing, are indicated by a caret at the exact point where the new matter is to placed. But when apostrophes, quotes, superior letters, or figures are to be inserted, their position is marked by a regular V written at the top of the line.

If a capital is to be changed to lowercase, the offending letter is slashed diagonally with a light stroke so the compositor can easily tell what it is. When several letters are incorrectly capped, they are circled as a group.

A lowercase letter that should be a capital is underlined with three parallel lines. Two underlines indicates that those letters should be set in small capitals. A single underscore calls for Italics, a wavy underline means boldface and a combination of the two means Bold Italics.

Whole lines often become transposed as Linotype slugs are shuffled. To transpose two lines, the top line is enclosed at the left with a bracket and from it an arrow half-circles down under the next line. At the right margin, a bracket holds the second line and the arrow goes up above Line 1.

If several lines are misplaced, their correct order is marked, 1, 2, 3, etc., in the left margin. *Tr lines* is the marginal instruction.

Insertion or deletion or interlineal spacing is indicated by a V lying on its side, its vertex pointing between the lines where the ledding is to go or come out.

It must be emphasized that every error requires two marks, one at the point of the error and one in the margin. Every time one of the marks discussed in the previous nine paragraphs is used, a proper sym-

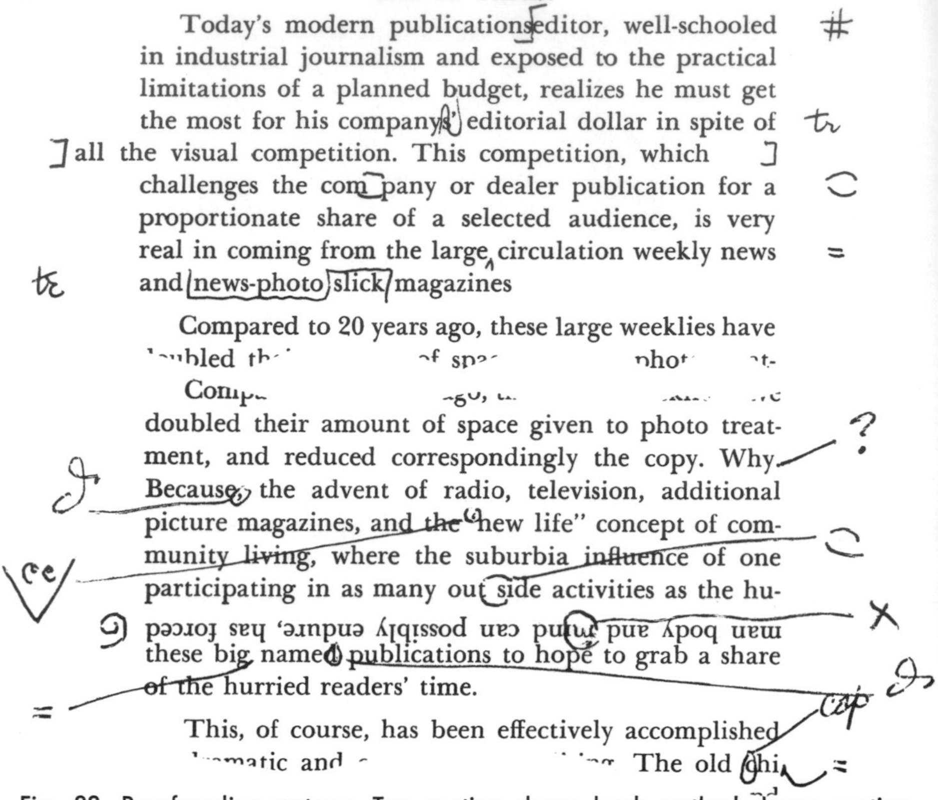

Today's modern publications editor, well-schooled
in industrial journalism and exposed to the practical
limitations of a planned budget, realizes he must get
the most for his companys editorial dollar in spite of
all the visual competition. This competition, which
challenges the com pany or dealer publication for a
proportionate share of a selected audience, is very
real in coming from the large circulation weekly news
and [news-photo] slick magazines

Compared to 20 years ago, these large weeklies have
doubled their amount of space given to photo treatment, and reduced correspondingly the copy. Why.
Because the advent of radio, television, additional
picture magazines, and the "new life" concept of com-
munity living, where the suburbia influence of one
participating in as many out side activities as the human body and mind can possibly endure, has forced
these big named publications to hope to grab a share
of the hurried readers' time.

This, of course, has been effectively accomplished

Fig. 33. Proofreading systems. Top portion shows book method; lower portion, guideline system.

bol must appear in the margin.

Busy as they are in catching other people's errors, proofreaders make
their own, too. When a "correction" turns out to be unnecessary, the
proofreader writes *stet* in the margin. That means: *Let it stand*—just
forget it! Then he underscores, with a dotted line, those letters or words
that were correct in their original form.

Sometimes the typesetter may follow copy faithfully and thus repeat
an error in the manuscript. Suppose the phrase *bays and girls* appears
in the galley proof. The proofreader checks the manuscript; it is the
same way there. He thinks that this should be *boys* instead of *bays* but
he, too, must follow copy. So he makes the obvious correction but at
the same time queries the author and ties the two symbols together
in a large circle. If the author agrees to the correction, he crosses out
the query sign and leaves the correction symbol stand. Or, if he were
attempting a pun and really wanted the word to be *bays*, he crosses

out both symbols, puts a dotted line under the word and commands, Stet!

All the signs and procedures discussed thus far are concerned with correcting typographical errors, those of the typesetter, and so called *office corrections.* The cost of making these corrections is absorbed by the printer as a normal expense.

But authors, too, are human; they change their minds or have second thoughts. These corrections and alterations must also be made to maintain accuracy. These are called *author's alterations—AA's—*and are charged back to the customer.

Suppose you are producing a catalogue for Amalgamated Widget Company. On page 7 of the manuscript, your typist hit the wrong key and the Super-Giant Widget is identified as C-105. But it should be C-106.

If the job is set in foundry type or in Monotype, it is comparatively easy to remove the 5 and replace it with a 6. But if the error is in a Linotype slug, the whole line must be reset. This takes more time—and costs more money. If the face used in this job is not on the machine at the moment, the operator must find the proper magazine and put it on, after taking off one in current use and storing it properly. This takes even more time . . . and the customer must pay for it.

People who buy large quantities of composition estimate that it costs $4 for every line that must be reset. This figure varies, of course, but it is indisputable that the cost is not inconsiderable.

This points up the necessity for close reading of the copy before it gets to the typesetter. Correcting the steno's bobble in the manuscript would have entailed two seconds, crossing out the 5 and writing a 6 above it. Professional copyreading will eliminate almost all such errors.

Now suppose that just before the catalogue goes to press, the sales department finds out that the Colossal Widget Corporation, your deadliest competitor, is selling their comparable model $3 under your price. "We've got to be competitive!" is the anguished cry. "Change the price from $159.95 to $153.88!"

The process of making this *author's alteration* is identical with that of correcting an error. This, too, is paid for by the customer. He is perfectly willing to assume this added expense that business exigencies have forced upon him.

But the author's alteration that can be costliest to make is an editing process that is done in type instead of at the typewriter. The cost may be not only in money but in time. Most printing is done under compelling deadlines and often the time involved becomes a major factor.

Let us suppose that the Super-Giant Widget has been described as a device that brings its own absolute contentment as the red sun slowly sinks in the west. The typesetter has dutifully converted this deathless prose into metal. The proof is delivered to the author. He has decided he doesn't like that word *red*; it lacks the fine feeling necessary to motivate the reader to rush out and buy a widget. He searches his memory, dictionary, and thesaurus and decides that this word should be *crimson*. He crosses out *red* and writes *crimson* in the margin and away goes the proof to the printer.

Now the typesetter resets the line in which *red* appears, putting *crimson* in its place. Alas! The new word has four more letters than the original. What does he do with them? He just breaks that long word at the end of the line and hyphenates it down to the next line. That means resetting Line 2, of course. But still he has those four extra letters. So he carries them, either in the form of hyphenation or as a smaller word, down to the third line, and then the fourth and so on. He may have to reset every line until the end of the paragraph before those excess letters find a permanent home.

So this alteration has cost, not the minimum $4 for resetting a single line, but several more dollars to reset many lines.

It was such second-guessing that kept the novelist Balzac on the fringe of bankruptcy despite the excellent sale of his novels. And it is this expensive revision that causes the most pain (mental and financial) today. There may be some legitimate occasion for making revisions at this late stage. But in the vast percentage of instances, if the need for change of content has not become apparent in the various editing stages, it is probably not necessary after the type has been set. All editing should be done by manipulation of a pencil on copy paper, not type on a galley.

The author, or printing buyer, usually sees the first revised proof. (The printer's proofreader has corrected the typographical errors— *typos*—on the original galley proof.) The second or third revise is also sent to the author so he can determine whether his corrections or alterations were properly made.

Great care should be given to reading the whole correction line, or lines, not just the single error that was originally marked. Correction lines usually have a higher incidence of additional errors than the original galley had.

When the typesetter has to set several lines in the process of making a correction or alteration, these lines will usually be indicated by blue brackets. They must be read even more carefully than on the first proofs for they are brand-new composition and subject to as many mistakes as the original setting.

In reading galley proofs, determine first that the face, size, and ledding are correct. If the face has long or short descenders, check that the proper ones are used here. If Old Style or Modern figures are available, make sure that the proper ones—and only these—have been used. The compositor should use ligatures throughout or not at all; mixing confuses the reader. The buyer of printing is ultimately responsible for both editorial and mechanical accuracy. So first read the proofs for content, punctuation, and capitalization.

Read it a second time for typographical errors. Even when the composition is lengthy, two separate readings will usually save time in the aggregate and will also insure greater accuracy.

Reading with a copyholder is the best method, but often not available to the typical printing buyer. Reading alone demands painstaking attention to detail and should be done in an area free from distraction.

A sharp, clear proof is essential and should be demanded.

In the second reading, ignore words and phrases, concentrate on individual letters. For single errors, make the correction in the left margin. If there are more than two or three errors in a line (an uncommon occurrence), succeeding notations should be made in the right margin.

Once an error is found, be sure to give unusual attention to the balance of that line. Often the proofreader feels overconfident and just skims on after making the initial correction.

This is especially true if a whole line is upside-down. The reader corrects this obvious mistake, then neglects to turn the proof around to read the topsy-turvy line. Errors in transposed lines are also very easy to overlook.

A few usages are automatic danger signals; when you see them, beware. If the copy mentions a series, as: *The first five states in automobile production are*—make sure that five states, not four or six, are listed. When names are repeated, make sure they are identical in each use. *The New Yorker* magazine delights in catching a character in a novel who turns from Anne in Chapter I to Ann in Chapter XXI, and perhaps to Constance somewhere en route. (And all too often her hair changes from red to black because author and copyreader dozed simultaneously.)

Remember that quotes, parentheses, braces, ellipses, and dashes are a pair of hands, holding phrases in apposition; one hand alone cannot enclose such set-apart material. Every time you see one of such a pair, look for the other. In some instances, the period may take the place of one of these separators. But never take that for granted. Nothing will disconcert a reader more than to wade through page after page of improbable conversation before he finds out that someone merely forgot to close a quote.

Whenever a date appears, it should be checked. Was December 22, 1959, really on Thursday? Is Sioux Falls in Iowa or South Dakota? Is Charles Smith's middle initial really *T*?

Hyphenated words require extra care. Have they been broken at proper syllables? Is it Eng-land or En-gland? Buttres-sed or buttress-ed?

Combinations of *l* with *t* or *f* are inherently dangerous. For *tl* can easily be confused with *tt* at a casual glance.

But the most insidious errors are those in which a single wrong letter creates a common—even if incorrect—word. The eye instantly recognizes *pxrt* as an error. But if it is *part* instead of *port*, there is a tendency to overlook it. So you cannot completely shut off reading for sense even though you should concentrate on reading letters the second time.

Reading page proofs of magazines, newspapers, and advertising requires attention to several new points. First, determine that the layout is correct. If any elements are out of position, indicate their proper place. Do not make tiny changes, though. Often the form is not locked as tightly as it will be on the press, and the elements may well shift several points to the proper position in the lock-up process.

Then check art work. Are the proper pictures used? Especially in commercial printing—the hypothetical widget catalogue, for example—there is often little difference between the 2×3-inch picture of an economy model widget on page 3 and a 2×3 of the deluxe model on page 12. Especially those cuts of identical size must be closely scrutinized.

Then check picture captions. Those four men identified around a conference table may easily be the four men at a sales meeting shown three pages later.

Count faces and names in each picture and accompanying caption. Here particularly (although this holds true wherever several names are listed), make sure that each name is complete. If John H. Jones's name appears sixth in a group of 24 names—and especially if it breaks from one line to the next—it is easy to overlook the fact that only *John H.* appears at the end of Line 5 and that Line 6 starts with Sylvester Q. Trumble.

If prices are set in a different, usually larger, face, make sure that they are correct. They have been set separately and it is easy to mix them up when the contents of several galleys are combined in the form.

In advertising, the buyer usually sees his first proof as a made-up form. Type is scattered into several separate groupings, not all together in a block the way it was in galleys. It is wise to set a ruler under each line, read it meticulously, and then put a checkmark at the right of the line to indicate it has been read. Before the proof is returned, inspect it to make sure every line—no matter how widely separated they may be—has been read.

Give special care to the address, phone number, store hours, or similar recurring material that has grown so familiar it is often accepted without reading.

Be particularly careful in reading headlines. Errors in display type—despite the fact that they are so easily overlooked by the proofreader—are especially glaring to the casual reader. Some people will tack proofs up on the wall, step back several paces, and read the display lines from a distance.

Finally, on ads, make sure that the signature cut is included. Without this identification, the ad is worthless; yet this omission is not at all infrequent.

Wise advertising men have checklists of the essential elements in each ad: headline, copy blocks, prices, art, address, phone number, etc., and insist that each be checked off (with the initials of the reader) before the proof is returned.

Proofs must be returned to the typesetter on deadline. If proofs are returned promptly, it can effect savings in money because the magazines may still be on the machine and the stone man is familiar with the style he has just been making up. Late proofs often mean overtime work to make corrections before an inflexible press time. This cost is passed on to the buyer.

Prompt return of proofs assures that the printer will be able to make corrections with at least a modicum of pressureless time. Late proofs just cannot be given that unhurried care that is essential to a perfect job.

Proofreading procedures vary in detail, depending on the job. In book work, details of typography are checked out on sample pages. The printer, the publisher, and the author read proof. The latter may read the same proof several times, especially in technical work, but the other two participants must limit theirs to one time because of the length of the work. They rarely work with a copyholder.

In advertising, the heads of several departments usually read proof, each concentrating on the area of his greatest interest, leaving the "author"—the advertising department—with the final responsibility of the total job.

If printing is done from plates instead of original type, proofs from the plate are also read.

The difficulty—and cost—of corrections depend, too, on the job. In book work, the number of corrections will be larger than in a two-page travel folder, and each correction line will cost less proportionately because overhead costs are prorated among many units.

To err is human; to correct errors efficiently and completely is the mark of the professional.

SUGGESTED READINGS

Lasky, Joseph. *Proofreading and Copy Preparation*. New York: New American Library (Mentor Book), 1954.
A Manual of Style. Chicago: University of Chicago Press, 1949.
Style Manual. Washington, D.C.: Government Printing Office, 1950.

8

Layout

PATTERNS TO PLEASE
THE READING EYE

Layout was no problem to the old country printer. He had an axiom that handled the situation nicely, thank you:

"When in doubt, set it in Cheltenham and center it."

Today layout is recognized as being far too important to be produced by this old home recipe.

Layout is the disposition of various printing elements—display and body type, illustrations and ornamentation, white space—in a pattern that is pleasant and attractive to the eye and that makes reading easy and convenient. It is an art, just as much as the disposition of oil paints on canvas or sounds upon human eardrums is an art. But it can be learned; individuals this side of genius have been taught to paint a picture or compose a singable tune.

A good layout should be *organic;* it must be *functional.*

Organic layout grows from the materials the designer has to work with. As he looks at the type, headlines, and art that must be used, these elements will often "make themselves up." Of course, it is not that easy, otherwise we could develop a layout machine and we would all be out of work. But as the trained eye of the layout man first sees his materials, it will tell him almost unconsciously how these elements should be arranged in relation to each other. This last phrase must be stressed. A picture that would occupy 80 per cent of a page with a certain head and block of type might be reduced to a tiny rectangle if combined with other pictures or with a different message to convey.

Functional layout is layout that is studiedly utilized to further the primary job of all printing: carrying a message. Anything that the layout can do to lift the message off the page, through the reader's eye and mind, and into his comprehension is functional. Anything that layout does to impede this flow of information is certainly non-functional and, in the graphic arts, most non-functional elements are automatically mal-functional. Anything that does not speed reading usually impedes it.

A good layout should be invisible. The reader should never be aware of the layout. As soon as he is conscious of it, his attention is distracted from the message. Communication then is less than ideal. We have already discussed the need for invisible type, but in the other arts invisibility also is important. When you look at a Corot painting, you want to see the picture, not an S-pattern or thrusting diagonals. When you listen to a *Brandenburg Concerto* you want to absorb the total music, not count off the beats or become aware that now the bassoon has modulated to a new key.

If we accept the yardstick of functionalism, we must first determine the job of layout.

First, it must attract or hold attention. There is a great difference between the function of the dust jacket on a book, its title page, and its page 102. The cover must compete for attention against many other gay designs that decorate other books on a shelf. The title page must attract the browser, give him a foretaste of the flavor of the book. Inside pages need not attract attention . . . but they must hold it.

Layout must make the message easy to read. All the techniques of readability talked about in Chapter 5 must be put into practice. Ink and the paper must give maximum legibility. Type blocks must be given enough elbow room. It is especially important to insulate them against other elements which might dilute or absorb all the reader's attention.

Layout must arrange our elements so that the reader can consider and digest each one in a logical progression. Reading is no longer convenient if the reader must ask himself, "Where do I start reading?" or "Well, I've read this; where do I go from here?" Then danger rears its ugly head; the reader may decide to dispense with this chore, and our printing becomes useless—worse than useless, in fact, because it has become an immoral economic waste, a form of creative "featherbedding."

Finally, layout must make reading pleasurable. This does not mean that the reader must obtain conscious sensual satisfaction or exclaim between paragraphs, like the fun-loving Rover Boy, "What a jolly good time!" But the process of reading must be pleasant, and the reader must derive some satisfaction, however unconscious, from the page as well as from the content. A child can gain this satisfaction from the drawings in a Dr. Seuss book, the attorney from the information he receives from a stark page in a law book. But this satisfaction, or realization of reward, must be present—or else the reader will not be.

The layout man has a big job on his hands. Possible solutions are endless.

Give the same raw material to a dozen layout men and you will get a dozen different layouts, just as the same scene would be rendered differently by El Greco, Utrillo, and Grandma Moses.

If the designers are all of equal talent, it will be impossible to say, "This is the best layout." All we can say is, "In my opinion, this will do the job best," or simply, "I like this one." For, just as the creation of art is subjective, so is its evaluation.

But a few elementary principles can be formulated that will enable us to discuss, evaluate, and create sound layouts.

As has been noted so many times already in this book, creations of human minds do not lend themselves to neat pigeonholing. When we must establish categories to facilitate discussion, we must always keep in mind that in reality these lines of demarcation are not sharply defined; overlapping areas are often greater than well-defined ones.

EQUIPMENT

Before embarking on the creative aspects of layout, we should consider those that are purely mechanical. The more familiar a person is with the technicalities of production, the better he can concentrate on esthetics.

The tools of the layout man are important. While a good craftsman can make a better chair with a jackknife than a poor one can with a complete set of power tools, it is also true that the craftsman can do the best work with good tools. The layout man should have adequate equipment, and it should be of good quality. The difference in initial cost may be marked but, amortized over many years and many jobs, it is wise economy to buy quality in the first place.

Every layout man has his own arsenal; it is impossible to make a "standard list" that will meet all needs and preferences. Some items are of basic necessity, a drawing board, for instance. It should be of medium size and non-warping, and the layout man should learn to hold it in the position that is most comfortable. Most artists prefer to rest it against a table or desk at an angle; some prefer to work on it flat.

A more elaborate table-type drawing stand may be convenient as progress or volume of work advances. This may be used at desk level so the designer can swing from desk to board. Others like to use a high table at which they can work while standing or seated on a high stool.

Thumbtacks should not be used for holding paper to the drawing board. After a few months the surface becomes so pitted that its usefulness is impaired or destroyed. *Masking tape* is best to hold your work.

A sturdy, accurate *T-square* and a right-angle *triangle* are essential to assure perfectly horizontal and perpendicular lines.

To meet specific and recurring needs, *French curves* and 60-degree triangles have many uses. A *protractor* may come in handy; often this is incorporated into a triangle.

Writing tools are essential and pencils are the foremost among them. Soft lead, in the B grade, is practical. Drawing pens should be at hand in good assortment, varying from the delicate *crowquill* to the broadest *Speedball*. The latter are used in C shapes, broad and narrow, for Roman lettering and in B, ball, for monotonal letters.

Brushes are used constantly; their size and shape is a matter of choice. *Flats*, corresponding to C Speedballs, are good for laying in large areas; *brights*, sharply pointed, execute finest detail.

Black India ink is the classic medium.

For color, *opaque tempera, showcard paints*, are ideal. Their range of color is wide and they mix easily to produce new ones. They can be used in ruling pens and compasses when properly diluted. A slab of glass, an old dinner plate or specially designed ceramic containers with small shallow depressions are handy for mixing paint or working it to proper consistency.

Some designers use colored pencils, colored India inks, or *pastel crayons*. In the latter case, a clear *fixative* must be used. This is now available in the popular "bomb" cans and comes in a variety of finishes, some of which can be worked over in any medium without blurring.

Grease pencils for marking photographs, sandpaper blocks for sharpening pencils, a *line gauge* (also called a *pica rule*), reducing or enlarging glasses, a *screen finder,* and a slide rule are all useful but not essential.

Erasers, alas, are a human necessity. Two kinds are generally employed: *Art gum* is useful for cleaning large areas; *plastic* can be delicately manipulated. Note that this "plastic" has nothing to do with synthetic materials designated by that term; plastic erasers are of high quality rubber.

Each designer has his own favorite paper. *Tracing paper* is most popular for it is easy to use to trace the exact outline of drawings, trademarks, or other elements. If a layout is generally satisfactory, but some element must be changed, tracing paper can be overlayed and units easily shifted, resized, or changed. By rubbing the reverse of the paper with a soft graphite pencil, then tracing on the face with a sharp pencil, it is easy to transfer any element. Tracing paper has adequate *tooth,* texture, to take any medium.

As for drawing paper and mounting board, there are so many varieties that each artist must experiment to find his favorites.

A wide assortment of printing papers of various colors, textures, and weights should always be at hand, and the designer must learn to work on all of them. Many paper manufacturers prepare portfolios of their various products for use by layout men.

Rubber cement is indispensable. When one coat is applied, paper may easily be lifted and shifted. When both the paper and the surface on which it is to be mounted are coated with cement and it is allowed to dry almost completely, an absolutely permanent bond is effected. Great care must be taken that the paper is placed properly the first time, as there is no opportunity for second guessing.

If the designer uses a great deal of rubber cement, as professionals do, he should have a can of solvent, or *thinner,* available to keep the adhesive at the proper consistency, quite thin. The cement sets up quickly and soon becomes a solid. Some artists fill a small oil can with solvent and allow a few drops to run under the paper to loosen the cement when the paper must be removed. This requires good paper that will not be affected, and great care, lest the solvent react on paint or ink.

A pair of good scissors, at least 6 inches long, is a constant necessity and razor blades are good for straight cuts. Never use a blade against a triangle, T-square, or other valuable instrument; it will nick even hard metal. Instead, cut against the metal ferrule of a cheap ruler. Many designers use single-edged razor blades without a handle. This can result in cut fingers; they heal—but blood stains can ruin a layout!

The artist's "reference library" consists of type specimen books or sheets, especially from the printer with whom he works most often. Specimen sheets showing a variety of halftone screens, Ben Day tints, Zip-a-Tone, Artype, and ink catalogues should be within arm's reach.

The *morgue*, or clipping library, is irreverently called the *swipe file*. This consists of clippings or specimens of printed matter, filed in as casual or elaborate a system as the designer desires or finds time to do. The swipe file should contain examples of all media of original art and all engraving styles. It is often time- and money-saving to refresh your memory before you commit yourself to a method less than the best.

Catalogues are good morgues themselves, especially those for merchandise with which the designer must work frequently. The finest illustrators find Messrs. Sears, Roebuck trusty friends on more occasions than might be imagined. How does a raglan sleeve fit into a coat? How far does the fender extend over the wheel? What is the angle of a golf-club head to its shaft? Where does a cat's back hump when it sleeps in a crouch? These are all answers we should know; we see these things constantly. But as you rack your memory for an answer, you realize how valuable a good "library" is. A standard filing cabinet is the most convenient storage place. Two-drawer files are desk high and make a handy *taboret*, a table alongside a drawing board for holding tools and materials.

This catalogue of tools may give the false impression that a person must be equipped as extravagantly as an astronaut to do a layout. This is not so—some of the finest layouts have been done with a ballpoint pen on the back of an old envelope. The beginning designer needs only paper, a pencil, and a straightedge. Other tools need not be added until the need arises, or when the frequency of a task makes it impractical to make-do with a tool that is adequate but inefficient.

DUMMIES

The layout man's first efforts are *thumbnail sketches*. These are small —1 × 2 inches can visualize a 24-sheet poster—and are hastily drawn.

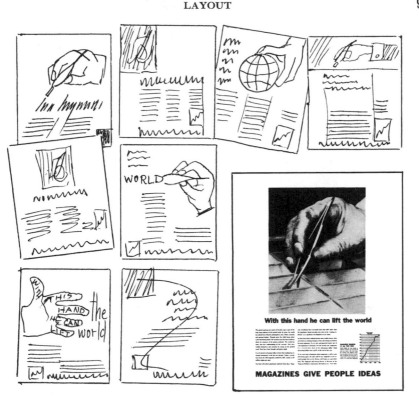

Fig. 34. Thumbnails. One at left center was basis of finished layout.

They are notes written in shorthand.

One of the most useful exercises in learning layout is to make thumbnails of all the ads or pages in a magazine, newspaper, or book. As hand and eye are trained to reduce a finished layout to a quick sketch, they are also trained in the reverse of this process, visualizing the completed layout from a few hasty notes.

Dozens of thumbnails will be scribbled as the designer experiments with patterns. This is an essential process; for ideas proliferate in a chain reaction; the more thumbnails he makes, the more possibilities the designer visualizes.

When he has arrived at a satisfactory one, the designer expands upon the thumbnail in a *rough*. This is also shorthand, but here it is written in complete sentences. The rough is the same size as the finished job. While it is not sloppy or amateurish, the rough is casual, with an incisive, quick character.

Thumbnails are sketched on anything from the backs of old envelopes

Fig. 35. This rough dummy was converted. . . .

corona builds reader traffic

That paper must have Corona appeal! Corona is a pleasure to look at, a pleasure to read. That's because it looks a full point-size larger than it is, gets your message to readers more attractively.

Advertisers get the message, too: more readers, more advertising dollars. Make the switch to Corona soon, and build the kind of reader traffic that you and your advertisers can count on.

This text is set in clear, easy-reading Corona type. For a more complete specimen sheet, just call your Linotype Agency, or write Mergenthaler Linotype Company, 29 Ryerson Street, Brooklyn 5, New York.

Fig. 36. . . . into this finished layout.

to restaurant tablecloths. Roughs are done on tracing paper, bond or ledger.

Illustrations are merely sketched, but they indicate the tonal value. Headlines, too, must show the weight of the type although the letterforms are not polished. Body type is suggested by parallel lines. Space between lines shows the point size, weight of the lines, and tone of the type. Color is added by any convenient means. If there are large areas, such as backgrounds or panels, a piece of colored paper may be pasted on and lettered over.

The rough is often presented in anything but rough form, affixed to a generous-size mounting board, often under a mat, and protected by acetate or tissue overlay plus one of kraft paper.

As work progresses, refinements are added, and by the time the third step—the *comprehensive dummy*, the *comp* or just the *dummy*—has been completed, it will be an accurate blueprint of the finished job. The comp has two purposes: (1) to show the printer exactly how to make up the form, and (2) to show the client exactly how the finished job will look. It is the latter function that requires the most work.

The printer is able to work from a sketchy dummy; he must know that a certain cut will be 4 picas from the top and 7 from the right margin; he doesn't care about the details of the bathing suit the model is wearing. But the client is not a graphic artist; he cannot flesh in the details and so they must be included.

In the comp, the headlines are carefully drawn or traced.

Tracing letters from specimen books or cards especially prepared for such use is another useful exercise. No other method teaches the eye to learn identifying characteristics of a type face as thoroughly, quickly, and painlessly. Niceties of letterspacing become apparent and the hand is trained to swift deftness. The ability to trace letters is not as childish as it seems; it will pay good dividends in those cases where dummies must be very detailed.

Body type is indicated still by ruled lines or with a Craftype that simulates type in various sizes. If art is already available, *Photostats* will be made to the desired size and mounted. Reverses are shown in the negative stats. Colors are applied in exact chroma and intensity.

If the art work has not yet been done, the layout man may produce a miniature of such high quality that the casual observer may think that it is the finished job. When the author of this book directed advertising for a manufacturing company, he often used art from the comp

Fig. 37. Comprehensive dummy. Notice that type blocks are indicated in self-adhesive Copy Block by Craftype.

or even the rough because it had a spontaneity that was often lost in a picture more painstakingly drawn.

The comp should be prepared for the use to which it will be put. If it is an in-plant job—the dummy of a newspaper page, for instance—it can be sketchy, but should be accurate, of course. If it is for a client, he is the determining factor. An old customer may be willing to entrust details to the taste and skill of the designer. A new customer, or a prospective one unfamiliar with your work or who must be impressed, will receive an extremely high-gloss comp. In the case of a booklet, it will be prepared on the same cover and inside stock as will be used in printing. Sometimes more than one comp must be prepared—if the elevator operator, the vice-president's mother-in-law, and the stock clerk must approve, as happens in too many companies. Often additional comps are assembled from photocopies, if various details must be checked by different departments.

Photocopying is valuable when the same basic layout or material is to be used in different forms. A newspaper ad may be revised for magazine use, as the cover or page in a catalogue, as a direct-mail piece, or a poster.

The *mechanical* is an exact replica of the finished piece. Usually the same size as the final job—sometimes larger, but never smaller—the mechanical may be used as copy for making plates or as a guide to assembling an engraving, form, or negative which has been made in several units for reduction or special effects.

Making layouts and dummies is like playing golf: You can learn the basic principles in an afternoon, then spend the rest of your life mastering details. This discussion does not pretend to cover everything a layout man must know about his craft, but it is adequate as a sound foundation.

Fig. 38. Mechanical for two-color job. This is brown plate; S/S symbol indicates it is to be reproduced same size. Shadows have been exaggerated to distinguish various elements. Before plate-making they must be opaqued out.

DESIGN

Having given attention to those mechanical or technical aspects of layout work that can be well defined, let us embark now into an aspect which defies such specificity—the creative.

Every creator has his own method and often it is not apparent even to him. There must be a period of gestation, a subconscious process that goes on while the designer works on another job, on his thumbnails, or just plays poker or sleeps. A serendipitous journey through the swipe file often switches on the light of a bright idea. This is a process that must be developed, not taught.

The following steps may be taken as a point of departure only. They are benchmarks from which each individual must blaze his own trail of creativity.

The designer should read the copy carefully to obtain the over-all impression of the piece. Is it calm, as the title page of a book of poetry? Is it rugged and masculine, a catalogue for a manufacturer of road graders? Is it traditional, a program for the consecration of a bishop? Or dynamic and modern, to announce a new jet plane schedule?

Then he must decide whether the type or illustrations will dominate the layout. Is the art already at hand? Which pictures are musts? If art must be commissioned, will delicate pen-and-ink or a bold oil painting best harmonize with the general tone—and aid communication? Type faces, colors, and paper will be chosen the same way.

Then the designer must decide on the size and shape. Often this has already been done. A client will tell the layout man to design an ad 5 columns wide by 17 inches deep, or a publisher will have decided on the size of the pages in a book. If the choice is the designer's, he weighs the factors of paper sizes and press capacities.

His proportions will usually be close to the *Golden Rectangle*. Its proportions were established by pragmatic artists centuries ago. By rule of thumb and their own esthetic appreciation, they established its ratio as *one to the square root of two* (1:1.414). This has been modified to 3 × 5 (close enough to the mathematical 3 × 4.24 for all practical purposes). A *regular oblong*, 2 × 3, is often used.

Mathematical formulas developed from instinctive solutions include the *line of golden proportion*. This establishes that a single unit within an area is best displayed on a horizontal plane three-eighths of the whole height from the top. Book page margins can also be established by geometry. The first method allows the designer to establish the outside margin, B', himself, as in Figure 39. One half of this distance, C', becomes the inside or *gutter* margin. At B and C perpendiculars are drawn and then the diagonal, AD, is drawn. Intersections with the verticals mark the top and bottom of the type area.

The second method is entirely mathematical. The gutter is one-eighth the width of the page, A'. The top margin is the same. The outer margin, C', is A' plus one-sixth; the foot, D', is C' plus 2 picas.

Having determined the size of the printed piece, the designer must choose between vertical or horizontal rectangles. The use of the piece is a determinant. We are used to vertical books and tend to read large masses or many pages most comfortably in this form. On the other hand, desk blotters or business cards are customarily used or read as horizontal units.

There may be shock value in using an unaccustomed shape, size, or axis. This should never be overlooked but must be used warily; too much shock may repel the reader and hamper communication.

Many publications require vertical composition in ads, restricting them to no shallower than a square.

If he decides on a horizontal rectangle, the designer soon finds he must subdivide the area in most cases, because his lines of type will usually be too long if they carry clear across. Or, if the type is large enough so that readability is not sacrificed by using them that wide, the resultant design is apt to be squat and stolid. There are exceptions, of course, but in most cases the vertical rectangle allows for more dynamic layouts.

Now the designer is ready to begin his composition. Because he appeals to the reader's eye, it is necessary to know a few things about eye movement in reading. From long habit, we look first at the upper left corner of any page or area, just as you looked first at that area on this page. We have been taught that this is the starting point for writing or reading and go there instinctively. (Readers of Arabic look first at the upper right; they read right-to-left.) The upper left is the *primary optical area* or *focal point*. Here we must place something attractive to the eye at first glance.

When you get to the lower right corner of this page you will automatically turn the page; you know that that area is the end. The eye keeps that goal in mind always and thus the basic movement is a diagonal from top left to bottom right. The eye does not follow this

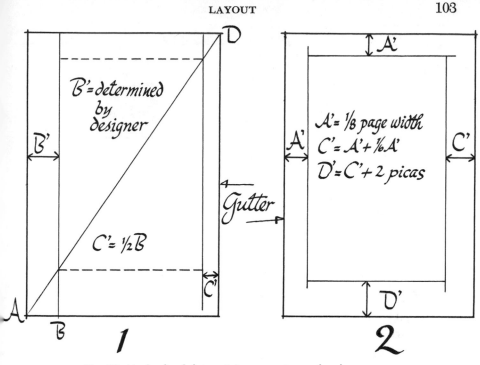

Fig. 39. Methods of determining margins on book pages.

line like a honey-laden bee but more like a beagle puppy in the park. It courses back and forth—the more flowing the loops, the easier the eye is working—but always toward the goal.

In many layout problems, notably in designing the front page of a newspaper, the layout man seeks to define the diagonal with strong display elements. Then, to attract the eye into the corners away from the diagonal, there must be some lure placed there, too.

The eye always wants to move downward. To attract it by an appealing element, and then to expect the eye to backtrack and read something higher on the page, is just not understanding human nature. If the eye should back up, it has been subjected to undue effort and irritation and the result is apt to be that the eye will stop reading before the whole page or area has been covered.

The eye, while small and delicate, is willful. It can be coaxed but it cannot be forced. It is susceptible to suggestion, and so designers try to cajole and guide it into covering all parts of a layout. Suggestions may be obvious: an arrow or pointing finger. They may be less apparent: the direction of an automobile or of fork tines, the gaze of a model

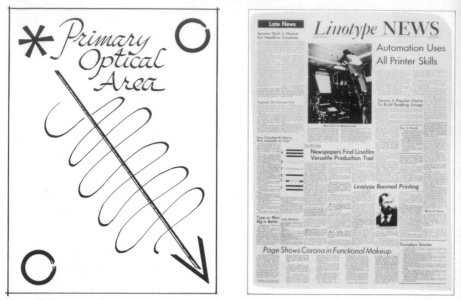

Fig. 40. Pattern of newspaper page defines diagonal on which reading eye travels. Asterisk designates primary optical area; circles indicate weak areas where eye must be lured by attention compellors.

in a photograph. Or they may be very subtle: the shape of a word or the sweep of a hilltop in a drawing.

A layout is a whole network of lines that the eye may subconsciously follow. The designer must make sure that the dominant lines lead the eye where he wants it to go. This is the *rhythm* a designer seeks in his layout.

Just as these suggestions can entice the eye to a path the designer wants it to follow, so they may distract him in other, undesirable, directions. The eye will follow any motion, real or implied. If a layout shows a child running with his dog, the eye will follow the projected path of the youngster. The layout man must make sure that this projection does not lead the reader right off the page or out of the printing area. Even motion implied as gently as that of a human profile or the direction of his gaze can urge the eye off the page. That is the why of an axiom: Pictures should always face into the page or composition.

Any non-parallel lines that would eventually meet to form an arrowhead will carry the eye in that direction, even if the lines would have to be continued far beyond the boundaries of our layout before meeting.

An excellent means for training your eye to detect these subtle lines

Fig. 41. Lines of force within ad (shown by arrows) direct reading eye.

of direction is to draw them, with heavy or grease pencil on advertise-ments or other layouts. As you learn to detect these "magnetic forces," you will also learn to harness them to your own needs.

There are many signposts that can be erected along the path to di-rect the eye. Initial letters are good. Decorative *paragraph openers* are good guideposts and the most common is the *bullet* or large period.

The layout must arrange each element so that the eye will reach it in logical progression. There must be distinct but unobtrusive order and neatness; the eye does not enjoy a jumbled page any more than we like a cluttered room. The designer may well heed the Japanese as they furnish a room: They use little furniture and few ornamental ob-jects, because in simplicity is the neatness we all enjoy. So typographic layouts should be simplified. For another exercise, take an ad or printed piece and, with white poster paint, eliminate as many details as you can, borders, ornaments, rules. It is surprising how much can be taken out of a layout without loss. The human eye will fill in many details, just as it does in a sketch—by a comic strip cartoonist or by Rembrandt.

Always apply to every element in a layout the criterion of func-tionalism: Does this do a good job? If not, throw it out.

As the layout man plans his patterns to attract the reading eye and make its task lighter, he uses contrast to give it pleasure. Here we may draw an analogy from music. Think of the opening four notes of Bee-thoven's *Fifth Symphony*. It opens with three authoritative G's and

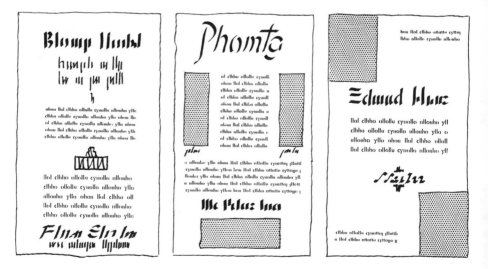

Fig. 42. Some basic patterns for symmetrical layouts.

then, just as the ear has grasped the pattern, it sings out with a startling E-flat. To mix metaphors, it is like the boxer who jabs three times with a left and then crosses with a right.

Contrast gives emphasis that perks the ears and perks the eyes. It may come from shape, size, or tone of any elements. It may be a big picture breaking forth from a group of smaller ones. It may be an Italic in the midst of a forum of Romans. It may be a vertical element rearing among horizontal ones.

When contrast is used, it must be marked. You cannot contrast Caslon with a Garamond; a 3×5 picture is little contrast against a $3\frac{1}{4} \times 4\frac{1}{4}$.

Remember that all emphasis is no emphasis. Designers who use more and more black type find their message no longer carries; typographically it is the boy crying "Wolf!"

Layouts may be categorized as *formal balance,* or *symmetrical,* and *informal balance,* also called *occult* (heaven knows why) or *dynamic balance.*

In symmetrical layout, everything balances on a vertical axis down the middle of the page. (For the rest of this discussion, we shall refer to the "page" as any area the layout man has to work with, even a business card or an ad which will be only part of the whole newspaper or magazine page.) In its simplest form it follows the old printshop dictum that opened this chapter: Center everything.

A trifle more complex is the layout in which identical cuts or type masses are mathematically balanced against each other. Occasionally a fillip of contrast may be added by some element that does not balance mathematically but does balance optically.

Formal layout has the dignity and stability that its name indicates. That stability is its main weakness; such layout is far too static for many needs. But symmetrical layout is ideal to express formality—as in wedding invitations; dignity—as in documents or the pages of a Bible; stability—as in an advertisement for a bank or a funeral home.

Dignity need not equate with stodginess and, while formal layout is solid, it need not be stolid. Its simplicity pleases the eye and there are many opportunities to use this layout with telling effect.

Informal layout balances its elements in a pleasant, less rigid manner. The designer should imagine a pivot at the optical center of the page, about one-tenth the height of the page above the mathematical center. Then he should envision each element as having physical as well as optical weight. He pastes these onto an imaginary board that hangs on this pivot in such a way that the board hangs almost, but not quite, straight up and down.

Elements balance like children on a see-saw; a fat little fellow has to get close to the bar to balance his skinny chum at the end of the board. But in this case, we do more than merely balance two children against each other—we scatter many of them around in the cars of a Ferris wheel.

The solidity of formal balance can be compared to the Washington Monument: It stands foursquare and strong. Yet this perfect perpendicular does not delight the eye as much as the curves of Japanese cherry trees at its base.

If you will take another look at your favorite picture, physically or by mind's eye, you will undoubtedly discover that it does not quite "hang straight." There will be some diagonal movement that takes it off the rigid 90 degrees. A good example is the portrait photographer. He may take his subject sitting perfectly erect; when he prints the picture he will crop it so the head or torso tilts a little. This slight imbalance is pleasing to the eye; it suggests interest and motion. This the designer should seek in most of his layouts.

There are no exact scales for weighing typographic elements. Tall and thin pictures tend to swing the layout away from the pivot more than square or flat pictures. Dark backgrounds outweigh light ones; square halftones are heavier than silhouettes. Boldface outweighs lightface, and Condensed or Extended weigh more than the normal letterform. Ultimately, the designer's eye must determine when all elements are in balance; this comes from trained or experienced instinct.

A picture with strong motion will tilt the board in the direction of that motion no matter what its tonal weight may be.

While you do not want your layout to stand as stiffly erect as a cigarstore Indian, neither do you want it to lean so far that it may fall on its face. It should be almost, but not entirely, perpendicular.

Within an already broad classification of informal balance, we establish subdivisions that are equally elastic; most layouts combine one, or even several, characteristics of these groups: *classic, geometric, vertical axis, rectangular, expanded,* and *connotative.*

Classic does not mean moth-eaten or longhair. It simply means that these are patterns of composition that were well developed by the great artists of centuries ago. They are not stilted. Durer's illustrations

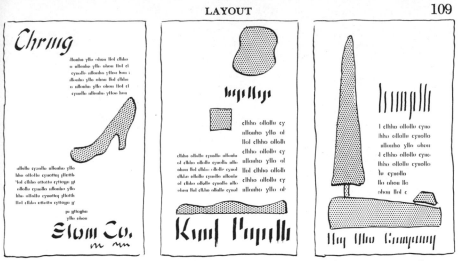

Fig. 43. Patterns for classic layout: Reverse S, left; triangle, center; L, right.

of Dante's *Inferno* are eminently classic in composition; they are certainly not stodgy.

The most famous of the classic patterns is the S or *reverse* S. The latter is extremely useful. It begins at the primary optical area and carries the eye, not only down the basic diagonal, but also into the opposite corners in the flowing curves that the eye loves. The *pyramidal* pattern of Da Vinci's *Mona Lisa* lends itself well to typographic layouts as does the reverse *L* of Whistler's portrait of his mother.

Geometric layout is an extension of the classic forms. It uses pictures or blocks of type to define geometric shapes more definitely than the classicists did. The simplest is to *anchor the corners*, place a strong element in each one. Common patterns are the *triangle*, facing up or down; a *T, U, Y,* or *L,* facing in any direction. *Bands—braces* or *brackets* —can run vertically or horizontally. A pair of L's can be arranged like hands to hold other elements. Figure 44 shows some of the most commonly used geometric patterns.

Rectangular layouts are "the poor man's Mondrian paintings." Here a large area is broken up into smaller units of varying shape and size and harmoniously related to each other. Sometimes these areas are defined, boldly or delicately, with rules or decorative border material. Sometimes, they are merely suggested.

Dutch artist Mondrian's paintings are amazingly deceptively simple. It is only when you attempt a design in this style that you realize the genuine artistry and delicate manipulation of areas that is involved.

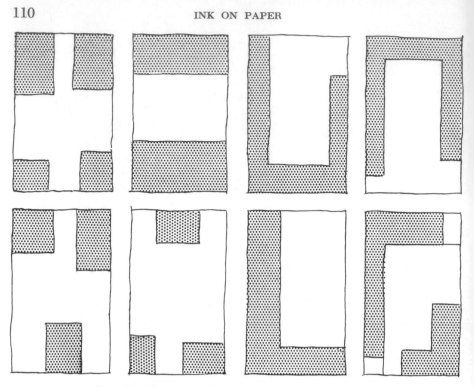

Fig. 44. Placement of pictures in geometric layout.

There is only one piece of advice that can be formulated for these layouts: Subdivision of areas should never be obvious; no line should be drawn at the half-, quarter-, or third-way mark. No area should be a third, quarter, or half of the whole, and none should be exactly the dimensions of another. Beyond that, the designer's experience and discernment must stand all alone.

Rectangular layout takes a long while to master. But long before the designer produces masterpieces he can create functional and pleasing layouts by this method.

The vertical axis is sometimes called the *totem pole* or *Christmas tree* to distinguish it from symmetrical balance, which is also on a perpendicular. The totem pole is not symmetrical; rarely, if ever, does the axis run along the center of the page. Projecting from the axis—which is usually imaginary but can be defined—are lines and blocks of type. Those at the left of the axis are flush right; those on the other side are flush left. Their inner margins, then, align along the axis; their outer margins may be ragged and, certainly, the margins of the

With acres of deck space, you can stroll to your heart's content on your trip to Europe aboard s.s. United States or s.s. America. Or stop and chat with your interesting fellow passengers.

Mr. and Mrs. John R. Friar and their sons John, William and Malcolm, returning from a military mission in Iran on the s.s. America. For the carefree life aboard, you'll find an expertly supervised children's playroom, heated salt-water swimming pool, first-run movie theaters, romantic Meyer Davis music, gourmet cuisine.

You'll re-discover a world of leisure on board the world's fastest ship

The gracious life aboard the s.s. United States begins for the Honorable Douglas MacArthur, U. S. Ambassador to Belgium, and Mrs. MacArthur. They'll relax in comfortable lounges with friends.

Though the s.s. United States, the world's fastest ship, speeds you to Europe in five days, your life aboard is leisurely and gracious. And whether you sail on the United States or the America, some of the world's most distinguished people will be among your fellow passengers.

s.s. United States —regularly includes a week-end in its 5 days to Europe, conserving time for businessmen.

s.s. America —popular, luxurious. Offers two extra days at sea for a more leisurely crossing.
10% round-trip reduction in Thrift Season (from August 16).

SEE YOUR TRAVEL AGENT OR

United States Lines

United States Lines, 1 Broadway, N. Y. 4, N. Y. Owner-operators of the s.s. United States, s.s. America and a fleet of 53 fast cargo ships to Europe, United Kingdom, Far East, Australia

E1

Fig. 45. Rectangular layout. (Courtesy United States Lines)

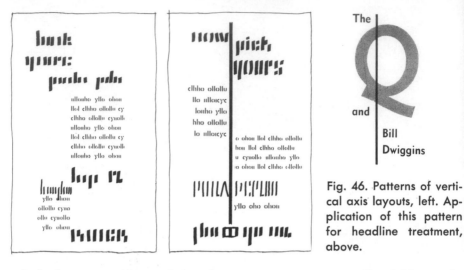

Fig. 46. Patterns of vertical axis layouts, left. Application of this pattern for headline treatment, above.

whole layout are ragged for the projections are usually deliberately made of varying length.

The *oblique axis* is a variation of the totem pole. In one form, the entire layout is tilted as in the first Figure 47. This is poor; the eye is accustomed to reading on horizontal planes and may become irritated by having to establish a new horizon. This danger can be minimized by tilting the top only between 30 and 40 degrees to the left. This is approximately the angle at which paper is held in writing, and the reader is not as aware of the angle as he would be if he had to cock his head to the right.

The danger of irritation is increased when only some elements of a layout are tilted. Here—in the center of Figure 47—varying horizons are emphasized to the discomfort of the eye.

The reader can be given the convenience of reading on the accustomed plane if the oblique axis is achieved as in the right Figure 47. Here the type is stepped down to create a diagonal block but each line is horizontal.

Expanded layouts create an optical illusion that enlarges the layout area.

Within the entire area of the layout, a smaller rectangle is drawn to leave a generous frame of white. The rectangle is well filled to define it sharply. Then a large picture breaks out of this area to touch one or two sides of the outer edge of the layout. The feeling of motion expands the entire layout and makes it appear larger. Because the thrust

Fig. 47. Patterns of diagonal axis layouts. Note angles at which type blocks are set.

of the picture shifts considerable weight with it, other display elements must be placed to make the composition hang almost straight.

A large headline can expand a layout but far less effectively than a picture does.

Connotative patterns are also called *jazz layouts,* a far more descriptive term that is often relegated to second position because it does not have a pedantic enough ring. It takes its method from that of the

Fig. 48. Typical pattern in expanded layout.

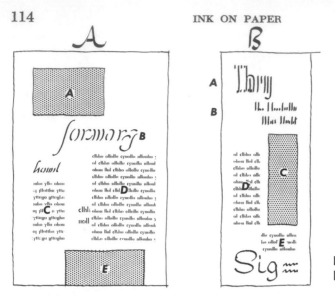

Fig. 49. Patterns of jazz layouts.

Dixieland jazz band. The band plays a chorus or two of a familiar melody to establish it in the listener's mind. Then each soloist embroiders a harmonic pattern around the now unplayed melody. His music line may approach the melody but never follows it exactly. So the listener supplies the "lead" and the soloist the "tenor."

In a jazz layout, the pattern is suggested but never totally defined. Again a rectangle is drawn within the area of the layout to provide proper framing. (This technique should be used with any layout; the frame of white space is as important as the mat on a watercolor. The frame is not the same width all around. Tops and sides are equal; the bottom is 50 per cent wider.) Now he alludes to the rectangle by suggesting each of its four sides by one or more elements. One element may suggest more than one side, but usually no more than two.

The principle is demonstrated in Figure 49. In Sketch *a*, a picture (A) defines the top and left margin. The headline (B) and a block of type (D) mark the right; another type block (C), the left again, while a shallow illustration (E) suggests the bottom margin. In Sketch *b*, the principle is used for a tall composition. Now the top is defined by a line of display type (A) and the right margin by a subhead (B), a type block (E), and a cut (C). Another mass of type (D) establishes the left margin, while the signature sets the bottom and both side margins.

In any informal layout, the *orientation system*—also called the *buddy* or *no-orphan*—may be used to insure a sense of orderliness. We have discussed how this quality puts the eye at ease and makes it more comfortable to read a layout. The eye wants a definite, even if most unobtrusive, orientation point for every element. It constantly asks: "Why is this picture (or headline or block) here instead of somewhere else?" If the designer cannot answer this question—even though it is rarely articulated—his layout has a dangerous weakness.

By this orientation system, every element is placed at some logical reference point vertically and/or horizontally. Each element has a companion piece, a buddy, just as a swimmer has at a Boy Scout camp. No element stands alone, hence no orphans.

Look at Figure 50, a layout for a newspaper ad. This is the kind of layout that often consists of many different elements, each of which must have its own readership yet be integrated with all others.

The dominant feature is a large picture of the product (A), a new sailboat. To position it, there are three basic orientation points: flush

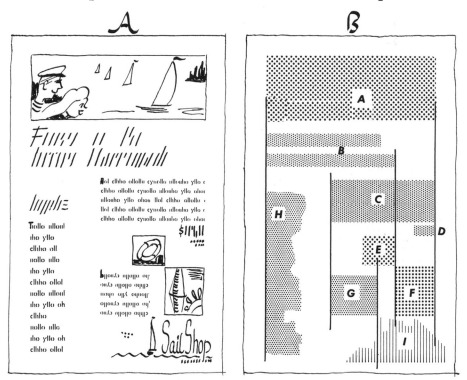

Fig. 50. Oriented layout. Diagram emphasizes how each element is aligned, horizontally or vertically, with at least one other.

left or right (on the white frame, not the outer edge of the layout), or centered. Let's center it. The headline (B) can also be placed at any of these three benchmarks, and for this demonstration it is placed flush left. Now comes a copy block (C); it too can go to any one of the three basic points, but now two new orientations are possible; it may align to the right or left of the end of either line of the head. Here it has been lined up flush right. The price (D), a separate element because of its size, also aligns at the right.

Two smaller pictures (E) and (F), show close-ups of optional equipment which is described in (G). Picture (F) is pushed flush right and (E) aligns with (F) at the left.

Now there are several possibilities for (G). Every time a new element is placed, at least one new orientation point is gained, unless that element only marks previous ones. Having placed (E) and (F), (G) can align with the left, right, or common axes, or with the top or bottom of either picture. Or it can align with the left margin of (D), or, as here, with the left margin of (C). It also lines up with the bottom of (F).

Most ads carry one or more subordinate items; in this case (H) is a whole list of sailing accessories, set flush left and aligning with the bottom of (C). The signature (I) lines up with the right margin of (G).

Now every element has a buddy: (A), (B), and (H) share the left margin; (A), (C), (D), and (F) the right; (E) and (F) buddy up, so do (C) and (G); (I) teams with (G). Not even the bone stands alone. (Notice that this has created a jazz layout.) Also note that in Figure 49 everything is paired with the exception of the shallow picture at the bottom of Sketch A which is nonetheless well oriented by being so definitely centered.

The same orientation system is used in Figure 51, a double spread for a magazine. Here the elements are more closely tied together by subject matter and the problem is not as acute as in advertising layout. But the principle remains valid.

Again a large picture is centered (not because this is the only orientation but because it seems best). The subhead (B) buddies, not with the picture but with an element therein, the stripped-in head *The Bleeding Land*. A silhouetted picture (H) also aligns with an element in the top picture, a windmill. Another square halftone (G) aligns with the right margin of the subhead.

Columns of type are rather definitely oriented by the format of the

Fig. 51. Oriented layout used for magazine spread.

magazine, but we buddy them vertically. Column (C) aligns at the bottom of the type page and (D) aligns at the top with column 1; (E) and (F) align with the bottom of the subhead, and (E) at the bottom with the shoulder of the standing figure; (F), of course, ends to allow plenty of breathing room for the cut (H). If spatial economy is a factor, type can be set to run around the cut in columns D, E, and/or F.

In all layout systems except the totem pole or the rectangular pattern, if areas are defined by rules, the initial placement is just that—initial. Once the pattern has been established, elements must frequently be moved around a bit to create the optical effect that matches the mathematical effect we seek.

To demonstrate the optical manipulation required, let's look at this word:

MOTEL

The letters appear to be perfectly aligned, don't they? Yet if you lay a straightedge, or squint from the side along the bottom, you'll see that the designer has made the *O* and *M* extend below the baseline. He has deliberately drawn these letters in such a way that they seem, to the casual observer, to be lined up properly.

The shape or color of a typographic element or the lines of motion within it, which have been discussed, may create an optical center of gravity that does not coincide with its mathematical center. It must then be moved a trifle to place it in proper optical reference.

In Figure 51, the weight of the top picture is toward the right. If it were not for the added weight of the surprinted head, we would probably have to push the cut a little to the left to make it look centered. The shapes of words affect optical balance. Look at these two:

thin

milt

Although both are centered, the top one leans to the left and the lower one to the right, because of the position of the ascenders.

All-cap words must frequently be *optically spaced* to make them look as if they are evenly spaced. Two straight lines, side by side, look closer together than a straight line—like the edge of an *M*—at the same distance from the outer segment of a circle, as *O*. The built-in white space under the shoulder of a *T*, below the diagonals of a *W*, or above those of an *A* must frequently be compensated for by adding extra space between the straight letters as shown on page 59.

Optical letterspacing is pure art; it cannot be reduced to formula. Only the compositor's eye can tell him when the desired effect has been created. In the same way, only the designer's eye can tell him when, and how much, an element must be shifted to make it align properly.

The designer's eye may be all the authority he needs in any layout. To the question, "Why is this element here?" a perfectly valid answer might be, "I like it here," or "This is where it looks right to me."

The systems outlined here are useful only as points of departure. They are not insurance policies, but they are good icebreakers. When a designer sits at his drawing board and ideas are conspicuous by their absence (a state of affairs that, sadly, does sometimes occur), he can say, as he otherwise would not, "Now I shall design an expanded layout." Often he will soon abandon his first attempts, but the mental log jam has been broken. For the person whose layout sense has not been well developed, following these systems will assure him of workmanlike results even though they may lack the spark that makes a truly outstanding layout.

There are no "rules" in graphic design, even if they are usually referred to as such. If there were rules, they would be meant to be broken. But when you break a rule, do so deliberately for a well-thought-out reason. In baseball it is a "rule" that the batter with a 3–0 count lets the next pitch go by. But the wise player will, when the occasion warrants or demands, take a lusty swing at the ball. If he gets a homer, he is a hero. If he misses, he is given credit for doing it on purpose, not out of ignorance. The same is true with the designer.

Today's typography stresses functionalism and simplification. "Throw it out if it doesn't do a good job," the designer is told. "Simplify your layouts to the essentials." It is no wonder then that we hear an occasional wail, "Can't I use *any* ornamentation?"

Of course you can; much ornamentation is functional. Ornaments are an integral part of the type library and many great type designers have drawn ornaments that are happily wedded to the alphabet font of type. W. A. Dwiggins designed a pleasant repertoire of florets and decorations—his Caravan series—that go with his type faces as tonic goes with gin. Rudolf Ruzicka has eight handsome Fairfield decorations.

Since Gutenberg's Bible, decorative initials have been grown like flowers on the vine of type. Today they are abundant and useful; so are paragraph marks, most designed with a specific font.

Borders and all rules except the straight line are ornaments.

How do we use them?

1. Ornamentation should be used with restraint.

2. It should be unobtrusive, felt more than seen.

3. It should never outweigh the type; it must harmonize with the other elements in weight, form, and feeling.

4. If color is used for ornaments, or solely as ornamentation, it must be chosen so the final chromatic ornament will be of the same tonal value as the basic black type. This often requires a heavier weight of ornament than if it were to be printed in black.

5. Ornamentation must be functional.

This statement is often unbelievable to the mind that stripped serifs off the Roman alphabet and porches off Victorian homes. But the initials in the Mazarin Bible do a job. And how better could one convey the flavor of the halcyon 1910's than to use a wide, ornate Jenson border or an intricate Cheltenham initial?

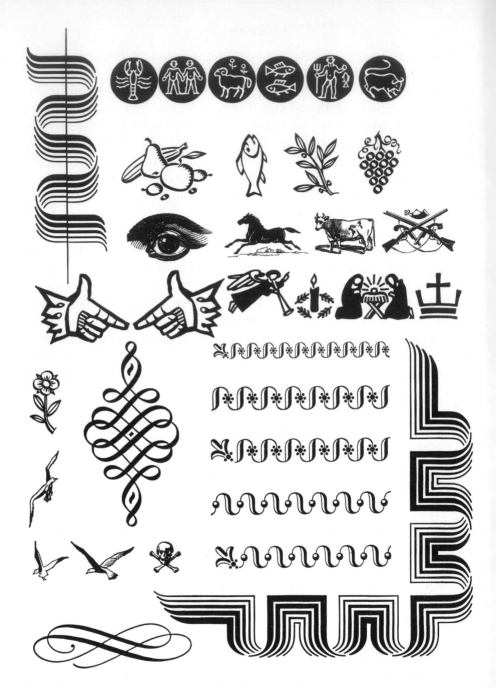

Fig. 52. Typographic ornaments. Top-left and bottom-right corner pieces are Ombree. Top two rows are Troyer. Series of five strips at lower right are Dwiggins' Caravan Ornaments.

The function of ornament is to convey a mood, direct the eye, or to add to the pleasure of the reader. The initials on a Gutenberg Bible do all three. They create a mood of dignity, awe, and authority; they attract the reader to the primary optical area or to major starting points within the page; they certainly delight the eye with their exquisite detail and rich color. Modern ornamentation must serve at least one, and preferably more, of these basic functions.

Ornaments should never be used just to fill space!

The mechanical practicability of ornamentation should be a factor in its selection. This is not a limiting factor, however; linecasters have a wealth of ornamental material and type founders even more. In photocomposition there is literally no limit.

A simple stick-up initial or a bullet to start a paragraph is ornamentation. The designer might choose the complex Raffia initial in type or have an artist hand-letter one. In any case, he can combine mechanics and esthetics without loss of either one.

Borders must meet the same functional standards. Rarely is a border, other than a hairline, necessary to separate elements in a layout or on a page such as a newspaper's. If a portion of a layout must be set apart, a *sideless box* is the best solution. This is simply a decorative rule at the top and bottom, acting like a pair of brackets. This will emphasize the enclosed type but will not impede the free sweep of the eye through the page.

Rules are far simpler than borders but they, too, must be chosen for harmony. The thick and thin parallels of Oxford rule are perfect companions for the thicks and thins of Bodoni and the Modern Romans. This Period Design

goes well with the Old Styles and this

with the Sans.

Linecaster rules are produced on *matrix slides,* 30-picas long. Borders are either in slides or in separate matrices that are used separately or join so cunningly they seem like a single unit. Border matrices are cast in constant increments; they should be arranged so that no single character must be sliced to fit the line. Border matrices often have separate corner pieces to terminate a line or bend it at right angles.

This is an interesting example of the use of border matrices:

Notice how right-hand pieces and southpaws tie in so tightly that they seem to constitute a single linear unit and form neat corners that turn the design without apparent break. The eye doesn't discern that this border is made up of 20 matrices.

If all advice on layout had to be summed up in two words, it would be: Have fun!

All creative work is fun; it satisfies the soul even though it has its moments of travail. When the designer has had fun and satisfaction in creating a layout, the odds are long that the reader will gain fun and satisfaction, too. If he does, he is in perfect receptivity to information.

With the treasure chest of materials available, and the greater freedom being given to designers today, layout work is one of the most gratifying of all phases of the graphic arts. Not the least of the contributing factors is the fact that this job, unlike so many others in graphic arts, is not done backstage; it always plays to an audience.

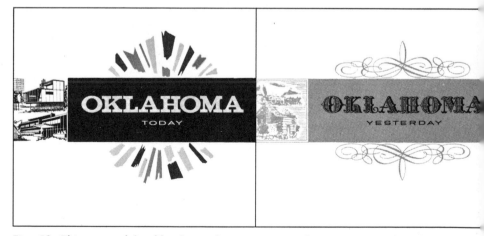

Fig. 53. This unusual booklet has split cover to emphasize contrast between old and new which the two "cover designs" do by means of type and ornamentation. (Courtesy Oklahoma Department of Commerce and Industry)

𝕿𝖗𝖆𝖉𝖎𝖙𝖎𝖔𝖓 und kultivierter Geschmack verbinden sich im

Liqueur Fonteney. Schon  erhielt

Chevalier de Fonteney das Privileg für seine Herstellung. Nach

der französischen Revolution waren die Rezepte nicht mehr auf-

findbar, bis sie vor einigen Jahren in einem alten Manuskript

wieder entdeckt wurden. Seit  erfreut

der berühmte Fonteney-Liqueur wieder verwöhnte Kenner.

LIQUEUR FONTENEY BORDEAUX

Fig. 54. Decoration of coat-of-arms and Hermann Zapf's Festival Figures add pleasant flavor to simple announcement. (Courtesy D. Stempel Typefounders, Frankfurt-
am-Main)

"190 TONS DROPPED ON OUR DODGES EVERY DAY!!"

our trucks work is equal to three on the road. We checked one of them at 150,000 miles. Not one part was worn enough to be replaced!" Stark Ceramics, Inc., Canton, Ohio

DODGE BUILDS TOUGH TRUCKS

Fig. 55. Type becomes illustration as well as channel for words. Note how headline conveys impression of heavy impact; bent lines of body type give effect of weight. (Courtesy Dodge Truck)

DODGE TRUCKS FOR 1962 are America's only Job-Rated trucks. More than 50 significant advancements make them tougher, more tight-fisted than ever. And they're priced lower than most of their competitors, right in line with the rest. See, drive and price the '62 Dodges!

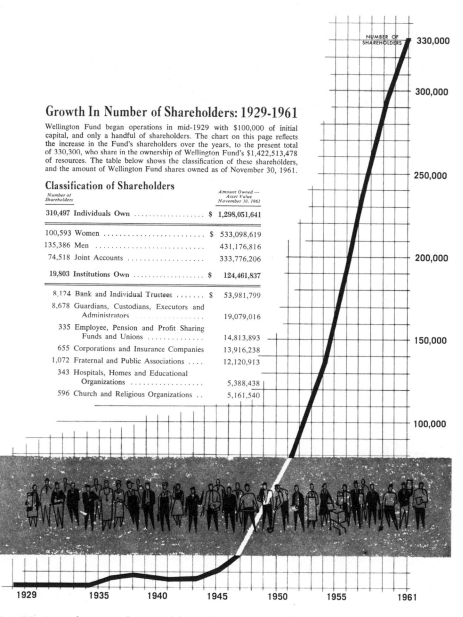

Growth In Number of Shareholders: 1929-1961

Wellington Fund began operations in mid-1929 with $100,000 of initial capital, and only a handful of shareholders. The chart on this page reflects the increase in the Fund's shareholders over the years, to the present total of 330,300, who share in the ownership of Wellington Fund's $1,422,513,478 of resources. The table below shows the classification of these shareholders, and the amount of Wellington Fund shares owned as of November 30, 1961.

Classification of Shareholders

Number of Shareholders		Amount Owned — Asset Value November 30, 1961
310,497	Individuals Own .... $	1,298,051,641
100,593	Women .... $	533,098,619
135,386	Men	431,176,816
74,518	Joint Accounts	333,776,206
19,803	Institutions Own .... $	124,461,837
8,174	Bank and Individual Trustees .... $	53,981,799
8,678	Guardians, Custodians, Executors and Administrators	19,079,016
335	Employee, Pension and Profit Sharing Funds and Unions	14,813,893
655	Corporations and Insurance Companies	13,916,238
1,072	Fraternal and Public Associations	12,120,913
343	Hospitals, Homes and Educational Organizations	5,388,438
596	Church and Religious Organizations ..	5,161,540

Fig. 56. Annual reports face problem of presenting tabulations in interesting manner. This page combines drawings with graph and chart. Basic color is dark blue; tint block under drawing and grid of graph in dull pink-buff. (Courtesy Wellington Fund)

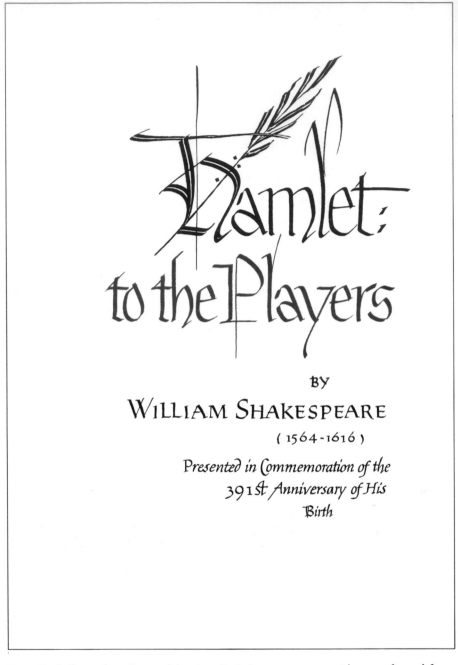

Hamlet:
to the Players

BY

WILLIAM SHAKESPEARE

(1564 - 1616)

Presented in Commemoration of the
391st Anniversary of His
Birth

Fig. 57. Calligraphy—"beautiful writing"—is happy partner with more formal foundry type. These "written" pages are by Raymond F. DaBoll, through whose courtesy they are reproduced.

Oh, might I in my exultation,
To all the world this joy impart!
Would I might clasp the whole creation
Lovers or Strangers, Foes or Brothers—
Would I might clasp them
The whole Creation
With fervent rapture to my heart!

Pilgrim Song
from the Russian of Count A. Tolstoi
English version by Paul England
(Music by Tschaikovsky)

Fig. 58. Record album jackets offer opportunity for colorful design. This one (a comprehensive by Elaine Golt) uses orange in two panels, top and bottom, and for tint block behind the numbers; type in black. Repetition of words not only accents content of copy but affords pleasant overall pattern.

SUGGESTED READINGS

Baker, Stephen. *Advertising Layout and Art Direction.* New York: McGraw-Hill Book Co., Inc., 1959.

Dwiggins, William A. *Layout in Advertising.* New York: Harper & Brothers, 1948.

Felton, Charles J. *Layout of Advertising and Printing.* New York: Appleton-Century-Crofts, 1954.

9

Basic Layouts

BOOKS AND LETTERHEADS

Just as a football player must learn the fundamentals of tackling and blocking, so there are fundamental layouts that the designer must master. If he can solve these problems well, he can handle most others.

BOOK DESIGN

The first of these problems is that of designing a book. Some critics sneer that books are no longer designed today, they are canned, like sardines. The truth is not quite as dour. The number of books published every year, like the soaring total of the national budget, increases constantly. Some books are canned; many, fortunately, are designed. Often the finest designed books are of such limited circulation that they are overlooked in the flood of cheap paperbacks.

To understand book designing, we must know something about the anatomy of a book.

The first a prospective reader sees of most books is not part of the volume at all, it is the *dust jacket*, more commonly today, the *jacket*. This is, in effect, a poster. It must give the name of book, author, and publisher, and must convey, or at least suggest, the subject matter or flavor of its contents. The jacket has three parts: the *spine* or *backbone*, the *front cover*, and the *back cover* (often used as an advertising area, although perhaps too subtly to be recognized as such). The jacket *flaps* (which fold around the cover proper) usually carry a synopsis of the book and biographical data on the author.

Rarely does the reader see more than one cover and the spine at one time, and usually only one cover. Thus each subdivision can be treated as a separate unit. Because the jacket folds over in a roll instead of a crease, there is no sharp definition of area, and there must be a physical blending of the two units as well as one of feeling and treatment.

The cover, or *case*, of the book itself, while often not seen until the dust jacket disintegrates, also identifies the book, author, and publisher. Just as definitely, but far more subtly, it must contribute to the over-all impression which the author seeks to make.

Economics of book publishing have long since simplified book covers. Expensively bound books are replaced by machine-bound; printing supplants stamping. But the many new plastics and fabrics, new photographic and printing techniques ensure that modern book covers can be as intriguing as classical ones.

A long-term debate about the direction of the printing—when it runs lengthwise on the spine—has apparently been settled, although there are still unreconstructed rebels. Such titles are now printed—in America but not in England—so that when the book stands on a shelf, the reader must tilt his head to the right to read the backbone. Or, to visualize better, when the book lies flat on the table and printing on the spine is right-side-up, the front cover will be visible.

The book itself consists of three parts: *preliminaries, text,* and *references.*

The first loose page in a book is half of the *end paper;* the other half is pasted on the cover. The first page on book stock is the *half-title page* or *bastard title.* This is unnumbered and carries only the name of the book. This is backed by a blank page, although sometimes a list of the author's other books is given here.

The *title page* is backed up by the page proclaiming the *copyright.* The *dedication,* if any, is the next right-hand page and it is backed with a blank.

Dedications were rare for a decade or two; they were too sentimental for a culture that allows such indulgence only on such peremptory occasions as Mother's Day and Christmas, or others set by commercial calendars. They are coming back, though, a happy practice.

None of these pages has been numbered. When pages are numbered,

Fig. 59. Book jackets are among brightest American designs. *The Pass* wraps illustrations around spine. *Salinger* uses rich brown and cerise as borders on black rectangles. For *The Negro Revolt*, striking black-and-white design is accented by bright yellow semicircle. *Prisoner's Friend* uses two hues of green plus black. (Courtesy Harper & Row, Publishers)

remember that right-hand pages are always odd numbers. That means that Page 1 always faces a blank.

But before we find Arabic numerals, we may have Roman ones. The *preface* and/or *foreword* come after the dedication and are numbered in lowercase Romans. Thus, the first page of the preface is, in this case, *vii*, for it is the seventh page even though the first six are unnumbered.

The next right-hand page carries the *table of contents* and a printed page number or *folio*. A *list of illustrations*, if there is one, runs on the next right-hand page and, on the next odd number, the *introduction*. (The preface is a formal statement of the purpose of the book and acknowledgment of help and encouragement. The introduction explains the particular point of view of the author toward his subject matter or toward other works in the field. The preface and introduction are written by the author; forewords by another person.)

All these pages are preliminaries. Not all of them appear in every book. Sometimes, to gain a vital page that would otherwise add a signature, two or more items may appear on the same page. Or, if a required signature contains blank pages, they may be interspersed in this section. Preliminaries may take through *page xiii* or more.

The first page of "reading," Chapter I, begins on a right-hand page. It carries the chapter number and/or title. This is the first page designated by Arabic numerals. It starts with 1, even though it may be preceded by many preliminary pages of "front matter." It may start with page 3 if the main body of the book is introduced by a *part title* page.

Page 2 is the first to carry the *running head*. Outside the main type area, the name of the book runs on even pages, of the chapter on odd pages. If chapters are not titled, the name of the book runs on both pages. Folios—page numbers—usually occupy the same space line as running heads to save space and simplify make-up. They should be at the top of the page; this is the easiest area to uncover as the reader thumbs through to find his place. Despite this, running heads and folios occasionally run below the type page; in some cases, heads are at the top and folios at the bottom, and sometimes there are no running heads at all, only folios.

Succeeding chapters may start on odd or even pages.

Reference pages contain one or more of the following: *appendix, supplement, bibliography, glossary, vocabulary, index*. They are usually set in smaller type than the text but should harmonize, and so are

Fig. 60. Well known colophons of book publishers. Above, from left: Viking Press; Oxford University Press, New York Division; Oklahoma University Press; World Publishing; Random House. Below: Fust and Schoeffer, successors to John Gutenberg (this colophon is now emblem of Printing House Craftsmen's Clubs); Harper & Row, Publishers; Modern Library; University of Texas Press.

usually kept in the same face. Often this material is set in two columns, because the line length, established to the page width for text faces, would be too long for a smaller face.

Occasionally a designer will use two pages for the title. This can be very effective, and one wonders why it is not a more frequent device, even if it may create folding and aligning problems discussed in Chapter 20. The title page is probably the most important page in the book. More than the cover or even the dust jacket, it sets the key in which the book is played.

The title page carries the name of the book—and perhaps some descriptive matter or subtitle; the name of the author—again with descriptive matter or identification if this is pertinent; a series title; name of collaborator or illustrator; previous books; the name and address of the publisher, and sometimes his *colophon* or trademark.

The colophon is the ancient mark with which every craftsman identified his product. (In silver we call it the hallmark.) Manutius made his, the anchor and dolphin, a respected symbol. Fust and Schoeffer, successors to, or grabbers of, Gutenberg, used two shields on a branch which today has become the insignia of the Printing House Craftsmen. Modern colophons are handsome—the torch of Harper & Row, the borzoi of Alfred Knopf, and the house of Random House being among the more distinctive.

The designer has more freedom with the title page than with any others, and more display material to work with. Restraint is therefore a laudable virtue. Type need not be the same family as that of the text, but it should either harmonize closely or contrast markedly.

Fig. 61. Title pages. Note double spread for *Confucius* and use of reverse for *The French Revolution*. (Courtesy Harper & Row, Publishers)

Decorations wax and wane in popularity; as in any printing, they must be functional. Should the publisher use a colophon, it would probably be all the decoration a title page can use. If there is any other, it must harmonize with the mark as well as the type.

The name of the book takes the largest type, the author's name the next size, with other elements considerably smaller. As there is unusually ample space to work in, the designer may be tempted to over-display the page. This should be avoided.

Because white space represents such a large portion of the title page, its disposition is critical. Instead of dispersing type all over the page, those elements which logically go together should be grouped: the title and subtitle, or the title and author. The principle of rectangular make-up which we have discussed applies to the placement on title pages; no line or ornament should be placed to define halves, quarters, or thirds of the page.

Because the title, in the largest type, heads the page, the mass of weight is always high, well above the optical center. By custom our eyes are used to this; title pages with the mass below the optical center disturb us. Being a right-hand page, the title page will have its widest margin at the right but, because there is so much white space here, the type page need not be moved quite as far to the left as text pages.

Chapter headings are the bridge between the title page and text. They must harmonize with either or both. Their typography is purely organic. If chapters are only numbered, treatment is different from that of chapter titles. Here again decoration is often used, but it must be subdued. Often when there is little material for attractive display—and other times, too, of course—the head may be *sunken*, dropped to the line of golden proportion or even lower. Or the head may be at the top of the page, with the body beginning at the line.

We have already discussed margination. The method of binding must be considered. If it is side-stitching, for instance, we must widen the gutter because so much of it will be hidden in the binding.

On text pages the designer's major decisions involve determining type specification, running heads and folios, and treatment of illustrations. After that, pagination is mainly the compositor's job. The very finest books do not begin or end a page with a widow and copy is sometimes rewritten to eliminate short lines. In *trade editions* these niceties are often ignored, because of their additional cost and of the American theory that it is better to make a book a little less than perfect available

*D*ear Davis: About halfway through this I began to realize I was writing it for you. It came to me after I had put down the account of your meeting with these three people, a meeting which I am sure had little or no significance to you. You were with them less than an hour and your mind was preoccupied with other things. It was significant to them, however, and even to me, though I was hardly conscious of it at the time, for the fact is you were a catalyst and without you the truth might never have been known. The truth, in that sense, is yours.

I feel I must explain why I have come to write in this particular manner. It is certainly new to me and I am not good at it. You know as well as I do how restricted and concentrated a surgeon's life can be and I am afraid mine was particularly so. I saw little of my friends (I hadn't many), there were no children, and it often seemed to me that my wife was my one constant communication with the human race, for you cannot call the removal of a tumor a form of communication

89

1

Tuesday, October 4   2:55 to 3:30 p.m.

Boy Kirton spent the most important part of his life in a box nine feet long by seven wide by eight high. The floor of the box was covered by carpet of soft, delicate gray. There was a desk, not a big one, and this desk was placed cater-cornered so that it formed a triangle with the meeting of two walls. He sat within this triangle in a position which for some reason he felt to be better than if, for example, he had sat with the light coming over his left shoulder from the metal-framed window which looked down seven floors into a side street. The box contained one other chair, a hat and coat stand, and on the window wall an abstract painting by a friend of Kirton's who worked in the art department of an advertising agency. Sets of printers' galleys hung on the wall behind him. The box had one brick wall. The three others were partitions, made of wood up to a height of four feet, and above that a latticework of wood and frosted glass. In one of these partition walls a door was set, and this door led out into a larger box of identical shape. Here the floor covering was haircord, there were filing cabinets, desks, noiseless typewriters. Another metal window looked out into the same side street. In this larger box lived Kirton's assistant Jack Smedley, Smedley's assistant Charlie Owens, and two girls who were sometimes called secretaries and sometimes research workers. This box again had one brick and three partition walls, and it differed from Kirton's only in the fact that there was clear and not frosted glass in the wall separating the box from the corridor.

1

Fig. 62. Chapter headings are chaste but connotative. (Courtesy Harper & Row, Publishers)

XVII

❧

MARTYR OF KULUKWI

❧

Standing on the hillside of his missionary home where Tom Bozeman drank in the refreshing early morning air and looked out upon the beautiful Baliem Valley that had been concealed from the rest of the world for slumbering centuries. Even as he stood there surveying the peaceful scene shortly after dawn in the spring of 1961, he knew that this panorama even yet had not been shared by many outsiders. Tom had known it as Cannibal Valley, a place of bloodshed and battles but now he thought only of the beauty of the peaceful landscape.

From Hetgima where Bozeman, and his family lived, you could look up the Baliem Valley in a northwesterly direction for a distance of almost forty miles. The floor of the valley is flat and the Baliem River snakes through it like a coiling brown serpent. From the north and west the river is fed by dozens of mountain streams that rush into the wider main river that sometimes glides peacefully and leisurely and at others roars angrily over the rapids on its inexorable journey to the southwest.

13

Eight

Talks with Thornton Wilder

"Whatever we succeed in doing is a transformation of something we have failed to do. Thus, when we fail, it is only because we have given up."
—PAUL VALÉRY

Did you happen to see, on the first page of the *New York Times* dated November 6, 1961, a two-column article by a feature writer named Arthur Gelb announcing the production in the near future of three one-act plays by Thornton Wilder, part of a double cycle of fourteen, *The Seven Ages of Man* and *The Seven Deadly Sins*, long rumored and hoped for? It was an important piece of journalism, illustrated by a flash photograph of the famed novelist and playwright, based in large part on an interview with him, full of the ethos of his art, and of those technicalities of staging which count for so much in the aesthetics of the theatre. "We have to kick the proscenium down," he told the *Times*.

Our great newspapers (I note) are apt to get essential truths and general principles right, but are not always accurate about dates and other small matters of fact. For example, in this article, Gelb stated that the announced triple bill at the Circle in the Square was to be Wilder's "first new stage work in nearly twenty years." To state this matter more precisely, it was his first *entirely* new stage work to be produced *in this country* since 1942. *The Matchmaker*, first given at the Edinburgh Festival in 1954 and brought here the following year, was a revision of *The Merchant of Yonkers*, a comedy somewhat unsuccessfully put on stage in the late thirties. In 1955 another play, entitled *A Life in the Sun*,

55

to a great many people than to restrict, by price, a perfect book to a small audience.

In children's books especially—although some fine editions of adult fare can be included—illustrations are an integral part of the page design. The illustrator works closely with the author or book designer and type is set and paginated around the art. As most such books are now printed by offset, the artist prepares the mechanical for each page —or at least specifies how it is to be arranged.

The growing popularity of *paperbacks* has opened a new field of book design. Here the cover combines the function and design of the jacket, the cover, and the title page. Such books do have title pages, but they are often treated very simply, almost like the conventional half-title.

In the public mind paperbacks are associated with paintings of period heroines (in low-cut gowns), victims of sundry mayhem (in low-cut, or no, gowns), or stern-visaged Westerners (with high-cut pockets). Books of this sin-sex-sadism genre require flamboyant display—and get it. But there are legions of good paperbacks whose covers are among the freshest designs of the graphic arts. Like dust jackets of trade books, these may use art work but many—and good ones—use only type.

LETTERHEADS

The next test of a layout man is a letterhead. On the face of it, this appears to be an easy job. Actually it is anything but easy. For the letterhead stands out like a matador in a bull ring, surrounded as it is with a wide arena of white paper. Letterheads are, of course, printed on colored stock, too; but it makes little difference if our bullfighter is spotlighted on yellow or white sand.

Functions of the letterhead are: to identify the sender; to connote the kind of business, especially when the name is ambiguous; to suggest the personality of the business, the solidity of a bank founded in 1798 or the modernity of an electronics plant; to create a pleasant page after the letter has been written.

A letterhead is always seen in connection with the letter itself. Because, by our usage, the formal salutation creates a block of type at the top left, it is wise to produce a balancing mass at the right.

The ingredients of a letterhead, other than the paper, are the name, address, phone number, cable address, and locations of agencies and subdivisions. These are the essentials. To these are added the *mosquitos*, the plague of the designer. The trademark is one, especially if it is not a good one. Officials of the company may individualize letterheads with the addition of their name. Organizations list all officers. Some companies have slogans of which they are inordinately, and sometimes undeservedly, proud. The worst of the skeeters is the picture of *Our Founder* or *Our Plant*. (If you listen carefully now, you may hear a sound like a distant surf. This is the sound of all the letterhead designers in America shuddering.)

On conventional letterheads (and woe to him who would change them), everything is centered at the top of the page. Modern letterheads often carry material at the bottom of the page and sometimes group long lists of names into thin panels that run down one or both sides. Color, in paper and ink, becomes more accepted every day.

Letterheads should be so designed that they can be used—as-is or with slight modification—on billheads, invoices, statements, and other business forms. The value of identifying all written matter from one source, by color of stock and ink and typographic treatment, is substantial.

Often the letterhead is reduced and used on envelopes, sometimes sideways to make it fit. In this usage only the name and address are necessary. The Post Office prefers the return address on the face of the envelope and its advertising value suggests this is the best location. By postal regulations, no printed matter can be placed closer than 3½ inches from the right edge; this assures room for postage and postmarks to be easily seen.

Most business letters are typewritten; they look best when margins of the typing align with those of the letterhead. The designer must keep this in mind. When window envelopes are used, it saves time if there is some device which will tell the typist where to begin the name and address. This can be unobtrusive, an agate period, for instance. Or it can be made highly visible, part of the total design.

Some letterheads combine inked or blind embossing, letterpress, offset, or Thermography in various combinations. Others use two-toned stock folded over an inch or so at the top with the letterhead printed on the side opposite that on which the letter is typed. If the letterhead performs its necessary functions, the only limit on its design is expense and good taste.

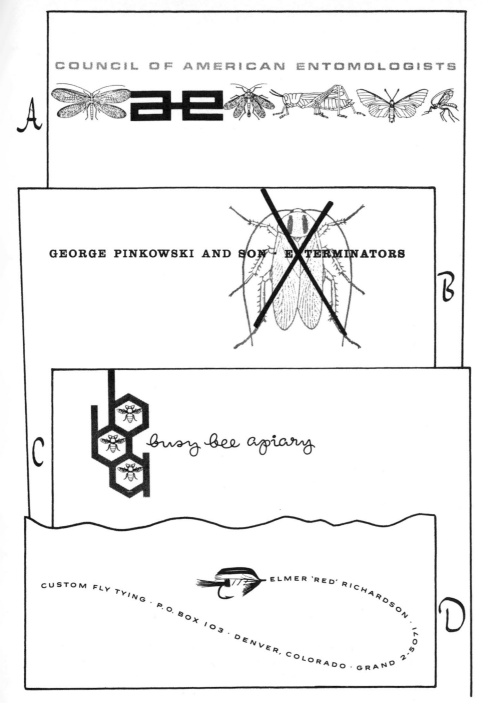

Fig. 63. Dramatic letterhead designs. A: type, olive green; art, black; geometric design, red. B: type and art, black; X, red. C: honeycomb, orange; rest in black. On these three, address is at bottom of sheet. D: fly, red, black and orange; type, black; this whole letterhead is at bottom of sheet.

Fig. 64. A: monogram, dull yellow; globe, blue; type, black. Note how type runs at side of sheet. B: address, light green; phone number, lilac; name, bright blue; initial, black. C: type, black; mountains, blue; sun, yellow and black. D: name and address and lower asterisk, black; sales offices and top asterisk, blue; S, dull yellow; note unusual placement of name and trademark at right of sheet to allow room for typed salutation. E: Bird's wing, metallic gold, rest in black. (All letterheads courtesy Whiting-Plover Paper Co.)

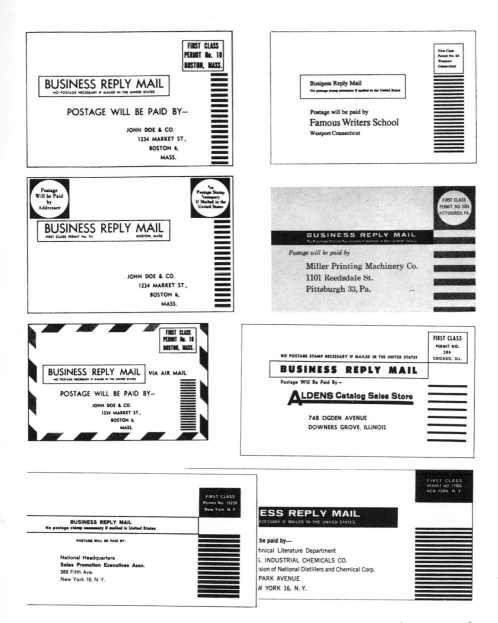

Fig. 65. Even prosaic forms as business-reply envelopes can be given design appeal. Top three designs in left column are examples shown by Post Office; others show design variations possible within regulations. (Courtesy *Advertising & Sales Promotion* magazine)

BUSINESS CARDS

Business cards contain most of the information of a letterhead plus the name of the individual presenting it. They must be businesslike, attractive, connotative, and above all easy to read, so that the recipient can grasp the entire message at a glance or use it as a convenient reference.

Business cards are small: $3\frac{1}{8} \times 1\frac{3}{4}$ inches is common. All elements, therefore, must be scaled down in proportion. There is not much room for maneuvering in an area this small; the designer must be surefooted.

It is said that if the layout man can handle letterheads and business cards successfully, nothing can daunt him thereafter. There is enough truth here to be an incentive to any designer to hit these tackling dummies at every opportunity.

One thing is sure, in most cases he cannot help but improve the present product. As a group, American letterheads fit the summary, "The average quality is well below average."

SUGGESTED READINGS

Bennett, Paul A. *Books and Printing*. Cleveland, Ohio: The World Publishing Company, 1951.

Carter, John. *ABC for Book Collectors*. London: Rupert Hart-Davis, 1961.

Tschichold, Jan. *Designing Books*. New York: George Wittenborn, Inc., 1949.

10

Letterpress

THE CLASSIC PRINTING METHOD

If you have ever used a rubber stamp, you have been a letterpress printer. This familiar gadget is a simple, and perfect, example of letterpress, the form of printing which is not only the oldest method but accounts for 82 per cent of all printing sales volume in the United States.

Letterpress is the method whereby a relief image of the character carries ink to the paper.

The earliest date we can attribute to printing is about 2000 B.C., when the Babylonians produced playing cards. The Chinese printed from carved wooden blocks by placing paper on the inked relief surfaces and rubbing or brushing the paper until the whole design had been transferred. This is similar to the way youngsters "print" wood blocks by rubbing the paper with the heel of a spoon.

Centuries were to pass before mankind found a method of producing the impression with a single movement. Although Gutenberg would be well enough honored as the inventor of movable type, many observers ascribe to him the first true printing press. This is undeserved acclaim. Wood blocks, which preceded metal type, were printed on a similar, if not identical, press. An ancient engraving of a press shows the date 1420 carved into the wooden structure.

The machine itself was not a drastically new device. As a matter of fact, it gets its name from the prosaic machine long used to press grapes and cheese.

Joining together two massive beams which ran from floor to ceiling was a stout wooden cross-beam. Through it passed a vertical wood screw. A waist-high platform held the type, and the *platen,* a flat plate that impressed the paper upon the type, was forced down as the screw was turned by a long horizontal lever.

The process was entirely manual. Untanned sheepskins, stuffed with wool, and fastened to stubby handles, were the *balls* by which ink was spread on the type. The paper was well moistened, so it would accommodate itself to the often uneven surface of the printing form, and a blanket was placed beneath the platen to make sure that irregularities in height would not leave any portion unprinted. These steps were done as the *bed* or form was pulled out from under the platen. Then, after the type was pushed back under the platen, the pressman would tighten the screw to make the impression, pressure was released by a backward sweep of the lever, the form was pulled out so blanket and paper could be peeled off and the whole cycle started over again—at the frustrating pace of 20 impressions per hour.

This press was standard throughout Europe for 150 years although minor improvements were made: The screw became copper; a sliding bed made it easier to ink the form; the blanket was transformed into a *tympan,* part of the platen; a *frisket* shielded the paper from areas which were not supposed to print. The first press in North America—that of Esteban Martin in 1534, or Juan Pablos in 1539, in Mexico City—and the first one in Colonial America—that of Stephen Daye in Plymouth in 1639—were basically the same in design. Daye's press still exists in the state capitol at Montpelier, Vermont.

The first press built in what is now the United States was the product of Christopher Sauer, Jr., in Germantown, Pennsylvania, in 1750. Until that time all presses were imported from England. There the Earl of Stanhope built an all-iron press in 1798 with the phenomenal speed of 300 impressions per hour. None was ever brought to America, for the new nation was fast becoming more than self-sufficient in this area.

The first press to be invented in America was the famous *Columbian,* a name still revered by all printers. Built by George Clymer in Philadelphia in 1813, the new model replaced the cumbersome screw with a system of levers actuated by a long lever, "the devil's tail." (It came honestly by the appellation; if pressure were unexpectedly released, the tail would sweep back like a whip and its heavy iron handle could knock a pressman into oblivion—or even into the obituary columns.)

An adaptation, the *Washington Press,* used a toggle joint instead of a lever complex. Both American presses handled forms of 27×42 inches, five times the area of earlier models. Washington presses are still in many a print shop today, most as museum pieces, a few still used as proof presses.

The *platen press* as we know it was born in 1830 in Boston. Stephen P. Ruggles developed a press with a clamshell motion that carried the platen from a horizontal position, upward from hinges at its bottom, against the printing form which was locked perpendicularly. Its action is similar to that with which the cover of a book is opened and closed as the volume lies stationary. This action gives the name *clapper,* by which platen presses are known familiarly today.

When patents expired, in the 1880's, Chandler and Price entered a market where it is still active. The *C&P* was, and is, the mainstay of many a printshop as was the picturesquely named *Colt's Armory* or *Universal Press.*

All these models were operated by a foot treadle which left the pressman's hands free, one to place blank sheets on the platen, the other to remove the printed sheets and pile them up neatly.

Many platen presses today are automatic; mechanical "hands" with pneumatic suckers feed and remove paper. But hand-fed platens are useful for short runs and many an exemplary piece is printed on tiny hand-fed and hand-powered presses that take only a 3×5-inch form. In commercial shops, platens account for well over 50 per cent of all presses in use today although, because so many are used for short runs, they do not produce anywhere near 50 per cent of printing volume.

The second most popular press now is the *cylinder press.* Here the form is placed on a horizontal bed, the paper impressed upon it by a cylinder that rolls across the form. The cylinder touches only a small portion of the form at any given time and thus pressure can be extremely uniform and the result is excellent quality.

A Saxony clock-maker, Friederich Koenig, patented the first cylinder press in England in 1810. He had found references to the use of rollers to print copperplates shortly after Gutenberg's day. He adapted the principle to letterpress, moving the bed back and forth beneath the cylinder which revolves on a stationary axis. The first cylinder was used by *The Times of London* and performed, to the proprietors' delight, at 1,100 copies per hour. This was improved upon by another Briton, D. Napier, who invented metal *grippers.* These clutched the blank paper which was then wound around the cylinder during the impression cycle, released, and then clutched by another set of grippers which pulled the printed sheets away from the form and onto the delivery table.

On the cylinder press, the bed of the press moves forward and back under a pyramid of rollers that ink the form evenly. During that cycle, the cylinder is raised from the form. Then, gripping a blank sheet, the cylinder drops down to roll across the form as it makes its second back-and-forth motion. As the form is inked again, the lifted cylinder sends the printed sheet to the delivery table. This is the *double-revolution* principle.

There are variations in the mechanical action that make for smoother or more precise operations. Cylinders may make only one revolution for each impression, the paper covering only half of the impression cylinder; this may employ the *stop-cylinder* action so the blank paper can be placed in exactly the proper register as the cylinder pauses. The cylinder may reverse direction during the inking-delivery cycle. Paper may be fed, manually or automatically, in single sheets or off a continuous roll. But the principle, a sound one, remains constant.

The proof press in most composing rooms is a small cylinder model.

Richard March Hoe, whose company built the first American cylinder in 1830, invented the third category of presses in 1846, the *rotary*.

The moving bed of a cylinder press must be massive, and thus heavy, to afford an absolutely smooth surface for the type form. This, plus the not trifling weight of the forms themselves, is a heavy mass to move many feet, stop, and move back again. This places an inherent speed restriction upon all cylinder presses, especially the giants that print newspapers. Hoe looked for a way to eliminate this reversal of direction which caused the problem. His answer was to place the type as well as the paper on a cylinder. V-shaped column rules held the type firmly against the centrifugal force.

This cylinder was large so that each individual line of type stood, in effect, on an almost flat surface. Indeed, the cylinder was so large that four impression cylinders fitted neatly against it. Each of these could be hand-fed at 2,000 copies per hour, making the total production 8,000. Later models added more impression cylinders and increased capacity proportionately.

Again the principle remains today, although one major improvement —curved stereotype plates—makes possible the phenomenal speeds of

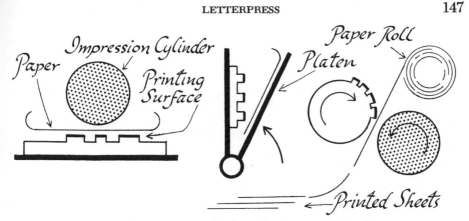

Fig. 66. Schematic of letterpress methods. Cylinder press, left; platen press, center; rotary press, right.

modern newspaper presses, and curved stereotypes and plastic or rubber plates have many applications.

R. Hoe and Company also invented a cutting and folding machine as an integral part of the *web-fed* press. It cuts the continuous roll of printed paper into proper-sized sheets and folds them into pages. (The principle of printing from a roll, instead of single sheets, had been invented in 1865.) These two inventions are essential in newspaper printing today.

Goss Printing Company first built presses that worked together as a team, printing several complete newspapers at one time. As early as 1889, only four years after its founding, the Chicago firm built a sextuple press for the *New York Herald* that printed off a roll unwinding at 25 miles per hour and produced 72,000 complete copies per hour. They were the first to build presses that could be expanded by adding additional units. Today, for instance, the *Chicago Tribune* links 95 Goss units into a single complex that prints two million 20-page papers (or any variation thereof) in one hour.

Most rotaries are *perfecting presses*. That is, they print on both sides of the sheet or paper *web*—the continuous sheet that feeds off a roll—and then fold the pages into signatures. Each *unit* of such a press prints the front and back of two or more pages. The paper must be fed through the press in such a way that the products of all units will fold together properly into a single newspaper.

A *perfector press* performs the same front-and-back printing on a flat-bed press with two cylinders.

Hoe and Goss, along with the Miehle Company, which produces

Fig. 67. Form locked up in chase. Note quoins at left and top and method of filling in non-printing areas. (Courtesy Emery Air Freight)

most of the country's cylinder presses, are leaders in the field although there are many other excellent manufacturers. Among these are Cottrell and Sons, who make the famous McKee rotary. This reverses Hoe's original principle. For it uses a single large impression cylinder and around it banks from two to five platen cylinders, each carrying a separate color so that the entire full-color reproduction can be printed in one revolution. The McKee is credited with making possible such large, huge-volume picture magazines as *Life* and *Look*, which must print precise color work at very high speeds.

The Miehle Vertical is another well-known American press. Its unusual feature is that the type is held in a perpendicular position and moves up and down to contact the impression cylinder. The Heidelberg press, made in Germany, became very popular in America after World War II. One of the unusual features of this platen press is that its mechanical fingers can pick up two blank sheets and print them, with duplicate or entirely different forms, at the same time. English-made presses are commonplace in Canada although not in the United States. Italian presses are building a following in this country in the few years since their introduction late in the 1950's.

The pressman is a skilled member of the printing fraternity. He has three ingredients to work with: paper, ink, and the printing form. Each poses problems which require his specialized talents.

He checks all printing elements to make sure that they be exactly type high. He cannot dampen his paper to make it snuggle down upon a wavy form. Neither can he *sock the type* into the paper. For, unlike the thick, almost spongy paper of Gutenberg's day, modern paper is thin and undue pressure will emboss the paper and make the reverse surface too rough to print upon. For most jobs he seeks a *kiss impression,* bringing the paper and form together exactly close enough to transfer the ink but not to bruise the surface.

To get this delicate juxtaposition, he utilizes *makeready.* If the printing elements are not exactly type high, he builds them up by applying the thinnest tissue paper under the low areas. This demands skill and care, especially when he must raise certain portions, sometimes very small areas, in halftone engravings. The pressman may have to compensate in an area smaller than a dime while leaving surrounding areas unaffected.

More commonly he achieves the same effect by building up or reducing the circumference of the impression cylinder. Around this finely tooled metal core are placed several thickness of paper, the *packing,* which is then covered by the blanket or a sheet of very tough *tympan paper.* By cutting away or adding to the packing, again in tiny increments of thickness, he can adjust the point at which paper and form meet. Makeready takes time, lots of it.

Whenever there is such an element of expensive manual work, there is pressure for mechanization; many an inventor has sought automatic makeready. The most promising method today employs a powder which adheres to a print pulled from the form. This, in effect, adds to the height of this area when the processed print is affixed under the tympan. This explanation is oversimplified. It is given only to emphasize that makeready is a costly step in printing, and that care must be exercised in keeping type and engravings at precisely type-high to minimize makeready time.

The pressman must know the intricacies of *imposition* so that after a printed sheet is folded each page will be in proper position. This is discussed in greater detail in Chapter 20.

The pressman must *line up* his forms so that margins are uniform. Hold a newspaper page to the light and notice how the right-hand margin of column 8 on page 1 aligns precisely with the left edge of column 1 on page 2. Line-up, depending on the kind of press, is effected by moving either the form or the grippers which hold the paper.

Similar manipulation creates perfect *register.* When more than one color is used, each must print in exactly the right position, even though one color may be printed days after earlier ones. The most common example of out-of-register printing, perhaps, is the colored comic pages. Often we see the red lips on Blondie's cheek instead of around her mouth or two sets of eyes, black ones and blue ones. Especially in full-color reproduction, *out-of-register* printing will make the picture fuzzy at best—or grotesquely distorted at worst.

Changes in humidity will make paper stretch or shrink. Impressions perfectly lined up and registered at the start of a run may be badly off at the end of the run after humidity has affected the dimensional stability of the paper. If partially printed sheets in one or more colors have to stand for days before extra color is added, the change in dimension can be irremediable. When paper is fed off a continuous roll, the weight of the paper *web,* the tension under which it moves, its momentum and the heat generated by friction all contribute to distorting dimensions. A *web break* is a major calamity in the pressroom, especially that of a newspaper where speed is so vital. (It is estimated that a delay of one minute on the press of a New York daily means the loss of 10,000 street sales!) On a rotary press, the press crew must thread the web through each of the many units in the press. Often the web must turn corners, by means of *angle bars,* and intricate arrangements of rollers are needed to make sure that, no matter how many pages an edition contains, it will come out of the press in such a way that they can be folded and cut into the familiar package that makes our newspaper.

(Before leaving the newspaper press, it is worth noting one of the most fascinating attachments to the modern rotary press, the *flying paster.* This ingenious machine grips the edge of a fresh roll of paper— some 40-odd inches wide, 6 feet in diameter and weighing a ton— applies adhesive to the leading edge and pastes it onto the tail of the preceding, exhausted roll—all without slowing the press even a trifle!)

To minimize paper problems, most modern pressrooms are carefully humidity-controlled.

By manipulating small set-screws, the pressman regulates the flow of ink into the form. Ink is applied by a series of rollers to assure equal and even distribution. Where the form contains heavy elements requiring a generous supply of ink, adjacent to light areas, the pressman has a difficult job of adjusting the ink flow. The heavy element may print light because its supply is minimized, while the light areas may be *flooded* and print so heavily that the ink will ooze and render the image fuzzy.

This problem can be minimized by the way in which the job is originally planned. When it becomes apparent that any layout will call for elements widely disparate in ink requirements, the layout man should consult with the printer before progressing beyond preliminary plans. Simple adjustments at that stage may prevent acute grief at press time.

After he has performed all his preliminary duties, the pressman still has an important function throughout the run. He constantly checks his printed sheets to make sure the register is holding, that ink is distributed perfectly (he makes adjustments almost constantly on the flow) and that there are no *work-ups.* Quads, ledds, and other spacing material, because of the pressure exerted at the sides of the form, have a tendency to be pushed upward high enough to accept ink and to print as ugly blemishes. The pressman must watch for these and, when they occur, stop the press quickly, with a minimum of spoilage, so he can hammer the work-ups down below type-high.

To avoid *offsetting*—or *setting-off*—smudging wet ink on preceding or following pages, highspeed presses have dryers built in. Sometimes this is only a row of gas burners over which the paper passes so rapidly that it will not catch fire but which will speed the drying of the ink. By the *spray* method, a fluid—sometimes a simple sugar syrup—or a powder is sprayed over the printed sheet. Immediately the paper passes through intense heat which causes the spray to crystallize. These crystals, although tiny, are thick enough to hold printed sheets far enough apart to prevent offsetting. In some cases a blank piece of paper, a *slip-sheet*, is placed on top of each printed page. Any offsetting is thus done on this worthless sheet rather than on the next printed page. This requires low press speed which—along with the extra operation—adds to cost.

Printed sheets are usually conveyed by moving *tapes*. The pressman watches to make sure these tapes don't get dirty and produce smudges on the paper.

Letterpresses have historically been far ahead of the other links in the printing processes; at the time the Linotype was unveiled, rotary presses were printing 48,000 eight-page papers per hour. Now, in the 1960's, more emphasis is given to new composing-room equipment than to the pressroom. Drastic changes in press principles and design will probably be few in the next decade, although minor improvements are apparent on each new model that reaches the market.

But the letterpress industry is making notable progress in the application of thin printing plates that can be wrapped around a cylinder and thus utilize the advantages of rotary press printing for many different kinds of work.

Letterpress, as the oldest printing method, has evolved specialized subdivisions for its major uses. *Fine printing*, as its name defines, seeks maximum quality whether its product be a magnificent lectern Bible, reproductions of famous art masterpieces, or letterheads. *Commercial printing* represents the great bulk of work that, too, may range from handbills for a farm auction to the handsome brochures of Tiffany jewelers. *Book printing* is highly specialized although its products include handsome limited editions and inexpensive paperbacks, as well as everything between. *Newspaper printing* represents a large percentage of the astronomical number of pages printed annually.

Any of these methods may print direct from type or from the plates that make the subject of the next chapter. But in all instances, the basic principles of the ancient Chinese block-printing, and the ubiquitous rubber stamp, are retained. Gutenberg, although he might be amazed, would not be baffled by a modern letterpress.

By its long history, its exemplary performance, and its self-adaption to changing needs, letterpress well deserves the honor of having its product described simply as "printing."

SUGGESTED READINGS

Printing Progress. Cincinnati, Ohio: International Association of Printing House Craftsmen, 1959.

Ryder, John. *Printing for Pleasure.* Newton Centre, Mass.: Charles T. Branford Co., 1955.

11

Printing Plates

PUTTING PICTURES ON PAPER

Pictures were our first "writing" and pictures were our first "printing." Pictures—many forms of illustrative matter come under that term —are an important part of the work that presses produce today.

In letterpress, which we shall discuss in this chapter, illustrations are printed from *plates—engravings* or *cuts*. With recent exceptions, all letterpress plates are made by utilizing the action of light on photosensitive compounds. Thus it is inevitable that the development of platemaking should be contemporary with that of photography.

Long before the invention of type, man was printing wood blocks. He simply cut away portions of a board to leave the remainder, in relief, as the form he wanted to print. (From here he advanced to cutting out words from the same wood.)

Carving was done on the side grain of the board. That made the block fragile; it tended to splinter away with the grain. But the printer's hunger for pictures continued their use and as early as 1638, the *Weekly News* of London carried a "news picture" engraved in wood. Seeking durability, engravers cut pictures out of metal, usually copper. These took far more time and money than wood blocks, themselves far from cheap.

It was Thomas Bewick, an English artist of the early 1800's, who discovered the *white line* engraving technique that combined the delicacy and durability of metal with the economy of wood. He carved his plates on the *end grain* of the board and achieved results which are still charming works of art.

This method provided most of the pictures that were becoming increasingly popular in nineteenth-century magazines and newspapers.

Sketch artists, comparable to our news cameramen, were sent to cover a story. Their drawings—finely detailed, or hasty sketches with marginal notations to help the draftsman at home complete the scene—were rushed to the publication. There, highly skilled carvers transferred the drawing to a block of wood and then carved a printing plate. Many methods were evolved to enable more carvers to work on a single picture. The most successful, and merely an improvement on earlier methods, was to bolt several small blocks together to form one large one. The desired drawing was copied onto the large block. It was then disassembled so that as many as 10 or 15 engravers could each carve a small portion. Reassembled, each block fitted in with its neighbors to form the original large engraving. It is amazing that the technique of the engravers was so uniform that each one's work would fit, unobtrusively, into a unified whole.

The Civil War intensified demand for news pictures; wood carving reached its height of excellence and volume in that period. Engravers found techniques to simulate the shadings of wash drawings and even photographs in wood. Soon they eliminated the need to trace original pictures onto wood by producing the image there photographically.

Photography, "writing by light," is part of the graphic arts. But, because so many good books are available on the subject, we will concern ourselves only with that aspect that applies to printing plates.

The first photograph was made by Joseph Niepce in France in 1826 —with an exposure of eight hours! It proved that man could truly "write with light." Two years later he entered partnership with L. J. M. Daguerre, who gave his name to the first practical kind of photography.

The first news photograph, a daguerreotype, showed the ruins of a conflagration in Hamburg, Germany, that raged for three days in May of 1842. Ironically, that was the very time that the first illustrated paper in the world, the *London Illustrated News,* was going to press with an imaginary scene of the fire, copied from an old print, with flames added by the artist, on a wood block.

Photography utilizes the fact that certain substances are darkened by exposure to sunlight. (While these include human epidermis, we cannot term America's sun-tanning rites as photography.) Silver salts are the most convenient photosensitive materials used today.

The simplest photoengraving is the *line cut,* also called a *zinc etching,* or just a *zinc,* because that metal is most commonly used. Tracing the steps in making a line cut, is a painless way to learn the basic principles of the process.

As its name indicates, a line cut reproduces black-and-white drawings made up of simple lines and masses and without gradations in tone such as a photograph or wash drawing.

Original *art* is placed before a camera in order to obtain an *engraver's negative.* Let the first example be something as simple as the capital *E* in Figure 68. The white paper surrounding the *E* reflects light through the camera lens onto a sheet of film, covered with an *emulsion* of silver salts. The letter itself, because it is black, reflects no light.

In the development process, that area on the film which has been affected by light turns black. The shape of the *E* has not been exposed on the emulsion, the silver has not darkened and it is washed away, leaving the clear film.

This is the *negative.* It is a copy of the original art but with the tonal values reversed: The black letter is white (or transparent) on the negative and the original white background is now opaque black.

When light is projected through the negative and onto a piece of paper covered with light-sensitive emulsion, the light passes through the *E*-shaped opening and affects a similar-shaped area on the photopaper. The opaque background prevents light from reaching that corresponding area on the paper. Where the light strikes, the emulsion turns black and the original *E* is duplicated; where no light has reacted with the silver emulsion, the paper remains white as on the original.

This is the rudiment of all photography.

In the engraving process, a negative is made as described above. But now, instead of passing light through the negative onto photosensitized paper, it is projected onto a piece of metal covered with a sensitized emulsion.

There is now a black *E* on metal. A special ink, which adheres only to that portion of the plate that has been struck by light, is rolled over the metal; it refuses to adhere to the unexposed areas but clings to the oxidized emulsion. The plate is washed by running water which removes the unexposed emulsion only. Heating the plate makes the ink tacky. A picturesquely named powder, *dragon's blood,* is sprinkled

Fig. 68. Schematic of making line cut by photoengraving.

over the plate and sticks to the inky adhesive. This powder is really a resin. As the plate cools, the resin hardens into a solid, acid-proof coating.

In an etching bath, nitric acid is sprayed against the plate. That portion of the metal covered with dragon's blood is unaffected, the balance is eaten away. The original image remains in relief to be inked and impressed onto paper. This is how a line cut is made.

What happens when we make our plate as an exact duplicate of our original *E?* When it is printed, it will create that pesky mirror image and the arms of the *E* will point to the left instead of the right. So we must produce the printing plate in *mirror form* of the original. That is done simply by turning the negative over before we expose through it onto the metal. This *flopping the negative* is an essential step in all photoengraving. Occasionally we see a picture in a newspaper or magazine where the "neg" has not been flopped. The result is wedding rings on right hands, men's pocket handkerchiefs on the opposite side of their jackets, and reversed letters on billboards.

By turning the negative so the *E*, in this form, points to the left, we produce a plate with a southpaw *E*, its arms pointing left also. When this plate is printed, the arms will properly extend to the right again.

This simplified description of the etching process ignored a constant danger. As the acid consumes unprotected metal, it will eventually start etching sideways as well as downward, and thus eat under protected areas. This *undercutting* weakens the printing areas which have remained in relief. Under pressure on the press, they crumple, and the plate becomes useless.

To prevent undercutting, the engraver allows the acid to etch only a shallow *bite* the first time. Then the engraver brushes additional resin on the plate to reinforce the original coating and to form new protection on the sides of those areas in relief. (It takes great skill to powder the sidewalls while leaving the bottom of the first bite exposed to additional etching.) Back into nitric acid goes the plate for the second, third, or even more bites.

Depth of the first bite varies from .0001 to .0005 of an inch. Total depth varies with the nature of the copy; it may be as shallow as .001 inch to 10 times that much, with such deep depressions lowered still more by *routing*, grinding them away with a small drill.

Small imperfections on the plate are cleaned up by hand. The plate is then *blocked*—affixed to a wood base that brings the printing surface to exactly type-high; or it may be delivered unmounted to the printer, who fastens it on metal base. The cut is usually held to the base by an adhesive or, on special metal base, by small clamps. In newspaper operations the plate is simply laid on the base with no fastening, if stereotyping is to follow.

The film upon which the negative was made consists of a thin layer of sensitized emulsion which is on a thicker, stronger piece of film or glass. This emulsion is peeled, *stripped*, off the reinforcing substance, and then flopped on a glass plate, a *flat*, with several other negatives. For economy, the entire flat is exposed onto a single piece of metal and etched as a single unit.

During exposure, the flat is held by vacuum to the plate so that no distortion results from buckling or warping of the thin emulsion.

Comic strips are a familiar form of line cuts. They are created by simple lines or masses of black and white. But effects of gray tones are achieved by using dots, lines, or cross-hatching. The artist can produce these with his pen or brush. Or he can use a mechanical aid, of which *Zip-a-Tone* is a familiar trade name. This is a *shading sheet* of transparent, self-adhering film upon which is printed a mechanically regular pattern of lines or dots in various combinations. In Figure 69, the artist drew his characters in simple line. To produce the gray effect, he chose an appropriate pattern of Zip-a-Tone. He peeled it off a protective paper backing and laid it over the entire cartoon. In those areas where he wanted the tone, he *tacked down* the shading sheet with a *burnisher*, a pencil-like piece of wood with one end cut at an angle. In the other end of the wood is a needle, the *stylus*. With this, the artist cuts around the outline of the shaded area and lifts off the unwanted shading. Now he rubs the film firmly onto the paper with the burnisher. A waxy substance affixes the film smoothly, tightly, and invisibly, except for the pattern, of course. The artist can use more than one pattern and he can develop new ones by placing one pattern over another.

There are dozens of patterns available under many trade names; Zip-a-Tone, *Craftint,* and *Contak* are the most familiar.

The engraver can create similar shading by the *Ben Day* process. The artist makes his drawing as before. In the areas where he wants shading to appear, he paints a wash of light blue, which is invisible to the engraver's camera. In the margin he indicates to the engraver which of the more than 200 Ben Day patterns he wants in the blue area. These patterns are embossed on sheets of thin celluloid. The engraver inks the proper plate; by printing this pattern onto either the negative or the metal and washing away the unwanted areas, he can make this pattern an integral part of the final plate. If he prints the pattern on the negative, it will appear white in the final letterpress reproduction. This technique is often used to *screen type,* placing a fine pattern of white dots on the type area so it appears gray instead of black.

Fig. 69. Cartoon using various patterns of shading sheets.

Fig. 70. Line engravings. Top: pen-and-ink by Barry Blackman; center: pen-and-ink by Inge Sorensen; bottom: scratchboard. (Courtesy Goodyear Tire Co.)

The Ben Day process is the older one, but shading sheets are so convenient that they become more popular day to day. Shading sheets, too, come in white as well as black and can be used for graying down type or artwork.

Pen-and-ink drawings (preferably in India ink) are the ideal line copy. But many other media can be reproduced by line etchings and many can by themselves create the effect of shading.

Black *crayon, litho pencil* (which produces crayon-like effects), *charcoal,* and *dry brush* can all be reproduced in line if done on a textured surface. Although the eye seems to detect grays in such original art, it is only an illusion created by tiny areas of pure black on the miniature hilltops of the rough paper while the vast valleys remain white.

Scratchboard, another favorite medium for line cuts, is a paper coated with a chalky substance. Black India ink is applied over portions, or all, of the paper surface, and the "drawing" is done with a sharp knife that scratches through the ink and exposes the clean white chalk. *Ross drawing board* is a scratchboard with a built-in geometrical pattern; *Rossco Stip* has similar patterns, in raised stippling on the surface, which appear when the paper is drawn upon.

Mechanical patterns can also be achieved by using *Craftone board*

Fig. 71. Use of Doubletone paper. A: line drawings. B: dark tone developed by applying fluid by pen or brush. C: light tone developed. Swatches at top show four of many Doubletone patterns. (Courtesy Craftint Manufacturing Co.)

and this is probably the most enjoyable to use. A pattern similar to a Ben Day is printed with ink invisible to the camera. The artist draws his picture in ink on that paper. Then, to those areas where he needs shading, he applies a developer solution with a brush. This solution causes the underlying pattern to become visible.

Craftint *Doubletone* is twice as ingenious. It has cross-hatched lines. When one developer is applied, it darkens only one set of lines to create a light gray effect. When the second developer is used, it darkens both sets of lines to create cross-hatching and darker gray.

Line cuts can be printed on any paper, but extremely fine lines or tight cross-hatching should be avoided with unusually coarse paper. Line cuts can be used in any color; the Sunday comics are good examples. When very fine detail is necessary, copper is used for the plates although zinc is by far the most common.

HALFTONES

The artist and photographer in black-and-white have a full palette to work with. It ranges from pure black to total white, with intermediate tones of gray created by using less pigment on the paper. Take a look at a photograph and notice how the grays vary in intensity as the silver deposit is thick or thin. Such art work is *continuous tone*.

But the printer normally has no grays to work with; he has only black ink and and white paper. To reproduce the intermediate tones of a photograph, such as a news picture in your daily paper, he must resort to an optical illusion with a *halftone engraving*.

If you look at a halftone in a newspaper with a magnifying glass— or even with the naked eye in some cases—you can see that it is made up of many small dots, ranging from 3,025 to 14,400, or even more, per square inch. Where the dots are large and close together, the eye sees that area as black or very deep gray. Where the dots are tiny and widely scattered, we see light gray and even white. Between these extremes, are varying combinations of dot sizes and dispersal.

This characteristic *dot pattern* is created by the engraver's *screen*. This looks like the one on your front door in the summer. It consists of two sets of parallel black lines, ruled on a glass plate, and crossing each other at right angles. On the plate itself these lines run at 45 and 135 degrees to the edges to make the resultant pattern less conspicuous in the engraving.

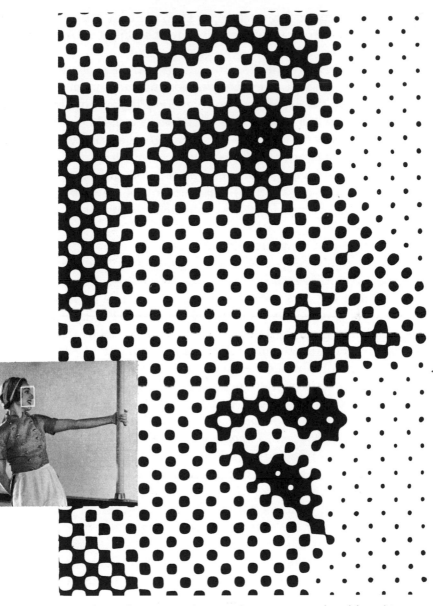

Fig. 72. Detail of halftone dots. Area of original engraving enclosed by white rectangle has been enlarged 31 times lineally.

Fineness of an engraving is indicated by the number of *lines* of dots per inch.

A 55-line-screen halftone is one made with a screen that has 55 vertical and 55 horizontal lines per inch. This, the coarsest screen in use, is most often seen in newspaper halftones. The finest in ordinary use is 150-line.

With one vital exception, halftone engravings are made as line cuts are. That exception is the introduction of the screen between the original art and the negative. The screen is placed a tiny fraction of an inch in front of the film. As the light reflects from the original art, through the camera lens, it passes through the fine openings in the screen, each one of which acts as a pinhole lens itself. Where the light is intense, it casts a bigger dot image on the negative. Later this large black dot on the negative will, in turn, block light to the negative, creating only tiny relief dots on the metal plate that will deposit a minimum of ink.

Etching is the same as for a line plate, except that one bite is sufficient in most cases. Occasionally a small portion of a halftone must be lightened up. All the other areas are *staged,* protected by an acid resistant, and the dark area is exposed to re-etching which eats down the dots and makes them smaller when printed. This is the *staging and re-etching* process. Re-etching can also be done without staging, by painting acid directly onto the area to be lightened.

Burnishing is the process of making dots larger by rubbing on them with a tool that flattens, and thus spreads, dots which were too small.

There are several common variations of halftones. The screen is a major one. Most newspapers use 55- to 85-line screen; most trade publications use 85- to 110-line. For enameled or smooth-finish paper, 120- to 133-line is best suited and on extremely high-coated paper, 150- to 175 is usable. Two hundred-line can be used only on cast-coated paper—such as Kromecote which has an almost lacquered surface— and then only with extreme care by the pressman.

Square halftones are those with right-angle corners, whether they are squares or, as in most cases, rectangles.

A thin black *finishing line* often encloses the square halftone; this is created by the engraver on his negative. This use is rare today but is occasionally revived for special effects.

The *silhouette* or *outline* halftone, as its name indicates, shows only an object with no background. A *modified silhouette* has only a portion of the picture in outline.

In a *vignette* halftone, the grays of the picture fade, almost imperceptibly, into the white of the paper. This calls for extremely skillful

Fig. 73. Styles of photoengravings. A: vignette. B: modified silhouette. C: silhouette.

New Cutler-Hammer bottom wrap inserter—shown on the job at Atlanta JOURNAL & CONSTITUTION—easily handles 40 bundles-per-minute. But speed is only half the story of this new inserter's superiority. The new Cutler-Hammer inserter features four-unit modular construction for easier inspection and maintenance. A pull-out drawer enables your own personnel to service the simple pneumatic control in a matter of minutes.

Fig. 74. Internal mortice in upper right of halftone. For external mortice, entire top right corner would be removed to create "notch." (Courtesy Cutler-Hammer)

work from the artist who first creates this blend with an airbrush on the photograph and from the engraver and the pressman. Because of the problems they present, vignettes are rarely seen in newspapers or magazines using uncoated paper.

A *modified vignette* is one where less than four sides of the picture blend out, the others being squared or silhouetted.

Oval and *circle* halftones are explained by their names.

Mortising is cutting out an area of an engraving so that type, or another cut, may be placed there. Its most common form is the removal of a rectangle from one corner, an *external* mortise or *notch*. *Internal mortises* are those entirely surrounded by the halftone. On rare occasions the mortise may be irregular in shape. But most often the design is more pleasing, the type fits more neatly, and the mechanics are simpler when the mortise is rectangular. Halftones with large uninteresting areas—the cloudless sky alongside a church steeple, for instance —that cannot be removed by conventional cropping are often improved by judicious mortising to focus reader attention to vital areas.

A *highlight* halftone—a *drop-out* or *facsimile*—is one in which the dots are completely removed in certain areas. Dots may be removed by *opaquing* them out with paint, by hand, on the negative. Those areas where the dot pattern is to remain may be protected on the metal plate, while the re-etching removes the unwanted highlight dots. *Tooling* or routing can cut or grind away unwanted dots on the metal plate. Shifting or rotating the halftone screen or moving the engraver's camera diaphragm only a trifle may often eliminate the dots on the negative by photographic means alone.

The *Kromolite process* is a most ingenious method for creating highlight halftones. It is the favorite method for the fashion advertiser who must have dropouts to reproduce the delicate wash and/or pencil and crayon drawings that lend themselves so admirably to fashion illustration.

Kromolite is a substance that is added to the artist's conventional wash without altering its monochromatic appearance. But when it is sprayed with a developer, the grays turn yellow.

When a yellow filter is placed before the camera, the art work resumes its original black-and-gray appearance to the lens and a halftone negative is made.

Now a blue filter replaces the yellow one and a line negative is shot. The blue filter makes the yellow areas appear jet black to the camera's eye. On the negative, this area is absolutely clear while the white areas have created opaque black on the film.

When these two negatives are placed together, the clear area of the line negative allows the dot pattern of the drawing to show through, but the opaque areas effectively mask out the unwanted highlight dots in the halftone neg.

Kemart is a similar process, as is *Maskomatic*.

In the *fluorographic* process a special solvent carries the pigments used in the original art work. Chinese white, dissolved in water, is painted on the areas where the dots are to be eliminated. A special filter is used then, as in the Kromolite process.

Fine screens retain more detail from the original than does a coarse screen. But sometimes, as in newspaper reproduction, it is desirable to retain the detail of a fine screen while actually printing from a coarser one. In such cases, a small halftone is made on copper. A proof is pulled and this becomes copy for an enlarged line etching.

Suppose a newspaper uses 55-line cuts and it wants a *blow-up* plate 6 inches wide. The engraver would make a 110-line copper halftone 3 inches wide. A proof is pulled. In a line camera, the image is enlarged to the desired 6-inch width. This means that 110 lines of dots that originally occupied a linear inch are now spread out across two inches and the screen is now 55. Before the second engraving is made, on zinc or copper, the proof may be retouched by painting out highlight dots or deepening the shadows.

Striking effects can be obtained by blowing up the original proof so the ultimate screen is as low as 20 or 25 lines per inch. This technique loses most detail, of course, but where bold effects are desired this is an excellent method of creating unusual impact from ordinary photographic copy.

A *reverse* plate gives the effect of white type on a black background.

Fig. 76. Reverse plate. (Courtesy
Stamps-Conhaim-Whitehead)

To create it, the engraver needs a negative on which type is black on a clear background. This he obtains by exposing the original negative —with clear type on black—onto a second piece of film. From this reverse negative the plate is made as any other line cut.

A simpler method is to have a negative Photostat made from the original reproduction proof of the desired type and shot as a normal line cut. This not only may be more economical but it enables the artist to see how the chosen type looks in reverse. Modern Romans or other faces with extremely thin lines are not suitable for reverses. The thin white lines may fill with ink and be lost in reproduction. For reverses, it is best to choose a strong-bodied type—a Sans or Gothic or the heavier Old Styles—no smaller than 12-point.

When reverses are used in advertisements, policy of publication may demand that the black areas be screened to lighten them down to dark gray. This screening is done by use of halftone *screen tints* which are applied by the engraver in a manner similar to Ben Day. Even when a solid black area is desired, it is best to use 90 per cent gray. Excess ink can then run into the tiny depressions on the plate instead of off the edges of the cut, and ink control is much easier.

When lettering is applied directly to a continuous-tone copy and shot in halftone, the dots will hide serifs, break hairlines and make vertical strokes serrated. All this lessens legibility.

For this reason, *combination plates* are used when line copy—which includes type—is combined with continuous-tone copy. Two negatives,

outstanding for performance,
simple to operate,
easy on film...

and above all,
DEPENDABLE

Fig. 77. Combination plate showing regular and reversed type on halftone back-ground. Line material could be drawing and could also extend beyond halftone area.

halftone and line, are shot separately, then are placed together and printed simultaneously onto the metal. Combination cuts can carry the line work in black or reverse.

Pre-screening continuous-tone art by the Velox process has many advantages. A *Velox* is a glossy photograph which has been broken into a dot pattern by a screen similar to that of the engraver. It is reproduced as a line cut.

Retouching is comparatively easy on a Velox. Highlight dots may be painted out for a drop-out. The shape and size of dots can be altered by hand; this is easier, and often gives better results with poor-quality photographs than to retouch the original. Contact letters may be affixed over a Velox for the effect of a combination cut; silhouetting is simple.

When a Velox is pasted up with other elements, the entire layout is shot as a single line unit. This eliminates the danger of stripping in a separately screened negative in the wrong place. Being able to handle all the elements of an advertisement as a single engraving saves time, especially for newspapers with tight deadlines.

SPECIAL SCREENS

Each square opening in the engraver's halftone screen acts like a tiny lens that takes a square picture. If that screen had only a set of parallel lines, with no cross lines, the picture that each opening would take would be an extremely narrow and long rectangle. This line would vary, not in width and length as the halftone dot does, but only in width. In effect, each one of these lines would be the equivalent of a column of halftone dots joined together.

While some detail is lost, parallel lines can adequately create the optical illusion of intermediate grays as well as reproducing black and white.

Often, especially in advertising, the effect of this *special screen* lends pleasant texture to an illustration.

Another special screen utilizes the same principle of parallel lines, arranging them as concentric circles. Not only does this give a striking effect, the center of these circles captures the reader's attention and can focus it upon an important area of the picture.

These are the most frequently used special screens, although others are used on rare occasion to give various textures.

An interesting effect is that created by shooting continuous-tone copy for a line negative. This drops out the intermediate grays with an effect of a crayon drawing. Copy for such treatment should be such that fine detail is not important and that deep shadows and highlights alone create a distinguishable image.

MECHANICAL ENGRAVING MACHINES

The many varieties of printing plates discussed this far are all produced by photochemistry. They account for a vast majority of all plates. But *photomechanical engraving machines* are producing a growing percentage of the total.

Such machines utilize the action of light to direct instructions, via electronic relays, to a mechanical instrument that removes unwanted areas of the plate.

The grandfather of such devices is the *Fairchild Scan-a-graver*. This was a long time developing; electronic progress during World War II and the return to civilian economy at its end brought out the first commercial models right after VJ-Day.

Fig. 78. Mezzotint effect (large photo) was obtained by mechanical variation of ordinary continuous tone photograph, inset. (Courtesy Lukens Steel Company)

Fig. 79. Continuous-tone originals shot as line work. (Courtesy *Print* magazine)

The machine produces halftone plates on thin plastic sheets, instead of metal, and removes non-printing areas by burning them away. There are two identical cylinders on the machine. On one is mounted the copy, on the other the plastic sheet. These revolve at the same rate of speed. A scanning eye moves slowly across the copy. As the cylinder revolves and the scanner moves laterally, every minute area comes under scrutiny.

On the other cylinder, moving at the identical speed, is a pyramid-shaped stylus, made red hot by electricity. Because their movement is identical, the eye and the stylus will always be at the same relative position on their respective cylinders.

When the scanner detects a bright white area, it relays instructions to the stylus. "I see a white spot," says the scanner. "You, stylus, bury yourself deeply into the plastic so that you burn away a large area which then will not be able to receive or deposit ink."

Similarly, the scanner instructs the stylus to leave an area unburned, so that it will print heavily, or in order to create different size dots for intermediate grays.

Because of its pyramidal shape, the deeper the stylus pokes into the plastic, the greater is the area of surface removed. The stylus oscillates at the rate of over 10,000 contacts per minute. Its lateral movement—equal to that of the scanner—is about one-third of an inch per minute. In that time it has produced engraving that wide and eight inches—the circumference of the cylinder—long.

To create the necessary mirror image required of a letterpress plate, the stylus moves from right to left while the scanner travels left to right.

The Fairchild has many advantages. The plastic cuts easily, and silhouette or modified silhouette halftones are easily cut out with a pair of scissors. Operators can be trained in a brief period to produce adequate engravings; settings can be made mechanically by means of dials and indicators. Actually, the settings are best made while inspecting the dot pattern through a stroboscopic microscope and the skill of the operator is still a major factor in the quality of the cut. The machine automatically turns itself off at the predetermined point, permitting the operator to busy himself on other chores while the cut is being made. A single picture can be converted into a plate faster than by photoengraving. But it should be noted that when a quantity of engravings are made, the photoengraver can turn out many times more the area of engraving in a day than the Fairchild can. The standard

Scan-a-graver can make 65-, 85- or 120-line screens, but changing line specifications is so long and delicate an operation that a machine will, for practical purposes, produce only one screen.

There are disadvantages. The plastic material is flammable. If the operator is careless, the stylus may not lift entirely free from the plastic as it oscillates. The result, as the hot needle drags on the plastic, is a fierce—if not merry—fire. Waste scraps must be kept in a water-filled metal container. Plastic plates do not lend themselves to stereotyping as well as photoengravings. Standard Scan-a-gravers produce only same-size plates; this often requires that a properly-sized copy photograph be made from the original art. Maximum size of a standard Fairchild plate is 8×10 inches.

An advanced model, called the *Scan-a-sizer*, will reduce or enlarge plates. This is only at a fixed ratio, however, and is not as flexible as the same procedure by photoengraving. Many newspapers leave appropriate areas blank on their curved stereotypes and paste the plastic plates right onto the stereos. Printing directly from the plastic results in excellent reproduction. If care is taken, two or more smaller plastics can be fitted together like a jigsaw puzzle to create a larger plate. A thin white line will appear where the portions butt, so cutting should be done along lines already in the copy to minimize the break.

Availability of the Fairchild opened a new era of photojournalism for smaller publications. Too small to warrant the investment of money and skilled labor in a photoengraving department, these publications usually had to mail copy to an engraver in another city. They were then at the mercy of the mails and of a premature deadline. The photomechanical engraver, available on lease, enabled production of plates in the shop by existing personnel. Smaller newspapers are the majority of Fairchild users although other publications, and custom engravers, use the machine, too.

The *Elgramma*, a Swiss product, and the *Photo-Lathe*, an American machine, are similar in principle. They use two cylinders and a scanning eye as the Fairchild does. But instead of plastic, they use a thin metal sheet. And instead of a stylus, they use a V-shaped cutting tool. As the graver cuts a thin or deep furrow, it leaves a correspondingly thick or narrow printing surface as a series of parallel lines such as the photoengraver produces with his special screen.

The pattern of parallel lines is more apparent to the reader's eye than the conventional dot pattern although fine detail can be reproduced. Horizontal lines seem to be less obvious than vertical ones, possibly because they resemble the similar horizontal scanning of the television screen.

The *Klischograph*, a German machine, gets its name from *cliche*, the European name for a cut. It also uses a metal plate, but is made of type metal that is non-distributive and can be remelted.

The blank plate is mounted horizontally on a metal table. The cutting tool can best be described as a tiny spade which "digs out" the unwanted metal, leaving the dot pattern in relief. The original art is mounted on the bottom of the table, directly under the plate, where it is scanned. The cutting, then, would start at the upper left corner of the plate while scanning begins at the upper right; the needed mirror image is produced this way.

The three machines that produce metal plates have advantages over the plastic-plate maker. They can make line engravings which cannot be produced on the plastic. In the case of the Klischograph, plates can, in effect, be reused. Stereotypers prefer metal plates, although it can be—and certainly is—debated whether this choice is based on hard fact or prejudice. The metal plates are so thin that they, too, can be bent and mounted directly on the curved stereo press plate.

As with the Fairchild, the other photomechanical engravers have made their greatest contribution by making it more convenient or economical to use photographs in printing. The written word is augmented much more frequently with pictures and smaller publications are using photojournalism so expertly that their aggregate circulation is showing a gain proportionately much greater than that of metropolitan newspapers.

DUPLICATE PLATES

There is need to make one or more duplicates of an original printing form, whether it is an engraving or a combination of cuts and type, when advertisements and news pictures appear in many publications the same day or publications are printed in several plants simultaneously. *Duplicate plates* are necessary in such instances.

Often it is not practical to print directly from type. Foundry type wears down quickly on the press and is expensive to replace. Machine-set type is of comparatively soft metal and its life on the press is limited. Engravings wear down and lose clarity. So it is customary, where the run is long as in book work, to make duplicate plates and print from them.

The most common duplicate is the *stereotype*. This method dates back to Colonial times, but it took another century before it became practical.

Stereotyping uses a cardboard-like sheet of paper, a *flong*, to create a mold or matrix of the original type or engraving. The flong, made of cellulose pulp, is placed over the original and subjected to extreme pressure, either by a roller or direct hydraulic press. (In either case, this is called *rolling a mat*. Because "mat" is used to designate both a Lintoype matrix or a stereotype matrix, this book will use the term "flong" although technically that is the raw, unmolded sheet of paper.) The flong is pressed onto and around the relief printing surfaces and makes a faithful matrix.

This matrix is light and durable, easy to transport and store. When molten type metal is poured upon it, an exact duplicate of the original form is produced. This is done in a *casting box*, by *flat casting*. The box consists of two iron plates, hinged together so they open like the pages of a book, one remaining vertical, the other horizontal. Upon the horizontal plate is laid the molded flong, face upward. Around it are laid three steel bars, *gauges*, one at the bottom, two at the sides. When the lower plate is swung upward, the result is a thin box, open at the top. Into the opening is poured molten metal, either with a ladle or by opening the vent in a metal pot above the box.

After the metal has cooled and hardened, it is removed, sawed to proper dimensions, and perhaps routed to further depress non-printing areas.

The thickness of the gauges determines the thickness of the cast plate. In some shops, stereotypers prefer to cast type-high. The cut can go directly into the printing form. Others *shell cast* the plate about a quarter-inch thick and then mount it on wood or metal to bring it to proper printing height.

Newspapers, daily or weekly, get most advertising illustrations in mat form either from a service or from manufacturers. Comic strips, panel cartoons, crossword puzzles, and feature pictures are also supplied this way; so flat casting is a familiar chore.

As invented by an Edinburgh printer, William Ged, in 1725, the mold was made of plaster of Paris. Moist clay was used shortly thereafter. Papier-mâché, used by Claude Gennoux in 1829, eliminated the breakage that plagued users of earlier molding material but it required pressure, heat and moisture—in the form of steam—in the molding process. *Dry mats* used today were developed in England and Germany, and were first manufactured in America as recently as 1917.

Mats can be rolled at the rate of three to five per minute and the cost of materials is not significant. Stereotypes can be remelted along with non-distributive type.

"Stereotyped material" in the context of the editorial worker takes its name from this mechanical process. Early in this century, when small papers, especially weeklies, had a hard time filling their columns, all kinds of editorial matter was supplied to the publisher in the form of stereotype plates—*boilerplate*. These were shell cast with a peculiar groove in the back, which accommodated a matching tongue on special base material to bring plates type high. Base was one column wide, in varying lengths, and was used over and over. Each week the express-man brought in a fresh supply of plates. Here were news stories—not very fresh, it is true, but interesting enough to the radioless reader—fiction, pictures, puzzles, and even ads. The editor used what he needed to fill the holes his handsetting couldn't cope with. After the plates were used, he either shipped them back or bought them for the price of the type metal that had made them.

This practice continued until after World War II when Western Newspaper Union, the last supplier, was forced to cease that operation on the grounds that it was a big, bad monopoly. Just who had been harmed was never made clear, certainly not the newspapers that expired immediately because they were so dependent on this adjunct to their own limited resources. The quality of this stereotyped material was high, far higher than the advice to the lovelorn and do-it-yourself medical diagnoses that appear in so many newspapers today.

Just as vital as stereotyping was to the smalltown editor, so another version of it is today for all large dailies. In the discussion of letterpress, it was noted that rotary presses have printing surfaces on a cylinder that opposes the impression surface, also a cylinder. A century ago wedge-shaped type had been used to create this curved printing surface. This was not practical for printing today's papers. There was always the danger that type would be loosened by centrifugal force and spewed all over the pressroom. It is hard to make up pages on cylinders; furthermore, modern presses need duplicate plates to print as many as 20 identical pages at the same time.

So the problem is, how to make up a newspaper page on a flat surface, then bend it around the cylinder of a rotary press? Stereotyping solves the problem neatly.

The page is made up conventionally and a page flong is rolled from it. This flat flong is then placed in a *former* or *scorcher* which bakes it into a proper curve to fit the press cylinder. It then goes into a casting box which duplicates this curve in a printing plate. Most plates today are *half-rounds* that occupy half the perimeter of a 2-foot cylinder. For some presses, they take up about 300 degrees of a much smaller cylinder. Most steps in the casting operation are automatic and four plates can be cast per minute.

While the presses are printing from these plates, the original type forms can be revised in the composing room to correct hitherto undiscovered errors, to include late-breaking news stories, or to vary the makeup for various editions. New flongs can be molded and new plates cast while the presses continue printing and stop only long enough to change plates. *Replating* thus becomes a common editorial term.

Stereotypes have disadvantages. A major one is that only coarse-screen halftones can be matted, and sometimes molding pressure breaks down fine details of type.

Another disadvantage of stereotyping has been turned into a virtue. The flong is made up of tiny cellulose fibers in the form of long cylinders that lie parallel to each other. As the flong is dampened to make a true matrix, the fibers swell in circumference but not in length. As they dry—to create a good casting condition—they shrink, again sideways. There is only insignificant vertical shrinkage.

As the fibers change in dimension, so the whole flong shrinks and contracts sideways. This fact has been utilized by newspaper publishers to effect savings in paper.

Newspaper pages are made up in 11-pica columns and then deliberately shrunken down during stereotyping to 10 picas. Because this shrinkage is horizontal, it is possible to print on a narrower roll of paper while still retaining the original vertical measurements on which the price of advertising is predicated. Because the cost of newsprint is about 40 per cent of a paper's expenditure, saving even a tiny strip on the edge of each page can amount to five or six figures annually.

Unfortunately, while publishers were making savings in newsprint, they were squandering readability. Individual letters are distorted in stereotyping, height remaining constant but width compressed. Although type designers have studiedly created letterforms to withstand such distortion, shrinkage is not uniform. The over-all shrinkage of a whole page can be controlled but column 1 may shrink twice as much as column 7. If too much compensation is designed into a letter, it may look equally as distorted if shrinkage is not up to expectation.

Another hazard of shrinkage is that it produces columns far too narrow for pleasant reading. The optimum line length for typical newspaper body type is 16 picas. When type is set at 11 picas serious discomfort results to the reading eye. When the column is reduced to 10 picas by shrinkage, it approaches an end to readability.

Plastic and rubber plates are used with varying degrees of success; both materials are rapidly being developed today after lengthy periods of experimentation. Advertisers find that plastic plates give good reproduction and, being so light, can be mailed at comparatively low costs to publications throughout the country.

The truest duplicate plates are *electrotypes*. These are manufactured by combining a molding process with the same electroplating that puts the chromium on your auto bumpers.

The original form—type, engravings or a combination of them—is used to make a mold similar to the stereotype flong. Instead of cellulose of the flong, the electrotyper uses lead, plastic, *Tenaplate*, or wax, although the latter is rare today.

This mold must be made electrically conductive. Once this was done by coating it with graphite, a dirty job that no one liked because graphite is very black, penetrating, even into human skin, and difficult to wash off. Now molds are coated with a fine, high-pressure spray of silver nitrate solution. This mold is suspended in an electrolytic tank in a solution of copper salts.

The mold is given a negative electrical charge. A copper bar hanging in the bath is charged positively. Copper ions in solution also have a positive charge which causes them to seek out the negative of the mold. These ions hug the surface of the mold as they lose their charge and are neutralized. Meanwhile the copper anode slowly dissolves and replenishes the bath with more copper ions. The thickness of the copper coating is determined by how long the mold remains in the bath. But it is never very thick.

This thin cuprous shell is removed from the mold. It is *tinned* or *plated* on its back and lead is poured onto the back to make a plate about a quarter inch thick. The lead gives strength; the tin assures a

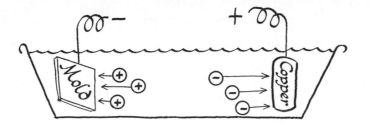

Fig. 80. Schematic of electroplating process. Positive copper ions are attracted to negative-charged mold; negative ions travel to copper cathode and form copper salt to replenish solution.

strong bond because copper and lead would not join.

If the mold is of plastic, it can be reused. If it is wax or Tenaplate, the mold is destroyed when the copper is removed. Tenaplate is a thin sheet of aluminum backing a sheet of wax.

Electrotypes are carefully finished by hand to correct low areas or defects. They are then mounted on wood by nailing or *sweated* to a block of solid lead with solder. Just as the boilerplate mentioned earlier was mounted on special base, so electros can be locked into proper position on grooved plates designed for that purpose. Unmounted electros are less bulky for easier shipment and storage and the metal base eliminates deterioration and dimensional instability of shrinking or compacting wood base.

The same electrolytic process is used to make steel or nickel-faced electros. These, commonly called *nickeltypes,* are very durable and are used when long press runs are planned or when extremely rough-surfaced stock will be used. Newspaper name plates are usually nickeltypes.

The use of electros grows constantly. Almost all magazine advertisements are delivered to publications in that form. Because electros hold finer detail than stereos, many advertisers prefer to furnish newspapers also with electros of their ads.

Most books are printed from electros. Should there be any damage to the printing surface, it is easy to make a new electro. Should signs of wear become apparent, new plates can be duplicated. If a new printing of the book is demanded, fresh electros can be made far more easily than resetting the type. And always there are the advantages of printing from a single element rather than from many linecaster slugs. *Curved electros* are used on rotary presses with greater fidelity than stereotypes.

To gain the advantage of the high speeds of rotaries, the printing industry has developed many techniques in recent years that are already commercially successful while improvements are being made constantly.

One of the most interesting has been the *Dycril plate,* a product of DuPont. This is a thin, light-sensitive plastic similar to nylon that can be etched by a solvent far less caustic than the engraver's acid. It accepts a fine image, can be etched easily and quickly and then wrapped smoothly around the printing cylinder. The plates are also used flat as conventional printing plates are.

Engravings of entire forms can be made on new alloys thin enough to use as *wraparound plates.*

The most flexible printing plates are made of rubber. *Rubber plates* are made by a molding process paralleling that of stereotyping. When first introduced, rubber plates were messy to make and lost detail; their most common use was for such comparatively low-quality printing as kraft mailing envelopes and paper bags. But constant improvement in technique and materials has made the molding of these plates no more difficult than casting from a flong and enables the plates to hold fine detail.

PREPARING COPY
FOR THE ENGRAVER

While it is the responsibility of the platemaker to produce good printing plates, the man who prepares copy for the camera and specifies plate requirements contributes substantially to the ultimate quality.

It is axiomatic that the engraver can get no better quality in his plates than is in the original copy. While not 100 per cent accurate, the statement accurately stresses the need for good preparation and handling of original art.

The specifier of plates must know those that will best reproduce his original copy. Line etchings are used for pen-and-ink drawings, brush-and-ink, dry brush, wood engravings, linoleum blocks, and scratchboard drawings. Highlight halftones are needed to capture the texture of pencil, charcoal, and wash drawings. Halftones will reproduce photographs and such continuous-tone copy as paintings in oil, watercolor, casein, and other media. Three-dimensional art can often be photographed directly through the halftone screen.

Line art should be done on good quality white paper, of which every artist has his own favorite brand. Tinted stock should be avoided except that which is blue-white. Ability to erase cleanly is essential. *India ink* is the best medium, smooth, and non-reflective. (Shiny highlights on black areas will reproduce as white.) It can be used with a brush, pen, ruling pen, or Speedball.

But India ink has a tendency to thin out at the end of a stroke and, when thin, assumes a brownish cast which results in a weak negative. When used to paint in large areas, it can wrinkle lightweight paper. For large areas, *lampblack* or *tempera* (poster paint) should pinch-hit for India ink.

Most engravers prefer to shoot original art that is larger than the finished cut. So artists consistently work at dimensions larger than the final engraving, usually two to four times in area.

Degree of reduction is a factor that must determine the artist's technique. Fine lines may disappear in reduction; so may white areas between lines. Some artists use *reducing lenses* to check on the strength of the reduced picture.

Halftones require glossy photographs for best results. Pictures on *matte paper* will tend to lose crispness in reproduction on the press. Photos should not be too contrasty; deep blacks and highlights must be separated by full gradations of gray. Most photographs are 8 × 10 inches but here, too, original copy should preferably be larger, and certainly no smaller, than the finished engraving.

Photographs often require retouching before going to the engraver's camera. Much retouching must be left to highly skilled artists who work on either the photographer's negative or the photograph.

Photos are retouched with brush or airbrush. Four or five tones of gray tempera paint are usually used; pure white and black are sometimes valuable but more often dangerous because the camera sees their extreme values more clearly than most human eyes do. Retouching should always be invisible to the ultimate reader. Retouching paint should be applied sparingly; heavy impasto layers cast shadows that the camera will pick up.

When many photos are cut into irregular shapes to form one large picture, it is called a *collage*. When a similar effect is obtained by printing several negatives onto a single sheet of photopaper, we call it a *montage*. Airbrushing blends tones and hides harsh edges of collages.

All hand art and retouched photographs must be protected. The common, and best, method is an *overflap*. A sheet of soft paper is cut the exact width of and about 3 inches longer than the artwork. The extra length is folded over the top of the art and fastened to the back with masking tape or rubber cement. It can then be lifted easily, like the page of the book, to expose the art and will automatically fall down to protect it. Some artists use two overflaps, one of tissue and one of strong kraft paper.

Crop marks, which indicate to the engraver the area to be eliminated from the cut, should always be marked outside the picture area. Four crop marks are necessary, two to show height, two for width. If no cropping is indicated, the engraver will shoot to the outside edge of the original. Occasionally the portion of the original to be used is on an axis different from the original. In those cases, one of the horizontal crop marks must be continued to the other side of the picture and it is wise to mark this "horizontal" so the engraver will know to what plane to make the sides perpendicular.

By placing crop marks outside the engraving area, they can be erased and new ones indicated, should the art work be reused. In the case of glossy photographs, crop marks are indicated with grease pencil which can easily be rubbed off.

Sometimes it is desirable to make an overlay of tracing paper and indicate the area to be reproduced. This is most useful in the case of an irregularly shaped cut or *internal mortising*.

If no cropping is required, it is usually best to affix a protruding slip of paper to the back of the picture and on it write directions to the engraver.

Never should instructions be written on the back of a photo. Even light pencil marks may indent the paper and raise the surface of the picture so that the camera catches highlights. Paper clips should never be used on glossies; they also indent the emulsion.

Engraver's copy should never be folded or rolled. Folds cast shadows which the sensitive camera will pick up and even carefully rolled materials will soon develop tiny ribs or creases.

Instructions to the engraver should be terse and explicit. The size of the cut should be written between the crop marks, in inches or picas. Traditionally, engravers, although they work solely for printers, have shunned the point system of measurement, preferring to work in inches. But it is simple to convert instructions given in picas.

Never specify size in words; "reduce one-half" is confusing. Does it mean that the total area of the engraving should be half of that of the original? Or does it mean that the width of the cut should be one-

half of the original? In the latter case, the height will also be one-half
so the area will be only one-quarter.

For halftones, the screen must always be indicated.

If the cut is to be a square halftone, no express directions are required. But should it be a silhouette, a drop-out, or other less common
kind, instructions should be precise.

Specify whether the cut is to be mounted or unblocked. *Flush-
mounted* cuts are becoming common; but if it is essential that one or
more sides be mounted flush, this should be specifically ordered.

If a number of line cuts are to be reduced at the same proportion—
same-focus—they can be mounted together and handled as one subject
until after the engraving is made. Then they are sawed apart and
blocked separately.

Halftones, too, can be grouped into a flat. This requires that they all

Fig. 81. Cropping marks and engraver's instructions are placed in margin of
photograph.

be reduced at the same focus, of course, but also that their tonal values be identical. It takes an expert to judge these values, and unless you qualify totally it is best to leave this grouping to the engraver.

Good engravings require time. It is wise to schedule work to avoid breathless deadlines. Tell the engraver exactly when you need the cuts. He can then place them into the routine of his shop in such a way as to assure maximum quality, often savings of time and money, and prompt delivery.

SCALING PICTURES

Most art, hand or photographic, is made larger than the finished cut so that the engraver can get sharp focus and so that any slight imperfections will be diminished to invisibility. Most photos are furnished in 8×10-inch size. Many artists work at linear dimensions 50 per cent larger than the finished engraving and some work at extremely greater dimensions.

The layout man must know exactly what the size of the engraving will be to render accurate dummies. So *scaling pictures* is a constant activity.

Scaling may be done arithmetically. The formula

$$W : H = W' : H'$$

simply states that the ratio of width (W) to height (H) of the original art will be exactly the same as that of the reduced width (W') to the reduced height (H').

Suppose we have a picture 8×10 and we want to reduce it to 4 inches in width. We have a simple equation:

$$W : H = W' : H'$$
$$8 : 10 = 4 : x$$

If you, as most graphic artsmen seem to, have forgotten your basic algebra: The product of the means equals the product of the extremes.

$$8 \times x = 10 \times 4$$
$$8x = 40$$
$$x = 5'', \text{ the new height of the cut.}$$

This was a simple reduction that really did not demand arithmetic or algebra. But it demonstrates the formula.

To avoid this mathematical chore, there are several mechanical devices based on the principle of the slide rule which enables the unknown factor to be found by simply matching up two numbers on a scale and reading the answer opposite the third known factor. These calculators—some like the conventional slipstick, others circular—are inexpensive, accurate, and easy to use.

But the simplest method is to use the *common diagonal.* If a diagonal were drawn from lower left of both the original 8 × 10 photo and the resulting 4 × 5 cut, they would both make the same angle with the baseline. If the small cut were laid on the original, the diagonal of the photo would be an exact extension of that of the engraving.

So, to find the scale for any reduction, or enlargement, this common diagonal is utilized as shown in Figure 82.

In Diagram X a photograph is to be reduced to a specified width. Draw the diagonal AC. Along the baseline AB measure exactly the desired reduced width, E'. At E raise a perpendicular until it meets the diagonal at F. Draw the line FG parallel to the line AB. Then F' is precisely the new height and the area of the cut will be AEFG.

In Diagram Y the new height is known and the new width must be found. Again draw the diagonal AC. Along the side AD measure off the desired height, E'. From E draw a line perpendicular to AD until it meets the diagonal at F. Now F' is no longer the unknown factor; the new width is known and the area of the cut will be AGFE.

On rare occasions you might want to enlarge the area of the original, as in Z. In this case draw the diagonal AC and extend it beyond the area of the original photo. Extend AB to the new required width, E'. At E raise the perpendicular to intersect the diagonal at F and learn the new height, F', and the area of the cut, AEFG.

Often such enlargement is done in planning a printed page but the photographer is then instructed to prepare a larger glossy so the engraver can still *shoot down* in making his plate.

These diagonals and perpendiculars are not drawn right on the original art, of course; tracing paper is laid over the picture. Care must be taken that the pencil is used so lightly it does not mar the surface of the art.

To make this system even easier, clear plastic sheets are overprinted with 1-pica grids. The layout man places the plastic over the original so it keys with crop marks. Then he lays a straightedge to define the diagonal. He simply counts off the known dimension and reads on the other grid line where his perpendicular hits the diagonal.

The diagonal system has two distinct advantages. It avoids cumbersome fractions in reducing the algebraic equation. It enables the layout man to visualize the photograph in its reduced size. For he sees its new dimensions imposed upon the original one and can thus gauge the approximate reduced size of any element within the picture. This is difficult to do when given only a set of numbers: Just how big is $2\frac{7}{8} \times 5\frac{3}{16}$?

Often the use of the overlay and diagonal will suggest a more effective way to crop the original.

The diagonal also shows where a picture must be cropped to fit a specific area. Figure 82, YY shows a photograph ABCD which must be cropped and reduced to fit an area Abcd.

Over the photo, draw the new area, Abcd, and extend the diagonal Ac until it intersects DC at E. Immediately you know that the original picture must be cropped the equivalent of E' to give it the proportions to reduce exactly to the required area. It's then easy to decide whether to crop off E', slice the same amount off the left at E" or divide the required amount, in any proportion, between both sides of the picture.

In all cases, care must be taken to draw the diagonals and perpendiculars accurately. In diagram YY, for instance, if the diagonal from A does not hit the corner c precisely, the error grows and E' is not correct.

Cropping photographs to maximum effectiveness is an exercise in discernment. The picture editor says, "I get the picture out of a photograph." He distinguishes between a photograph, as a technical product, and a picture, as a communication.

His basic axiom is: Crop ruthlessly. All elements that do not contribute to conveying information—especially those that confuse or distract the eye—should be eliminated. So the question to ask is: What *is* the picture in this photo? To show a watchmaker at work, the editor would probably crop down so that the timepiece, his hands and his tools occupied the whole picture area. But if his workshop were photogenic, or the subject of the picture, the editor would use far more of the photo.

Cropping ruthlessly gives assurance to the reader that it was done on purpose. To slice off just the top of a man's head, like a surgeon trepanning a skull, makes the reader uncomfortable. When the photo is cropped to just above the eyebrows, he knows his attention is being directed to the face. Never crop a standing figure at the ankles; cut him at mid-shin or mid-thigh or, better yet, at the bottom of the rib cage.

It is almost impossible to crop too tightly; the reader's mental eye will fill in details.

Cropping is also done to make a photo fit into a layout. The vastness

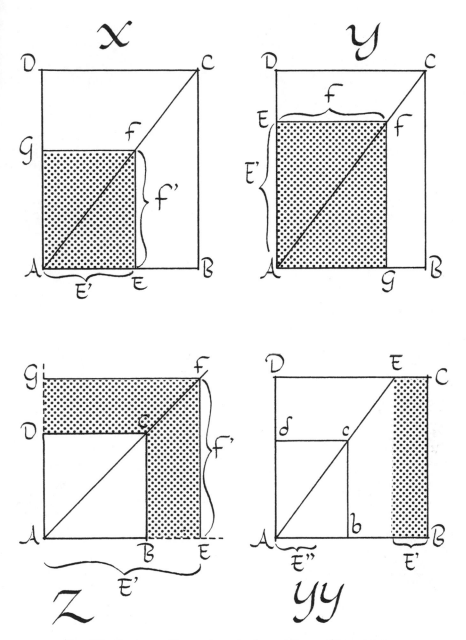

Fig. 82. Common-diagonal method used for scaling pictures.

Fig. 83. Cropper's L's used to determine most effective area of photograph.

of the ocean can best be conveyed by a very shallow picture; a tall vertical composition lifts the eye and mind like a rocket. So you can enhance mood as well as provide strong movement in a layout by judicious cropping.

Cropper's L's are useful tools for determining how a photo can best be cropped. These are L-shaped pieces of paper or plastic, usually 2 inches wide and 12 to 24 inches long on each arm, with inch or pica increments indicated on the edges. With one guide in the position of a normal *L* and the other one upside down, they can define any area of a photo and show its dimensions.

It is an interesting exercise to see how many pictures can be cropped from a single photograph. While I was editing a picture magazine during World War II and photographic materials were hard to come by, one extraordinary photograph was used repeatedly, each time making a most effective picture that looked as if it had been shot specifically for the layout in which it appeared. Even as simple a photo as a portrait can be cropped to several pictures.

Especially for a graphic designer who works with the same subjects much of the time—as in the ad department of a manufacturer of shoes or cartons, let's say—the ability to crop stock photos into interesting pictures is an important talent.

If areas of a photo are confusing, but cannot be cropped out because of the shape required by a layout, the background may be *ghosted*, covered with a dimming layer of thin white paint or Bourges sheets or darkened by the same processes. Depending upon the intensity of the toning, the main features may still be recognized but annoying details are melted away.

Working with illustrations is one of the most satisfying phases of the graphic arts. The designer should learn the technical aspects so thoroughly that he can perform them instinctively and not diminish his pleasure or effectiveness by having to divide his attention between picture and procedure.

SUGGESTED READINGS

Flader, Louis, and Mertle, J. S. *Modern Photoengraving*. Chicago: Modern Photo-engraving, 1948.

Line, Halftone and Color. Chicago: American Photoengravers Association, 1961.

Maurello, S. Ralph. *Commercial Art Techniques*. New York: Tudor Publishing Co., 1958.

Mertle, J. S. *Photomechanics and Printing*. Chicago: Mertle, 1957.

12

Color

COMMUNICATING BY THE SPECTRUM

Ever since early cave dwellers rubbed tinted earth into the drawings they made on rocky walls, color has been a close companion of the written word.

Egyptians painted their hieroglyphics; Gutenberg *illuminated* his Bible, as scribes had been doing for centuries; Currier & Ives tinted their engravings by hand. Today color makes rainbows of printed pages, with magazines producing exemplary work on high-speed presses and newspapers constantly expanding color on their forbidding paper.

Color has many important functions. It amplifies communication by giving information black and white cannot convey. It sets a mood that makes the reader more receptive to the message or makes the message more meaningful. It provides accent or contrast that makes reading more pleasurable. It helps direct the reader through the printed page. It can give identification as instantaneous as a trademark. It emphasizes: As the advertisements say, no one can ignore the familiar yellow sheet of a telegram.

Color should be used only when it serves at least one of these functions. Color cannot—nor should the designer try to make it—hide poor typography, layout, or printing.

The theory and use of color has intrigued the creative mind since history began, and probably before that. In the contemporary generation we have added volumes to our knowledge. Here we shall not discuss more than the fundamentals necessary to understand the value and application of color in graphic arts. Much of this can be done by defining terms. Standardization of those terms is recent and still incomplete.

All color comes from sunlight. When white light is broken into its components, we have the rainbow. *Reflection* and *absorption* of sunlight produce the effects we know as color. A lemon is yellow because it absorbs all colors except yellow and reflects that to stimulate our nerves of vision. In an unlighted room a lemon is not yellow; it is not visible at all. Under dim light, the yellow rays it reflects will be so weak we see it as gray.

There are two kinds of color: *Chromatics* are all the true colors, the rainbow and all its mutations; *achromatic* colors are black, white, and grays.

Black and white are, theoretically and commonly, not classed as colors. Black is the absence of all color; white is the presence of all; grays are mixtures of black and white.

Hue is that quality which creates color as we know it. It is the element that makes red red.

Tone or *value* is that variation of hue resulting from the addition of a small quantity of black or white. Adding black to color creates a *shade*. Addition of white makes a *tint*. (Most of such mixing is done by the ink manufacturer but often the printer must do so. In that case, tints should be made by adding color to white ink; shades by adding black to color.)

Adding one color to another, creates a *hue*—note the difference in meaning from "hue" as a quality. Jade green or peacock blue are hues made by mixing different proportions of blue and green.

Chroma—the *intensity* of a color—is its strength and brilliance. A "bright green" has higher intensity than a "dull green." Acute lack of intensity is referred to as *muddy* or *washed-out* color.

Despite contrary theory in physics and psychology, the printer classifies red, yellow, and blue as the *primary* colors. With these he can produce any of the others. *Secondary* colors are the product of any two primaries. Red and blue make violet; red and yellow, orange; blue and yellow, green. Mixing two secondaries gives a *tertiary* color: Green and violet result in olive; violet and orange, russet; orange and green, citrine. Mixing primary and secondary colors create *intermediate* colors.

Beyond that, possible combinations—each creating a new hue—are staggering to contemplate, and when the shades and tints of varying degrees are created for each hue the peacock pales in comparison.

There are *warm* and *cool* colors, so named for their natural associations. Fire and sunshine naturally make red, yellow, and orange the warm colors; water, sky, and the shadows of deep forests make blue, violet, and dark green cool. Warm colors are gay and exciting; cool colors are calm and collected.

Advertisements for air conditioners would use cool colors; those for furnaces, warm. Some colors are on the borderline; green can be cool or warm depending upon its hue and intensity.

Painters use this "temperature" of color to create effects of distance. Cool colors recede; warm colors project themselves closer to the viewer. Taking this effect into consideration, the designer prefers to use cool colors as a background on which to surprint black type; they recede and do not detract from the type.

Warm and cool colors can be used together with pleasant effect. But the over-all effect should be of one or the other. Thus the designer would use one kind of color sparingly, as an accent or contrast, rather than use equal amounts of cool and warm colors.

Color combinations add to the legibility of type. It is because black type on a yellow background has the highest legibility that highway traffic signs are painted in that combination. Black on red has the lowest legibility. Certain red-green combinations set up such dissonance that the eye is actually pained.

Psychological effects of color are strong. Of pure colors, women prefer red, blue, violet, green, orange, and yellow in that order. Among both tints and shades, they prefer violet. Yellow is preferred in tints far above its pure color or shades.

Blue is the favorite color of men, then red, violet, green, orange, and yellow. Blue is also preferred among tints and shades.

Children, as well as people and peoples whose educational and cultural development is not far advanced, prefer bright primaries and secondaries. Older persons prefer softer color, just as they prefer softer music.

Bad psychological effect comes from the unnatural use of color. Printing a steak in green not only fails to add to communication, it actually detracts from it by creating a strong sense of repulsion on the part of the reader. Such distortions as yellow skies are exaggerations, not

Progressive proofs of four-color process. On preceding page, yellow and red separation proofs. On this page, yellow and red plates in combination. On facing page, blue plate, alone and in combination with previous two. Overleaf, black plate and final product using all four colors. (Courtesy Harper & Row.)

MYRTLE R. WALGREEN

MYRTLE R. WALGREEN

perversions, of natural phenomena and so do not disturb the reader.

Red is the color of boldness and power. It can easily become overpowering and then banal. But used sparingly, like red pepper in cooking, it gives lift to a page. As a background, red must be reduced to a pale tint to counteract the forward movement of warm colors. In pure form, red is a good background for white type (in a reverse cut), if the type is large and devoid of thin hairlines.

Blue, with its intimate association with sky and water, is a quiet color of hope and patience. As the favorite color of a majority of people, it can be used with no fear of adverse psychological effects. Its coolness makes it a good background color, in tints for black surprinting, in full strength for reverses.

Yellow generates the buoyant happiness of a sunny day. In large masses it lights up a page, but it is too weak to provide legibility to type unless it is on a black background. Yellow on black has legibility almost as high as black on yellow.

Orange is a happy color, too. Its resemblance to gold gives overtones of money and prosperity. Its use should be in the same manner as that of yellow.

Brown, a shade of orange, is a most versatile color. Its shades have enough body to carry type; its tints are never anemic. Men associate it with wood and leather, women with fine furs. Like blue, it has no inherent weaknesses and so can be used in a wide variety of jobs.

Green is another universally popular and widely used color because the grass and foliage it suggests are universal. Like brown, it can be used in large masses, in small accents, or for type.

Violet, especially its shade of purple, suggests robes of royalty, the dignity of church vestments, and the pomp and splendor of high ritual. It can be used in many ways but its lighter tints, although popular with women, are too reminiscent of lavender-and-old-lace to appeal to men.

Using color combinations often brings unexpected reaction. You may wince at the man who wears an orange necktie with a green shirt; he likes the combination. The combination of red and green that delights at Christmastime becomes a visual nightmare if the hue or value of both or either is changed just a trifle.

The artist with a keen color sense creates precise and deliberate effects with unconventional color combinations. Jon Whitcomb, a popular contemporary illustrator, often gives his cover girls a green-tinted skin that makes them more glamorous than nature does.

The human eye can distinguish about 10 million variations in color.

Of these, 17,500 have specific names listed in various dictionaries. The average person probably uses no more than several dozens of these; the rest are mainly the coinage of fashion publicists: Shocking Pink, Eleanor Blue, or Kelly Green. Many of the coined names compound confusion. "Football" is a blue, so is African Green; Swedish Red is orange to the average man's eye.

In 1899, A. H. Munsell, a Boston teacher, began research that resulted in a system of noting color. Starting with 10 hues, he charted values on a numerical scale of nine steps ranging from black, 1, to white, 9. Chroma is shown on a similar, but longer scale. As chemists have not yet found pigments to make ink in all known colors, the chroma scale for some colors is greater than for others. There are, for instance, 14 values for red but only eight for its opposite, blue-green.

A bright, strong red is $R\ 5/12$. The 5 indicates that this red is halfway between dark and light and the 12 that it is a dozen steps away from neutral gray in intensity.

Maroon is designated as $R\ 2/6$, with low value and chroma. Pink is $R\ 8/4$.

(*Five value*, the halfway point on the tonal scale, is that level to which the eye unconsciously and constantly adjusts itself. The most successful use of color—in a painting, a package or a piece of merchandise—is usually at this intermediate, five value.)

The *Munsell system* was adopted by the National Bureau of Standards which for 28 years more labored over a similar system of nomenclature. Early in 1962, Kenneth Kelly, a Bureau physicist, announced a new method of designation.

He devised charts with 28 familiar colors and modified each in value and intensity to yield 267 different color names. These names are prosaic in contrast to the advertiser's Lilac Champagne or Hot Tomato. But the no-nonsense scientific attitude that devised such names as light-grayish-yellowish-brown, vivid red, or moderate pink does create a reasonably accurate vocabulary for describing colors verbally. While the new system was greeted with pleasure by people who must work with colors, the general public will still call pink just "pink" for at least as long as they call a flower a daisy instead of a *bellis perennis* or *chrysanthemum leucathemum*.

But the average printer, like the average person, has not developed or been born with such acute color perception. So the printer has devised a color wheel, Fig. 85, whereby he can reassure himself

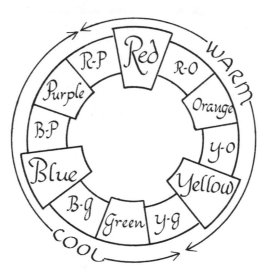

Fig. 85. Color wheel.

when combining colors, that he will create acceptable harmonies.

Around the wheel, in a triangle, are placed the colors comprising the *primary triad*. Halfway between them come the secondary colors produced by each pair. In the remaining blanks are the intermediate colors, named by combining the name of the primary, first, with the secondary: red-orange, for instance, never orange-red.

COLOR COMBINATIONS

There are six basic color combinations: monochromatic, analogous, complementary, split complements, triads, and T-harmony.

Monochromatic uses two or more tones of one color. In practice, this is produced by using one color of ink and screening some of the elements to tints; or the color of ink in a deep value may be printed on paper in a lighter tint of the same color.

Analogous harmony comes from two colors that are adjacent on the color wheel.

Red and orange will harmonize, for orange is after all the child of red. Orange also harmonizes with its other parent, yellow. But two parents and a child do not harmonize as a threesome.

Complementary color combinations are made from colors directly opposite each other on the wheel: blue and orange, red and green, and yellow and violet. This combination always consists of a cool and a

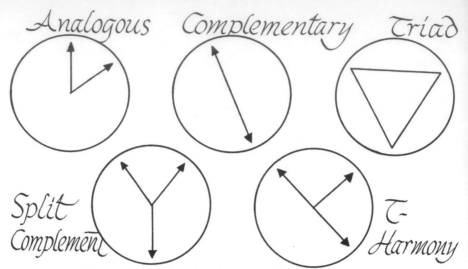

Fig. 86. Use of color wheel to determine pleasant color harmonies.

warm color. The result is a dramatic combination in contrast to the genteel softness of analogous combinations.

In the beloved Yule combination, green is best in large masses with red as an accent. In the blue-orange complement, often considered the loveliest of all combinations, blue should dominate.

Yellow and violet are the calmest of the complementaries; here either can dominate, but never should both be used in equal quantity. Combinations of complementary intermediate colors are more subdued, but all complementaries are striking. One color should be a shade, the other a tint, never both pure.

Split complements are found by choosing any color on the wheel, determining its complement straight across the wheel and then using a color adjacent to it. The split complement of blue, therefore, would be yellow-orange or red-orange, the nextdoor neighbors of the complementary orange.

The *triad* is a combination of three colors. To find a triad, visualize a triangle that connects the primary colors. Then, as you turn this triangle to any position, its points will designate the colors of the triad. Another way to determine the triad is to choose the first color, then count to the fourth color (in either direction) to find the second color and four more for the third.

The triad of primaries is primitive and almost brazen. The triad of the secondaries is more refined, that of the intermediates is the most delicate.

The triads should consist of one strong color, one light in tone, and the third one about halfway between. Always use just one color in large quantities, with the other two in definitely smaller amounts. *T-harmony* also uses three colors; its other name, *complements and a third,* describes the method. Choose your complementary colors and draw a line between them; at the center of the circle draw a perpendicular line in either direction. It will point to the third color.

Any of these combinations can be created on white stock with colored inks. The paper, on the other hand, may furnish one of the colors, or the combinations, in ink, may be printed on colored stock, thus adding yet another color. When colored paper is used, it should be a tint of one of the inks for harmony although it is possible to use an adjacent color to any one of the inks with pleasing effect.

Black, white, and gray are not colors in the strict sense, yet any one of them will harmonize with all other colors. Black and red is undoubtedly the most widely used of any combination; red-orange affords more contrast than pure red in this case. Gold and silver are not true colors either but also harmonize with all others. Gold and purple produce the richest, most elegant of all combinations.

Red and blue do not harmonize by any mathematical scheme. Yet in our flag the combination satisfies not only our patriotic but our esthetic values. The reason is that the colors are separated by white bands. In a layout also, non-harmonic colors can be used pleasingly, if they are kept well separated by white paper or by bands of the "non-color colors" we have just discussed.

Wisely used, color is a powerful tool for the designer. For this reason, and also because it is exciting to work with color, the typographic designer should study it and experiment with it just as enthusiastically and thoroughly as Picasso did when he used the blue of his palette for paintings of a whole period.

SUGGESTED READINGS

Bustanoby, J. H. *Principles of Color and Color Mixing.* New York: McGraw-Hill Book Co., Inc., 1947.

Cheskin, Louis. *Color Guide for Marketing Media.* New York: The Macmillan Co., 1954.

Maerz, A., and Paul, M. Rea. *Dictionary of Color.* New York: McGraw-Hill Book Co., Inc., 1950.

13

Color Printing

THE RAINBOW ON THE PAGE

By reversing normal procedures and considering the more complex use of color first, we can actually simplify an interesting subject. So we shall discuss *process color,* a more sophisticated form of the sleight-of-eye that the engraver produces in halftone reproductions.

Process color is that printing in which primary colors interact to create the impression of all other colors. It may utilize two colors or many, although three are adequate to reproduce the full spectrum.

The chemist's *analysis* and *synthesis* is a close analogy to the work of the engraver and printer in reproducing a picture in full color.

By electrolytic analysis the chemist breaks water into two parts of hydrogen and one of oxygen. By synthesis he combines these two gases, in proper proportions, to make the familiar fluid. The engraver analyzes full-color copy by breaking it down into the three basic colors. The printer puts them together again to make the original, chromatic image.

Imagine, for example, a picture of a red barn standing on the crest of a green hill with orange foliage and a blue sky behind it. This is to be reproduced by printing.

The engraver places the picture before his camera, just as when making a black-and-white halftone, for all process printing uses halftone plates. But he adds one more factor, a *filter,* a sheet of colored gelatin sandwiched between glass.

If he places a red filter between copy and film, red reflections from the picture will be absorbed by the filter. If he also places a blue filter before his lens, all blue rays will be absorbed. Then only the yellow reflections from the picture will pass through to affect the negative in his camera.

In practice, he would combine red and blue filters into a single sheet of violet for convenience.

Now the engraver has a halftone negative which represents only— and all of—the yellow in the original picture. There is a large amount of it in the orange of the trees and also in the green of the grass, lesser amounts in other areas of the picture, probably none in the sky.

By using a green filter, he bars all yellow and blue reflections and captures only red reflections from the original. In the barn of the picture, red will be intense. It will be lighter in the orange areas and in other places will be so faint the naked eye does not discern it as such.

Blocking out red and yellow light with an orange filter allows only the blue to create a halftone negative.

The filters actually used in color separation are *magenta,* a slightly bluish red used instead of violet; *cyan,* a greenish blue used instead of pure green, and *yellow,* used instead of orange. Standard printing inks are keyed to this analysis. These three filtering steps are *color separation.*

From each of these three negatives, the engraver makes a halftone plate. The analysis is complete.

(*Life* magazine's research division has invented a machine which produces color separations by scanning original copy in much the same way that Wirephoto or Fairchild systems scan black and white. The process is electronic, complicated, and costly but results are excellent.)

Now the printer performs synthesis. By printing each plate in the proper color, he produces the original in all its hues. The red plate has re-created the barn and blends with the yellow to make orange. The yellow has combined with the blue to reproduce green grass. The blue makes the sky and blends with the red to make deep shadows under the eaves.

This is *three-color process.*

There are important points that have been left out in this simple explanation. The inks do not mix physically to create secondary and subordinate colors; the reader's eye does this mixing. As each separation negative is shot, the screen is rotated slightly. The yellow plate is made with the dot pattern running perpendicularly and horizontally. When the red negative is shot, the screen is rotated 15 degrees to the right; for the blue negative, the screen turns to the left, from 90 to 105 degrees. The result is that the halftone dots are not superimposed in printing but lie side by side. The reading eye sees not a tiny blue dot snuggling up to a small yellow one, but one large green one. Occasionally two dots will overprint but their effect is negligible; the eye does the vital mixing.

The engraver proves his plates individually and in combination, in a series of *progressive proofs* or *progs*. He prints the yellow plate in yellow ink and the red in its color; then he combines the two. Next he pulls the blue plate alone and then over the yellow-red combination. These proofs serve two purposes: They indicate needed color correction, and they show the printer the proper inks to use.

Color correction is made on the plates by burnishing, staging, and re-etching or even by making dots smaller physically by hand. Another correction method is to make continuous tone *positive separations*, then retouch to make color correction, finally making screened separations. Both these methods obviously require an unusually keen sense of color, acute eyesight, and skilled hands. Correction is one of the factors that makes process color costly.

By showing the printer exactly what color ink to use, progs assure faithful reproduction of the original. A chemist must use the same two gases for synthesis that he obtained from analysis; if he mixes hydrogen with nitrogen he will not produce water. Similarly, if the printer does not use exactly the colors produced by separation, his printing will not be true. If the engraver breaks down the green grass to a mixture of lemon yellow and robin's-egg blue, but the printer uses chrome yellow and Prussian blue, the grass on the printed page will be far different from that of the original.

To avoid this obvious danger, most process color is printed in *standard process colors*.

These standard colors cannot reproduce all copy faithfully, however. In El Greco's painting *View of Toledo,* for instance, there are blues, greens, and grays that are unique to his palette. The trained eye of the color separator will tell him that the three standard filters will not produce proper analysis. Instead of the cyan filter he normally would use, he might choose one of another hue which would allow different quantities of red to pass through. The printer must then use a red ink that matches exactly the red that affected the engraver's negative.

Register must be precise in process color. *Register marks* are drawn on the original at at least two points. The most common form is this:

It is easy to overprint these marks precisely and assure perfect register. The marks are removed from the plate before actual printing begins.

Three-color process is most common in newspaper work, although it has many other commercial uses. But it lacks the strength and sharpness of *four-color process*, the most common.

In four-color, a black plate is added. This gives definition, produces intermediate grays that cannot be achieved by mixing primaries, and adds strength to the shades of other colors.

There are seven proofs in a set of four-color progs: that of the black plate and of the black on top of the three primaries in addition to the five of three-color process. Progressives are usually pulled yellow, red, blue, and black, the same order in which the printer normally uses them, though it is not necessary to follow this sequence because each set of dots lands on white paper anyway.

In a great deal of process work, the first color is allowed to dry before the next is run. But for magazines and other high-speed work, *wet printing* is necessary; there is no time to wait for drying. This requires special inks but the principles remain unchanged.

Sometimes, especially in offset, more than four colors are used for utmost fidelity, and in letterpress six are not unusual.

Two-color process does not even attempt to reproduce full color although some recent experiments with red-orange and blue-green inks give surprising chromatic range. Generally two-color is used for paintings that have been done in only two colors.

A common and useful two-color process is *duotone*. This commonly uses black and a lighter color, although any combination of dark and light can be used. The effect here is only of a third color; the eye does not see the original two. Duotones add an illusion of depth to a picture and the effect is far different from that created by mixing the inks and running the job through the press only once.

Some graphic artists do not consider duotone as true process color. They point out that there is no optical interaction to create intermediate hues as well as the original colors; the eye sees only the total, not the components. Duotones are made from a single black-and-white continuous-tone original.

Fake color is an interesting process whose most familiar product is the old-fashioned picture postcard which depicts items of local pride. Today souvenir cards are usually four-color process, but the older version well explains color faking. Suppose an engraver were handed a black-and-white photo of the West Siwash city hall and asked to prepare color plates.

He would shoot four black-and-white screened negatives. One he would arbitrarily designate as his "yellow separation." He knows that the grass and foliage in West Siwash is green, so he would leave yellow dots in those areas and also in the building which is orangey brick. But he would remove all the dots in the sky.

On his "red separation" he would leave small dots in the building and in the stripes of the flag and perhaps to indicate crimson blossoms, but again would remove them from the sky area. On the "blue separation" he would leave large dots in the sky and smaller ones where they are to mix with the yellow in the grass. But he would remove them from the building.

When the job is printed, the foliage is green, the sky blue and the building brick red. These colors would not be exact reproductions of the original but they would be close enough for the purpose.

Fake color is often useful in catalogues. A manufacturer might be bringing out a line of colored plastic wastebaskets. Rather than shoot several color photographs, he can make one black-and-white and fake the color to show the complete line long before all the colors had come off the assembly line. Fake color is far less expensive than full color in this and similar cases.

Preparing fake separations can be done on the negative or the engraving.

FLAT COLOR

Flat or *spot* color is best defined as any color which is not process. This is a broad definition, but so is the use of flat color.

Sunday comics are a good example of flat color. Into areas defined by the black or *key* plate are laid primary colors in various values, full intensity or tints. These may fake secondary and other colors but they vary in this use from process color in that they are created from line and Ben Day, not halftone, plates.

A familiar use of spot color is a letterhead in which the type is printed in black and the trademark in red. This is a *two-color job.* The number of colors or the elaborateness of their use in flat color printing has no bearing on its classification.

Flat color may be used to create other hues, as in comic strips, or one color may be surprinted on another to create the third. Spot color may be used to print halftones, or for tint blocks behind halftones in another color. The distinguishing mark of flat color is that it has no interaction of halftone dots in different colors to create the illusion of full color.

A headline printed in red is spot color. An orange, printed in orange ink instead of in yellow and red, is flat color. A panel on which type is surprinted is flat color. So is a broad area of blue that suggests the sky behind a black-and-white halftone.

Flat color, like process, requires one trip through the press for each hue or a separate plate for each color on multi-cylinder presses.

Copy for spot color is generally prepared by using *overlays.* Art is all done in black and white; only on the press is actual color used.

Suppose the artist wants the word "SALE" to print in orange on a blue background, both colors to be provided by ink, not paper. He letters the word in black on white paper. Over this he places a *tissue overlay,* a sheet of tissue or tracing paper. On it he lays orange crayon over the letters and blue on the background. The engraver shoots two negatives. One makes the orange plate. The other negative must be reversed to leave "SALE," in orange, print on white paper, not on blue ink.

The engraver may have to touch up his negatives to give proper register by one of three varieties.

Loose register is used for decorative color where its position need not be precise. For newspaper work and other processes where register may be a problem, loose register is often chosen because it does not lose effectiveness even if its position shifts as much as a pica or two. *Hairline register* brings two colors up to each other with no overlap and no gap. This is the most difficult for artist and pressman to achieve. *Lap register* provides a small area—about a thirty-second of an inch—where

Fig. 87. Key-line dawing for two-color mechanical separation. Letters will print in one color, background in another. Thin outline of letters will be common to both plates and will provide overlap of thickness of line. Reduced one-third by width from original.

color overlaps. This is the easiest for every craftsman involved.

When the platemaker has made his two negatives from the "SALE" copy, he has hairline register. He must add a thin edge to one to provide an overlap.

Key-line overlays are used for *painting up* to provide lap register. The area to overlap is drawn with a fine pen. The areas within and outside these lines are filled in with black to about a sixteenth of an inch, leaving a white area on both sides of the line. Again a tissue overlay shows the color scheme, and again the engraver shoots two negatives. On one film he removes the background; this is easy and fast because he need not work down to a fine line but only to the area left blank outside the line. This makes the orange plate. In the same way, again with no close work, he opaques out the inside of the letters to make the blue plate. The original outlines of the letter are common to both plates and provide the overlap.

When large areas of color are to appear, they need not be painted solid on the original art. The area is merely indicated with accurately drawn red lines around the perimeter of the color and the engraver opaques two negatives as indicated by a tissue overlay.

Acetate overlays are most frequently used for *mechanical separation*. The artist prepares separate art work for each color. One element, usually the key plate in black, is drawn on art board. A piece of frosted acetate is affixed over the board. On it, still in black ink, he draws the areas to be printed in the second color.

Acetate is sufficiently transparent to position each element precisely and its matte surface has sufficient tooth to make a good drawing surface.

Register marks are drawn on the original and, with greatest care, they are duplicated on the overlay. Additional overlays are used for each color. The engraver then shoots each piece to make a separate plate.

Techniques for preparing offset copy, discussed in Chapter 15, are applicable in many phases of color work.

The *Bourges* (pronounced Burgess) *process,* which has recently been developed as a versatile tool for color work, is far too broad for more than cursory inspection here. Basically, it consists of transparent plastic sheets in 10 standard printing colors, each in five values from 10 to 100 per cent, that duplicate standard printing inks.

When the artist prepares overlays, he uses the same colors the printer will use. Thus he can see just how the finished job will look. Such sheets are valuable, for the same reason, in preparing roughs and comps.

The sheets are augmented by pencils and inks, again exact matches to printing inks. White, grays, and black are also available; these have great value in ghosting backgrounds on photographs but this is by no means the limit of their functions.

The Bourges method is also used for process color, most notably in pre-correction of color separations.

When spot color is to be used with all type, there are several methods to make the separation. In the simplest, the form is made up with all the elements as for a one-color job. Then those which are to be in color are removed by the compositor and placed in an adjacent form in exactly the same position. The space left vacant on both forms is filled with quads or furniture. Printing is done from original type.

A mat may be rolled from the original form and two stereos cast from it. On one all the color elements are routed out; on the other, routing removes all elements to be printed in black, leaving only those to be in color. The same technique is used with two electrotypes.

Or the artist can take a black-and-white proof, cut out the elements and mount them separately as copy for two line cuts.

For very intricate copy, color separation may be made with

engraver's filters, shooting in line. This is rarely done, however.

Tint blocks are a simple yet effective means of using color. A tint block is a mass of color that carries no detail or tonal variations. It may be in full value or lightened by an over-all pattern, usually of dots, in which case it is often called a *screen,* another graphic arts word of many meanings.

A common use of a tint block is as a background upon which type is surprinted—or overprinted—in black or dark ink. This adds interest, emphasis and sometimes even legibility to the type. Such all-over backgrounds can enliven black-and-white halftones, too. A fire scene gains excitement from a red tint block; light blue can make a winter scene look even colder.

Sometimes a tint block makes only a *silhouetted background* for a halftone. In such use, color does not run behind the halftone and its highlights expose the white of the paper. This is more striking than if highlights showed the color of the tint block. Silhouetted tint blocks can be run in far heavier colors and 100 per cent intensity, while over-all blocks must be screened to well below 50 per cent, for most colors, lest they drown details of the halftone.

Tint blocks in deep colors may carry reverse type or, when screened, letters in full, unscreened values. Purists insist that these are technically not tint blocks because they then carry detail. But for practical uses, we would call tint blocks "those areas of color which are in simple shapes, if there is no gradation in tone." A silhouetted jack-o-lantern which ran under part of a full-page ad, for instance, would function as a tint block even though it carried detail at its outline.

Any engraving that does not meet the definition of a tint block is called a *flat color plate,* whether or not it is surprinted by another element.

With the exception of layouts using only type, color is used in half a dozen basic categories:

1. Full-color paintings, in oil or watercolors of various kinds; drawings in crayon, pastel or colored inks; combinations of line drawing with color wash.

The engraver may encounter some difficulty with highly varnished oil paintings that reflect light. But special filters control the situation and most oils reproduce well. Watercolors must be painted either in transparent or opaque paints; mixing the two creates difficulties in the whites because white paper will not affect the engraver's film exactly as white opaque paint will, even though they look the same to the eye.

2. *Photographic color prints* produced by any commercial method. These are still the favorite copy for most color separators. But there is a growing use of:

3. *Photographic color transparencies.* Brilliant results are obtained from such copy. But transparencies have disadvantages: they are difficult to retouch, to handle in collage, or to letter over.

4. *Hand-colored photographs.* These must light in the original black-and-white so that colors laid over the image will be captured clearly by the engraver's lens. Brilliant colors are hard to achieve from such copy, but art with delicate hues makes good plates.

5. *Line drawings with color added* by Ben Day (or Zip-a-Tone) or in simple areas.

6. *Continuous-tone* black-and-white photos or wash drawings, with Ben Day adding color.

Spot color, of course, can be used to print any kind of plate, from square halftones to line to combinations. Plates with fine detail are not suited to lighter tints; detail washes out.

Although production techniques vary slightly, process and flat color are produced by the same basic method for all printing processes and their use is the same.

NEWSPAPER COLOR

In newspapers color is designated as *ROP, run of the paper,* to distinguish material which is printed on regular newspaper presses from that produced on special color presses.

Newspapers use both process and spot. One of the pioneers in this field has been the *Milwaukee Journal,* which still runs more color advertising than any other American paper. It has done extensive research in the area. The *Journal* ran its first ROP color January 5, 1891; to herald the inauguration of a Wisconsin governor, it printed groups of horizontal lines in red and blue across page one. But not until 1937 did the first ROP ad run in that paper.

The *New York Journal* in 1897 reproduced sketches drawn by Frederic Remington in Cuba as the earliest use of true color for editorial purposes.

Three-color process is a favorite with newspapers. Pages can be made over between editions without changing register of color plates, because news type is all in the black plate which is entirely independent. Where time is short, as in a newspaper plant, it is also advantageous to eliminate the black plate which, because it carries the heaviest color, requires the most hand work by the engraver.

The Milwaukee paper's case histories testify to the power of color in advertising. Typical is that of a stove manufacturer who found that, although color advertising costs were 70 per cent higher than black-and-white, it drew 395 per cent more returns. A full-color ad sold 500 per cent more merchandise for a department store than did black-and-white.

(The *Milwaukee Journal* ran a spot-color ad that is a classic example of restraint in the use of color. A men's store ran a large photograph of a man in a gray suit with the tie in maroon. The only color on the page, this small spot had impact far exceeding that of large masses of red.)

In reporting its own story of developing ROP color, the *Milwaukee Journal* preached the definitive sermon on the use of color:

"Experience [showed] that color added to a poor black-and-white ad made it worse, not better. Improperly used, color could often make a good black-and-white ad bad. Good layout men, thrilled with the opportunity to use color, concentrated on it and sometimes forgot their fundamental training and knowledge of good design, headline- and copy-writing."

While the reference is to newspaper advertising, it applies to all areas of the graphic arts. Color must be used functionally, and only to make a faster, clearer, and more pleasant transmittal of information.

The function of color is to capture attention, give information that words alone cannot convey, guide the eye in reading, and create a mood that makes the reader more receptive to the printed message. Color should perform at least one, and preferably more, of these functions. It cannot—and should not be used to—disguise unsound layout by mere dazzle.

The hallmark of a good designer is not only how he uses color but how he does not use it. Color adds expense to printing; extra engravings must be used or a form must be broken down into two or more parts. And there must be at least one extra press run. So there is always strong temptation to "get your money's worth." The mediocre designer will start on a two-color ad by putting an illustration or headline in red, let's say. Then he will decide, "I've already paid the surcharge for this red. If I set the signature in color, it won't cost me a penny more."

So the sig goes in red. By the same logic he makes the prices red. Then he uses his—absolutely free now—color for the border. Soon the eye cannot tell whether this is a black-and-white ad with red added or a red-and-white with black.

Color should always be used functionally. It should also be used sparingly. Color is an accent, just as spices and herbs are. If a cook uses just a pinch of paprika, his goulash is a gourmet's delight; if he uses too much spice, the whole dish is spoiled. So it is with color; it should just bring out the flavor of the typographic design, never supplant it.

SUGGESTED READINGS

Paschel, Herbert P. *First Book of Color*. New York: Franklin Watts, Inc., 1959.
Sipley, Louis Walton. *Half Century of Color*. New York: The Macmillan Co., 1951.

14

Intaglio

LEGACY FROM THE ARMORER

One of those folk tales that no one cares to disprove because it is charming tells the origin of *intaglio* printing.

A knight, off to fight a dragon, stopped to embrace his fair lady. His varlet had just polished his master's suit of armor, but had neglected to wipe the dirty fluid out of the fine, ornamental designs that were incised into the metal suit of every well-dressed knight. So, as the dragon-slayer pressed his beloved to his steel-encased chest, her white dress absorbed the cleaning fluid and the design in the armor was thus printed on her frock.

This is exactly how intaglio printing is done. The printing surface is *incised*—that is what intaglio means—into a metal plate. Ink is spread across the entire plate, then wiped off the top of the plate, leaving only that within the incised depressions. As paper is pressed against the plate, the ink transfers from the incisions onto the paper sheet just as it did on the lady's dress.

Intaglio printing derives in fact from the armorer's craft. It was fashionable to decorate armor, shields, and swords, and the handles of other lethal instruments with intricate engravings, which were sometimes inlaid with enamel or precious materials. When the engraver achieved an especially successful pattern, he would actually print it for future reference.

It was only a short step from this process to true printing, and the earliest known intaglio print is a German copper engraving dated 1446 —the period when Gutenberg was holding forth.

The purest form of classic intaglio today is encountered in engraved wedding invitations and the etchings that young women are tradition- ally invited to "come up and see." The most common is the rotogravure section of Sunday newspapers; not common enough is paper money.

The intricate design of our currency is incised, by a team of crafts- men, into steel. After hardening in potassium cyanide, this plate is pressed into a softer steel. This in turn is hardened and pressed into soft steel plates, which do the actual printing in sets of 12. These dozen plates, and those to replace worn ones, can all be made from only one original engraving. The formula of the ink is so secret that at the end of each day all left-over ink is gathered and stored under guard. (Ink on our money never dries completely. You can test this by rubbing a bill—especially the green side—over a sheet of clean paper.)

Engraving like this, especially when several men work on different areas, cannot be duplicated by another hand or even by the camera. This is the bane of counterfeiters and a consolation to the legitimate earner of money.

Steel engraving has a spidery, wiry quality of line that has kept it from being a popular art medium. Its major secondary use today is for formal invitations, announcements, and stationery.

The *etching* is an original art form that employs chemicals—spe- cifically acid—to incise the design. (It should not be confused with the engraver's line etching, a relief plate.) A thin plate of copper or zinc is coated with a *ground*, a mixture of wax and mastic. With an etcher's *needle*, the artist draws his design through the wax to expose the plate. He need not draw thick or thin lines; the acid will ultimately create the desired weight of stroke.

The back and sides of the plate are protected by an acid-resistant *stop-out varnish* and the plate is immersed into a mordant—usually nitric acid but sometimes potassium chlorate, iron perchloride, or a mix- ture of two. The etchant bites into the metal only where the protective ground has been removed by the needle. Fine lines are then stopped out (as for re-etching of photoengravings) and the plate is re-immersed to bite deeper in other lines. Another method is to scratch in only heavy lines, etch them, remove the plate, and scratch in lighter lines. The heavier ones are re-etched as light ones are subjected to the first bite.

Etchings are printed in a press that resembles an old-fashioned clothes wringer. It is customary for the artist to number each print he pulls; their value often depends on the number of copies that have been made. Then he may destroy the plate by gouging a large X across the plate. He pulls a print of this, too, as proof that the limited edition will not, some time in the future, become unlimited.

Etchings can be recognized by running a finger across the printing. It will be raised, not only because the ink lies high on the paper but also because the printing process slightly debosses the reverse side of the paper as it is forced into the incisions of the plate. The obverse side is then embossed into slight relief.

Other variations of etchings are properly discussed in Chapter 16 under "fine art." But an understanding of the principle helps in examining commercial intaglio, *gravure*.

Although two kinds of such printing are designated as *sheet-fed gravure* and *rotogravure* (from rotary gravure), both are produced on rotary presses. Because the paper must be squeezed onto and into the incised ink bearers, extreme pressure is required, and gravure presses must be husky and heavy. Sheet-fed gravure is usually produced from thin copper plates which are wrapped around a cylinder. Rotogravure plates are themselves heavier copper cylinders. Both are produced by the same photographic method.

The curved-plate principle is old; it was used as far back as 1785 to print intaglio designs onto textiles. The gravure principle was invented around 1779 by Karl Klic in Vienna.

Gravure is a complete screen process. There is no line art; everything, including type, is screened. Thus gravure is a medium ideally suited to reproducing art and far less ideal for type or other line. Its greatest impetus came in printing the picture sections of newspapers in the familiar sepia ink.

The printing surface of a gravure plate consists of a vast number of tiny holes or wells, at least 22,500 per square inch. They are all of identical size but vary in depth, and hence in the amount of ink they carry.

Though no one can learn to make these intaglios by reading a book, a knowledge of the basic process is necessary to assay the strengths and weaknesses of this printing method.

All the elements of the page—body and display type and illustrations —are pasted into position. (Although photographs are the ideal original for gravure reproduction, any medium that can be photographed can be reproduced.) This exact-size paste-up is photographed without a screen.

It must be kept in mind that, when the printing plate is etched, intaglio is exactly the opposite of letterpress. In photoengravings, the non-printing areas are eaten away by acid; in gravure plates, the printing areas must be exposed to the etchant. Therefore a *film positive* must be used for gravure plates. To make such positives, the negative from the camera is simply printed on film instead of photopaper. Retouching may be done on either the negative or positive film.

Meanwhile the screen pattern has been printed onto a *carbon tissue*. This is a sheet of paper, whose only function is as a bearer, covered with sensitized gelatin. The gravure screen is similar to the photoengraver's with two notable exceptions: (1) It is finer (150-line) than most letterpress screens, and (2) it is positive rather than negative—instead of black lines crossing to form small transparent windows, the gravure screen has transparent lines enclosing small black squares.

The sensitized gelatin hardens to the degree of light to which it has been exposed. The white lines of the screen allow maximum light to hit the gelatin, with the result that the entire surface of the carbon tissue has now been cross-hatched by strips of gelatin which is so hard it will not allow penetration by the etchant.

Now the transparent positive is printed on this gridded carbon tissue. Light, varying in intensity of white and dark of the positive, reacts upon those little squares of gelatin that were protected during exposure of the screen.

Deep blacks of the original photograph, and of the film positive, allow little if any light to pass through onto the gelatin. This unexposed area is entirely soluble; it will allow the etchant to work unimpeded and create a deep well. This will hold a maximum quantity of ink which will print heavily. On the other hand, highlights in the positive will allow a great deal of light to strike the gelatin and harden it. There the etchant will be able to eat away just a shallow well holding only a small amount of ink and printing only a small highlight dot. In printing the screen onto the carbon tissue, those intersecting lines create the sides of the little wells.

Now the carbon tissue is squeegeed onto the copper plate or cylinder face down (the equivalent of flopping the negative). Moisture makes the gelatin adhere to the plate; the paper, its job done, is stripped away. Etching done with perchloride of iron, a mild etchant, requires 20-30

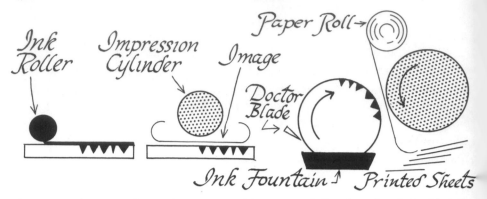

Ink Roller *Impression Cylinder* *Image* *Paper Roll→* *Doctor Blade* *Ink Fountain↑* *Printed Sheets*

Fig. 88. Schematic of intaglio printing. Diagram at left: plate flooded with ink. Center: plate wiped, leaving ink only in incised areas as paper is impressed onto it. Right: rotogravure process.

minutes to do its work, in from three to six bites. Type matter, which only needs half as much etching time as pictures, is staged out until the last portion of the etching period.

On the press the cylinder dips into an ink reservoir, and each of the millions of tiny wells picks up its full capacity of ink. A *doctor blade* wipes away the ink from the outer surface of the cylinder, and the paper is then impressed into the wells to pick up their contents of ink.

Gravure can be recognized by the screen that covers the entire printing area and by the uniform size of all dots, shadow or highlight. In a modification of the basic gravure principle, the *Dultgen* (sometimes called Dultgen-News) *process,* tonal values are controlled not only by the depth of the ink wells but also by their area.

Color gravure has advantages inherent in the method. Whereas in letterpress only the full strength of the ink can be printed, in gravure different quantities of ink are deposited; in one printing 15 different intensities of ink can be transferred to the paper. Gravure ink is transparent. The white of the paper shows through to lend luminosity; the color of the lower layer of ink will shine through that of a superimposed color to create very subtle gradations in color and hue. Black-and-white gravure has a richness unmatched by any other printing process. The extremely fine screen also contributes to fine gradations.

That screen, however, is also a liability in printing type. Being broken by a screen, no matter how fine, destroys the sharpness of type. If the hairlines are extremely thin, they may be completely severed. If the type runs as a reverse, fine lines may fill in.

Fortune magazine solves the problem neatly. On many pages it prints illustrations by gravure and type by letterpress. But, as this doubles the press run, it is not a panacea for most printers. If more than one color is used, however, it is comparatively easy to combine gravure and letterpress at no extra cost if the color can be run from gravure plates and type from relief.

To minimize the dangers of screening, no type smaller than 8-point should be used and 10-point is the desirable minimum. A full-bodied face—one without fine hairlines or marked difference between thicks and thins—should be selected. Monotonal Sans Serifs or Gothics are best for gravure work despite their basically lower readability.

There are many examples, notably the *New York Times* Sunday book section, which indicate that these minimums allow a goodly margin of safety. But, although these limits can be extended under certain circumstances, the restrictions are basically sound and impose no limitation on the typographer which he would not voluntarily accept in the interest of readability.

Photographs are the ideal copy for gravure. Line work should not be the open, sketchy kind; this wastes the resources of gravure. Instead, line art should have a wide tonal range. Pencil, charcoal, and crayon work should have well-defined middle tones and wash drawings are best in flat, poster-like technique. Oil paintings must be done in smooth technique; conspicuous brush marks or *impasto* effects will be exaggerated in reproduction.

Non-contrasty photographs reproduce best. Soft-focus photos will become even softer in gravure and thus should be used with full realization of such added diffusion.

A major asset of rotogravure is the ability to reproduce fine detail on inexpensive paper. There can be no better example of this than Sunday newspaper roto sections. The quality of their color work, especially, is a wonderful demonstration of the worth of this ancient printing form that has nobly weathered the transition from knights to satellites.

SUGGESTED READINGS

Cartwright, H. M., and MacKay, Robert. *Rotogravure.* New York: David McKay Co., Inc., 1951.

15

Offset Lithography

OIL AND WATER DON'T MIX

The invention of *lithography* is so recent (1799) that not only can we credit it to a well-identified individual, we also have his own journals to document the extraordinary labors that preceded its birth.

The inventor was Alois Senefelder, like Gutenberg and Mergenthaler, a German. Like them, he had an almost unbelievable tenacity—and needed it. Also like theirs, his invention so thoroughly covered all the basic principles involved that subsequent changes have been only refinements.

The son of an actor in the Royal Theater of Munich, Senefelder too wanted to wear greasepaint. His father insisted on a career in law for the boy; but Alois found time to write for amateur theatricals and one of them made for him a substantial profit of 50 florins.

When his father died leaving the family penniless, Senefelder decided to embark on full-time playwriting, but with less than resounding success. Like most authors of that time, he had to publish his own works; when he ran out of money, he decided to print his own plays. This objective was soon forgotten as Alois began to encounter difficulties. For he was a man who apparently derived great satisfaction from solving insoluble problems and the game soon became more important than the prize.

First, he attempted crude stereotyping by punching letters of steel into hardwood and casting from the wooden matrix. Then he trained himself in mirror-writing so that he could make gravure copperplates. But copper was expensive and he owned only one plate which had to be reground after every experiment. Eventually it became too thin to work on. Looking for a cheaper substitute, he caught the idea of using a slab of stone on which he mixed the various inks he concocted for his experiments. This was Kelheim, a variety of Bavarian limestone from Solnhofen which polishes down easily to a smooth, silky surface excellent for making intaglio plates.

Lithography means *writing on stone,* and now Senefelder had the material for his great invention. But his experiments, now only in intaglio, still had to go through letterpress before he found the third major printing process.

Then came one of those happy, illogical occurrences that have led the way to many a great invention. One day his mother sought throughout the house for a piece of paper on which to make a laundry list; Alois had used it all up. The washerwoman grew impatient with the delay and Frau Senefelder was more than a little annoyed with her son. She stalked into his laboratory and demanded that he find something on which to list the laundry.

Somewhat desperately, he took the newly polished slab of Kelheim and wrote the list on it with a new ink he had mixed consisting of wax, soap, and lampblack.

When the laundry was safely returned and he could wash off the stone for new experiments, Alois suddenly decided to use it, just as it was, to test another thought. He built a wall of wax around the stone and onto it poured a solution of *aqua fortis,* nitric acid and water. The acid ate away the bare stone but the ink protected the stone it covered. The result was a relief plate, very shallow but sufficiently in relief for careful letterpress printing. This process was good enough to set Senefelder up in the business of printing sheet music.

Alois had long since mastered mirror-writing but his workmen had not. So the process of transferring music from the composer's right-reading copy onto the wrong-reading image on the stone was laborious and prone to errors. Again, faced with a problem, Senefelder bull-dogged it into submission. He found an ink with which he could write normally on paper and then *transfer* onto the stone. In fact, he could print right from paper to paper. Great care had to be taken to avoid tearing the original sheet, however, and he sought for a more durable

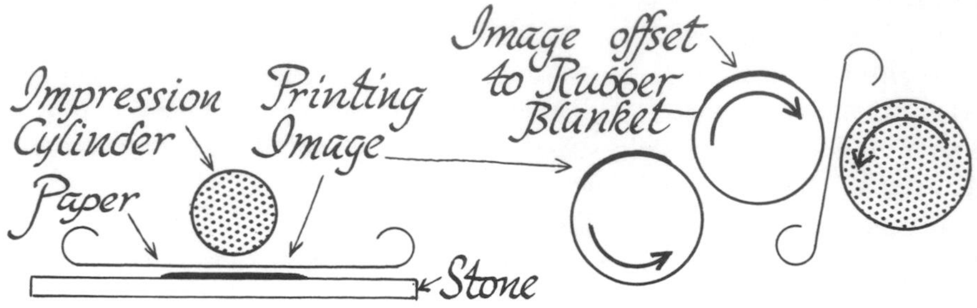

Fig. 89. Schematic of planographic printing. Left: lithography; right: offset process.

printing surface. Again he turned to his stone.

During these transfer experiments, he noticed the inherent repulsion between grease and water, and after countless steps harnessed this principle.

Finally he learned to prepare his stone by washing it with soapy water and then writing on it with a greasy ink. With aqua fortis, he removed the greasy coating left by the soap and re-washed the entire stone with a water solution of *gum,* a colloidal substance produced by plants of the mimosa family.

This is how he printed from his stone: He wet the entire stone with water, which was repelled by the greasy ink but attracted by the gum-washed blank stone. Then he rolled an inked brayer across the entire stone. The water on the stone repelled the ink, but the image he had drawn was most receptive to it. When he laid a piece of paper against this image, it was transferred perfectly. Subsequent impressions required only additional wetting and re-inking.

This is the process of lithography for which, in 1799, King Maximilian Joseph of Bavaria granted a 15-year patent, whose principle remains intact.

Senefelder even discovered the variations which are used today. He found that copper or zinc plates could be used as well as stone. He invented a press which automatically dampened and inked the plates. He wrote a textbook, published in 1818, so lucid and comprehensive that it remained the definitive textbook for decades after his death in 1834.

Like Gutenberg's, Senefelder's invention spread rapidly.

The inventor himself used color and, as early as 1806, banknotes were lithographed in color in Berlin. French artists, such as Toulouse-

Lautrec and Daumier, found it a perfect medium for their art. Music, always a problem for the typesetter, was produced economically by the new method. Johann Andre, an intimate of great musicians such as Mozart, became a business partner of Senefelder at Offenbach, Germany, the same year lithography was invented, and soon branches were opened in London, Paris, Vienna, and Berlin.

Lithography flowered in the nineteenth century. By 1870 it was common to have up to a hundred high-speed lithographic presses, printing from stones, in one plant. Posters, labels, maps, packages, pictures of all kinds, and reproductions of famous paintings could be produced in this manner with exemplary results. In the United States the most famous lithograph was a painting, *Custer's Last Fight*.

It was among the first, and certainly the most popular, of advertising giveaways. Anheuser-Busch Brewing Company distributed over a million copies since the early 1880's. Today it is a classic of the naive genre paintings of a simpler era. But the fascination of the picture is as great now as it was when our grandfathers lifted their steins in a silent toast to the golden-haired cavalryman who waved his sword in final defiance in a place of honor over the bar.

When it was first produced, by hand lithography, the picture required 33 colors—and 33 hand-drawn plates. Today it is reproduced by 11 colors and travels six times through a two-color offset press; the twelfth application is a coat of varnish.

Using newer techniques, the painting could be reproduced in eight colors without appreciable loss of quality.

One more step was required, however, to make lithography into *offset lithography*, its contemporary form.

Offset lithography can, in simplest terms, be demonstrated by an ingenious technique used by forgers in America a few years ago when ballpoint pen first came into use. The forger would obtain a genuine signature, written by ballpoint, and press his thumb firmly upon the writing. The signature was thus "lithographed" from the paper onto his thumb. Then he would press his autographed thumb onto a blank check. The signature would transfer from his skin onto the check paper. This second step is the "offset" process used in modern offset lithography. (Lest any reader be tempted to a life of crime, it should be noted that manufacturers changed the ink in their pens so that this method is no longer feasible.)

In modern offset the stone has long since been replaced by a metal or paper plate, but the same grease *vs.* water principle is maintained. Instead of lithographing the image on paper, it is first transferred onto a rubber roller from which it is offset to the paper.

The elasticity of the rubber offset plate enables it to take the ink off the image plate faultlessly and to transfer it perfectly onto any stock, combining finest gradations with sharpness and color intensity. Only minimal pressure is required, and the image, therefore, can be transferred cleanly onto rough or hard paper, cloth, and metal.

As a matter of fact, direct lithography was used to print on tin in the late nineteenth century, and the practitioners of this process were the ones who invented offset. Patents for offset were granted in France in 1881 and eight years later in Germany. But it was not until 1905 that the first offset printing on paper was done in the United States, and that same year it was used to print cardboard cartons in England. It followed by just a year the accidental discovery of the offset process by Anton Rubel, an American zinc printer. Casper Herman, who had lived in the United States for several years, is credited with decisively influencing the growth of offset more than any other individual. He was the first German offset printer and the first in that country to build an offset press (in 1906). Coincidentally, he died just a hundred years after Senefelder.

Today offset is used in many forms. The simplest is exemplified by the small office duplicators using paper plates, which can be prepared with a typewriter equipped with a special ribbon or drawn upon with pencil, crayon, or brush. At the other end of the range are huge four-color presses that will print 6,800 sheets—each sheet almost 4 feet long and over 5 feet wide—per hour, and newspaper presses that feed from rolls at much higher speeds.

Growth of lithography and offset was greatly stimulated by the development of photographic process, and most plates used today are prepared by photography.

Lithography is called *planographic* printing, printing from a flat surface. The printing image is neither raised, as in letterpress, nor incised, as in gravure; it lies on the same plane as the bearing surface. (There is an apparent exception in the case of deep-etch plates, but it is only apparent.)

The most common offset plate today is the *albumen* or *surface plate*. Of grained zinc or aluminum, this plate is flexible and durable. It is coated with a photo-sensitive solution, either by the platemaker in his own shop, or by the manufacturer as *presensitized* plates.

The image to be printed has been photographed, and the platemaker uses a negative just as does the photoengraver. He exposes the plate through the negative and by photochemistry creates, not an acid-resistant image, but a water-repelling one.

It should be noted that the offset platemaker need not flop the negative. For the offset plate is a *right-reading positive*. The mirror-image needed for printing is produced when the image is lithographed onto the rubber transfer blanket.

The *deep-etch* plate is used for long runs, from 50 to 200 thousand. It prints by planography but is produced, in part, as in intaglio plate.

The image is etched into the plate, but the depression is filled with a grease-attracting substance to the level of the water-attracting surface. By providing a mechanical container for the greasy image, deep-etch plates reduce the erosion of the unprotected image on an albumen plate.

A version of the deep-etch is the *bimetallic* or *trimetallic* plate. Each one constitutes a sandwich of thin metal. Chromium, stainless steel, or chemically prepared aluminum is on the face. Next comes a layer of copper, then—in a trimetallic plate—one of steel or other metal to give strength to the plate. The facing metal is eaten through, as in the case of deep-etch plates. The facing metal has an affinity all its own for the dampening agents, while the copper has strong attraction for the ink-receptive substance. Thus a minimum of water is required, solving many press problems. The face is ungrained and its smooth surface provides better printing of fine type and halftones.

Bimetallic and trimetallic plates have long press life, often exceeding runs of a half million. Because they will not corrode, they can be stored for future use.

Offset can use far finer screens than can letterpress; 250-line work is common and 300-line is not rare.

Offset color work—flat or process—is basically the same as in letterpress, with two essential differences. Color correction is not feasible on the offset printing plate as it is on halftone engravings. Offset ink is thinner than that in letterpress, and thus the same richness of color is not possible in photolitho work.

Dot etching is the process used for offset color correction. While it is analogous to staging and re-etching of halftones, it is performed on the photographic negative, instead of the printing plate.

Each tiny dot has a *core* which is denser than the *halo* around the edges. By exposing the dot to a solvent, the halo can be dissolved to leave the dot at the size desired. The solvent—called a *reducer*—can be applied after staging or directly, with a brush, for very delicate manipulation.

The term "dot etching" is as confusing as many other graphic arts terms. The dots are not etched to create relief; only their area is changed.

Dot etching is most frequently used with deep-etch plates. Remembering that the dots in such a plate are actually shallow intaglio receptacles, we realize that a screened positive is used to print the image onto the plate. So most dot etching is done on this positive film, with the added advantage of making it easier for the retoucher to see the tonal changes his etching is effecting.

The disadvantage of thinner ink is often overcome by running more than the four standard colors. Often pinks, grays, or blues of varying hues and tints are added to maintain true tonal values; sometimes several additional colors are used. Eight-color offset is far from rare. The cost of extra plates is usually not an inhibiting factor because much of this work is done on inexpensive albumen plates; deep-etch plates carry more ink and seldom require supplementary colors.

Dry offset, sometimes called *high-etch,* is an interesting variation originally used chiefly for printing safety paper such as the background for checks. The printing surface, in slight relief, is letterpressed onto the transfer blanket. The relief lines pick up full color while the shallow depressions are inked only lightly to create the familiar two-toned effect. Recently dry offset has been expanded to many uses. One of the most interesting is printing pencils. The printing surface is a right-reading Linotype slug (cast from *patrices* instead of matrices). The slug prints onto the rubber blanket which then offsets the image onto the pencils as they roll down from a huge hopper.

An interesting product of direct lithography is *decalcomania,* a name almost unrecognizable to most Americans because its abbreviation *decal* is so much easier to say. Decals are composed of several layers of colored ink, faced with an adhesive to make them cling to windows, doors, truck panels, or practically any surface, and a protective paper coating which is peeled off after application. Decals are usually printed from stones on flatbed presses.

The economics of offset printing are discussed in Chapter 21, but there is one obvious advantage that directly concerns the designer. *Copy* or *art,* they are synonymous, can be prepared in final form on the drawing board instead of in the composing room; this gives the obvious advantage of having make-up done in the studio instead of the print shop. (Many offset printing plants do not even have a composing room.)

The letterpress compositor makes up a form in a chase; the offset compositor *pastes up* his form at his drawing board. Instead of metal type, the paste-up man has *reproduction proofs* of hot metal, cold type (discussed in the next chapter) in film or paper, or typewritten copy, produced with a fresh ribbon—preferably a silk one—on good white paper.

Display lines come from similar sources or may be hand-lettered. His "cuts" are original art, line or continuous tone, proofs of engravings (often cut out of other publications), or Veloxes.

He works in exact size in most instances because this is easier to see what the completed job will be; reduction is possible if not too extreme.

Reproduction proofs are usually pulled on dull-coated paper (although every lithographer has his own ideas on the subject and unanimity of opinion is non-existent), but much fine work is done on *acetate* or *Kromecote,* an extremely high-gloss paper. Ink cannot be too stiff lest it cause *picking* of the paper surface, which makes white spots appear in the type. Too-soft ink will spread and cause soft halos around the letters. Impression must be completely even; high letters will punch into the paper and the camera catches shadows on the shoulder of the impression indentation.

Repro proofs must be thoroughly dry, of course, to avoid smudging in the paste-up. A clear fixative can be applied as protection.

Paste-up is done on a sturdy, hard, smooth-finished board—4-ply Bristol, 182-pound index or illustration board. Cold-white stock, without a trace of yellow or cream, should be chosen.

Rubber cement is the best adhesive. It lays the paper flat, without wrinkles; it permits paper to be lifted easily, yet holds it securely; excess adhesive can be rubbed off easily with a finger.

With a light blue pencil, invisible to the camera, the paste-up man draws the outer dimensions of the job. Then, using a T-square constantly, he places all type in the proper position. He uses meticulous care for, once the platemaker's negative is shot, it is expensive to straighten up a line of type.

If his art is also the same size and, in the case of continuous-tone pictures, has already been screened as a Velox, he pastes that into position, too.

If illustrations must be shot separately, to screen or reduce, the paste-up man indicates their position in one of several ways. He may draw the outline of the picture in red ink or pencil. He may have a Photostat made of the art work in the proper size and paste that into position; in this case he must plainly indicate "for position only" so that the platemaker does not use it for actual copy. He may use a blue-print proof of the platemaker's screened negative. These methods are most frequently used for *outsize* art (which must be reduced) or for irregularly shaped pictures.

For square halftones, two common methods are: to rule the exact-shaped rectangle in red ink, or to mount a rectangle of black paper into position. (On the negative this black square becomes a clear "window" into which the platemaker can strip the screened negative.)

A variation of the latter is used when there is more than one picture of similar size, shape, and subject which might confuse the plate-maker. A properly sized Photostat is pasted into position and then covered with red acetate. The red photographs as black and creates the clear window for stripping. Yet it is transparent, enabling the plate-maker to see exactly which screened negative he should place into the opening.

When repro proofs and line art are pasted up, they should be sur-rounded by at least one-eighth of an inch of the paper. If pasted-on paper casts a shadow, the platemaker can retouch it out of his negative without opaquing type matter. If thick sheets or board must be pasted up, edges should be *beveled* to avoid heavy shadows and time-consum-ing opaquing. An extra set of repro proofs should be kept on hand in case type in the paste-up is accidentally damaged.

When the copy is delivered to the platemaker, it is an exact replica of the final job except for stripped-in art. The platemaker's "proof" is a *blueprint, silverprint, brownprint,* or *Vandyke,* inexpensive photocopies using the negative from which the offset plate will be made.

Corrections are made on the original copy. A word or line is reset and simply pasted over the error line.

Copy for offset color is prepared as for letterpress.

Newspapers are using paste-up in growing volume today. Offset presses have been designed for newspaper needs and, in 1961, 689 weekly and 42 daily papers were printed by this method. With the growing practicality of photocomposition, many letterpress papers are pasting up display advertising. Although the paste-up then goes to a photoengraver, the technique is the same. Newspapers customarily use paste-up sheets which are ruled with light blue grids in pica increments, sufficiently fine for this kind of work. The grid obviates the need for T-squares and speeds up the process. Instead of rubber cement, a thin layer of wax is applied to the back of the material. This too allows the paper to be removed and repositioned, yet holds it firmly in place. Wax has a distinct advantage where speed is essential, as in a newspaper; it eliminates the danger of the rubber cement container being spilled, and there is no excess adhesive which must be cleaned off.

Offset has many advantages that are constantly finding new uses. It can print on almost any surface, as handsomely decorated metal containers on your kitchen shelf will testify. By its very nature, it gives "soft" effects which make it ideal to reproduce delicate art; watercolors reproduced by offset are often almost indistinguishable from the original. Line art costs nothing to add to a job; halftones require only the screened negative, not a costly engraving. Because the printing plate is so light, offset presses need not be as sturdy and heavy as letterpresses of comparable size; there need be no rugged construction to prevent disintegration by centrifugal force while running at high speeds.

While offset will probably never replace letterpress, it undoubtedly will increase its volume above the present 18 per cent of annual printing sales it now produces. It is such an important area of printing that everyone in the graphic arts must have a working knowledge of the fruit of Senefelder's success story.

SUGGESTED READINGS

Cleeton, Glen U., and Pitkin, Charles W. *General Printing*. New York: Taplinger Publishing Co., Inc., 1958.

Strauss, Victor (ed.). *The Lithographers Manual*. New York: Waltwin, 1958.

Tory, Bruce E. *Offset Lithography*. New York: Pitman Publishing Corp., 1957.

16

The Fine Arts

THE CRAFTSMAN AS AN ARTIST

The "graphic arts" of the fine artist are the "fine arts" of the printer.

If this sentence is confusing, it is only because the terms are. Confusion can be dispelled at least a little by a closer look at these dual-named processes.

From the point of view of the fine artist, his "graphic arts" are *printmaking*: lithographs, woodcuts and wood engravings, linoleum blocks, etchings, aquatints, mezzotints, dry points, and serigraphs. These all utilize the three basic printing processes, except serigraphy, which is a stencil process. Therefore, they all fall within the vast area of the graphic arts as defined by the printer.

The artist considers his "graphic arts" as fine art because no mechanical or photographic process intervenes between the creator and his creation. Every etching or lithograph is as much an original work of art as a painting by Rembrandt or a violin solo by the composer himself.

In commercial graphic arts, this fine art is important only as a source of illustrative material. The engaging picture by John DePol (Figure 90), for instance, is a wood engraving done originally in two colors, black and yellow. The artist printed a limited edition by hand. One of these prints was used as copy for a photoengraving. Proofs of this were used as engraver's copy by hundreds of publications to mark the

Fig. 90. Wood engraving by John De Pol, famed American artist, shows Whitelaw Reid inspecting first slug produced by Ottmar Mergenthaler on 1886 Linotype. (Courtesy Mergenthaler Linotype Company)

75th anniversary of the invention of the Linotype.

Every cultured person ought to have a nodding acquaintance with all the arts, and personnel of the graphic arts ought to be particularly conversant with those fine arts that are so essentially a part of their field of interest and activity.

Wood was the original printing plate. Although the mechanical age has replaced it with metal, wood remains a favorite vehicle for the artist.

The difference between a *woodcut* and *wood engravings* is slight but distinct. A woodcut is made in the grained side of a plank, using knives and gouges. Its basic effect is of large black figures on a white background. Wood engravings are cut with *burins* and *gravers* into the end-grain of a wooden block. It produces white lines on a black ground or thin black lines. Wood engraving reached its zenith with Thomas Bewick, whom we met a few chapters ago. Unlike most other art forms, it has not been improved upon by later generations; today it lies fallow, awaiting some artist to reawaken it and realize its untapped potentials.

Linoleum blocks are but a variation of woodcuts. Battleship linoleum is worked just as a wooden plank would be. It is cheaper and easier to handle and, though its plebeian name may flare the nostrils of the dilettante, it is an honest and vigorous medium.

Purists are also disturbed because some contemporary artists use such unartistic materials as masonite or plastics—any surface that will yield prints—and work them with a flexible drill. As if this were not disquieting enough, these contemporaries nail wire screen or paste string, barley, cheesecloth, and other prosaic materials onto certain areas of their wood block to create unusual textures and printing effects. They puncture large areas with nails of various sizes, or harry the smooth wood with rasps, files, or screwdrivers.

A highly inventive artist in wood is Antonio Frasconi; John DePol, already mentioned, combines the quaintness of colonial days with a pure contemporary feeling.

The classical *etching* has been examined in discussing intaglio. It has long been a favorite art form and continues to be today. Some of the great artists of history have found the copperplate to be a powerful medium. Probably the most famous etcher is Albrecht Durer, whose work packs the same potency today as it did in his heyday in the early 1500's. Rembrandt loved etching, and it is interesting to note that Rembrandt is Rembrandt with a burin as well as with a paint brush.

William Hogarth's biting satire of eighteenth-century England combined etching and engraving; Goya could protest against "Disasters of the War" or exult in Spain's pageantry. William Blake used etching to create his soaring illustrations of Biblical themes and America's Whistler found the acid as delicate as his watercolor.

Dry point is another of the many confusing terms in the graphic arts. It is considered an etching, yet there is no "etching" process involved. Instead of using acid to incise his lines, the artist cuts them with a metal, diamond, ruby, or sapphire needle. Actually, he plows a furrow and the displaced metal piles up along the sides of the line. This *burr* catches the ink that, even after the plate is wiped, gives drypoint its distinguishing flavor and mellowness.

Close cousin to the drypoint is the *mezzotint*. Its entire surface is covered with burrs, produced by a *rocker*, an instrument with many small teeth, that is rocked across the plate. The burr acts like intaglio wells. In desired areas it is either removed entirely with a *scraper*, or flattened out with a burnisher to create lighter areas of gray.

Another of the intaglio art forms that adds texture to etching is the *aquatint*. In this technique a ground of resin dust is sprinkled on all or certain areas of the etcher's plate and heated to make it adhere. The etchant penetrates between the fine grains to bite countless tiny intaglio wells that print in a soft texture. Salt and sugar are also used for aquatints, and sometimes sandpaper is pressed into the ground before etching. Aquatint is usually combined with bitten lines and so the texture must be applied after the linework has been etched.

The resin technique of aquatints is used in *photogravure*. Powdered resin is applied to a metal plate as in an aquatint. A carbon tissue, just as in rotogravure, is exposed to a film positive. But no screen is used; the minute granules of resin, with tiny areas between them, act as the screen. The "screen" is extremely fine, of course, and has a pleasant irregular pattern, somewhat like that of a mezzotint, that makes the dot pattern virtually indiscernible.

Except for the one photographic step, the making of a photogravure is entirely a hand process. Printing, after hand-wiping, is manual and 500 prints a day is maximum production, striking contrast to that of roto.

Photogravure is practically never printed with more than one plate. But the artist may carefully apply different colored inks to various areas of the same plate and print several colors at one time. This is not "color printing" though, in the accepted sense of the word; each print is an individual, and variable, product of the artist. (This same color technique is utilized with mezzotints also.) Sometimes photogravure is printed in a light ink and the print tinted with watercolors. This harks back to the days of Currier & Ives.

The fine-artist lithographer goes back to Senefelder's early techniques. He works directly upon a stone that he has himself ground down to a smooth surface. He can use lithographic crayons and pencils; he can apply a liquid *tusche* as in a wash drawing; with his fingers he can apply *rubbing ink*. He may apply large areas of ink and scratch, rub, scrape, or burn (with mild acid) designs or texture. It must be kept in mind that this "lithographer" does not reproduce other people's work; he creates his own. Lithography has been a facile medium for such famed artists as Goya, Daumier, William Gropper, and Diego Rivera, to mention only a fragment of the roster.

Fig. 91. Effect of media and techniques. Above: watercolor wash. On the opposite page: bullfighter in ink wash; woman, pastel; man, charcoal; landscape, pencil. All on textured Charko-Board. (Courtesy Crescent Cardboard Co.)

Although the use of stencils is ancient, its most sophisticated version was developed as recently as the 1930's by the WPA Federal Arts Project. This stencil printing is *serigraphy* or *silk-screen* printing. Although purists have sneered at serigraphy because it is not "true printing," it is recognized by most people as a legitimate member of the fine-arts graphics.

The silk screen that gives its name to the process is of raw silk, stretched tightly onto a wooden frame, that allows paint to be forced by a squeegee through pores of the fabric onto a paper beneath. When certain areas are covered with a gluey substance that does not allow the paint to penetrate, the stencil effect has been obtained. This insoluble tusche can be painted, brushed, dabbed, spattered, or dotted

to create pleasant effects and reproduce masses of color or details.

Transparent and opaque paints are used and their interaction produces a wide range of colors. (Most of the "graphic fine arts" can, and do, use more than one color on occasion.)

Commercial silk-screen printing has grown tremendously in the past few years, especially since photography has been developed as a tool in preparing the stencil.

Commercial stencils are silk, or other fabrics, covered with *frisket paper*. The frisket is cut away by hand, or is sensitized, exposed, and dissolved away by photographic processes to form the desired stencil. In this case the silk is merely the bearer for the paper stencil.

In the familiar stencils used to address packing boxes, it is impossible to print conventional letters. The inner portion of the O, for instance, must be held in place with a tiny strip that connects it to the stencil around the outside of the letter. Indeed, the bowls of all letters must be so connected and this gives the familiar effect of stencil lettering. With the silk acting as a bearer, the middle portion of the O—or any similar element—is supported by the fabric and need not be connected.

Special "presses" have been developed for speedier production of silk screen printing. The process can be used on any surface, from beer cans to athletic sweaters. Overprinting of transparent paints gives a full palette to the designer. A recent extension is to print an adhesive, instead of paint, and then spray *flock*, tiny particles of rayon, on the design to create a velvet effect.

Collotype and *aquatone* are two interesting printing processes that use gelatin as a printing surface. Technically speaking, these are not "graphic fine arts" because they are commercial processes. But as a major use, especially in color, is to reproduce art works, it seems more logical to discuss them here than in the chapter on lithography, which they resemble. Both rely on the mutual repulsion of grease and water.

Collotype, also called *photogelatin*, was first produced in England in 1865. It uses no screen but produces continuous-tone copies of continuous-tone originals.

A thin layer of sensitized gelatin is exposed to an unscreened negative. Then it is thoroughly dampened with water and glycerin. Those areas which were light in the copy will absorb most moisture; those dark portions, which were exposed to maximum light through the negative, are almost dry. All the intermediate tones of the original are reproduced, in varying degrees of dampness, on the gelatin. The gelatin plate accepts ink in close ratio to its dampness, taking the most where the gelatin is most nearly dry.

Only four colors are used: gray, yellow, red, and blue, usually printed in that order. The transparent inks and the unscreened surface give finely diffused layers of color that reproduce art work in beauty and richness. Dependent as they are on moisture, gelatin plates must be made and printed under strictly controlled humidity. No retouching is possible on the plate; it must all be done on the negative.

Commercially collotype is used, in monochrome usually, where fidelity of reproduction is required but only for short runs. For longer runs, new plates must be made; this slows down an already slow process to the point of impracticality.

Aquatone combines the principles of gelatin printing with that of offset. Here a screen is used, but the interrelation of the smooth gelatin and the rubber offset blanket is such that 400-line screen can be used. Like collotype, aquatone is handicapped by its slow rate of production.

Familiar examples of monochromatic collotype are the large posters used by theaters. Because it has no screen, the process is useful in making blow-ups from smaller copy. Lobby posters are often several-diameter enlargements of smaller ones that have been produced by other processes.

Aquarelle, although similar in name, has no relationship to aquatone except that it, too, teeter-totters across the line dividing the fine from the commercial graphic arts. An aquarelle is a printed picture to which color is added by applying water color through stencils, one for each color. This is a slow, manual application. The skill of the painter has noticeable effect on the quality of the added color and this pushes the process toward the fine-arts category.

Products of the fine-arts processes discussed in this chapter are known generically as *prints.* This is unfortunate; for the public associates "prints" with cheap reproductions of other art forms. So it must be stressed again that these prints are original works of art. Many an art collector has begun by acquiring prints. The price is low; an original Picasso can be bought for $10. This appeals to young connoisseurs, especially, whose beer budget will not permit the acquisition of champagne-priced oil paintings.

Printmaking also appeals to the creative instincts of many people who long for the relaxation and satisfaction of creating something with their hands after a day of mental work. Materials are inexpensive; few tools are required (the heel of a spoon, or even of your hand, makes a satisfactory "printing press"); the basic technique is quickly learned. Once it is mastered, there are enough challenges in any of these media to intrigue an artist for the rest of his life.

SUGGESTED READINGS

Heller, Jules. *Printmaking Today.* New York: Henry Holt & Co., Inc., 1958.
Strauss, Victor. *Modern Silk Screen.* New York: Pied Piper Press, 1959.

17

Cold Type

SETTING TYPE PHOTOGRAPHICALLY

Letterpress needs physical type to deposit ink on paper. But planography and intaglio need only a picture of the type from which to prepare plates. Ever since the latter processes came into practical use, men have sought ways to compose type photographically. They knew that manipulation of light photographic film or paper would effect substantial savings of time, energy, and money over the more laborious assembling of weighty metal.

As early as the 1880's patents had been granted for phototypesetting machines, but it was not until after World War II, when the whole graphic arts industry was in a ferment of research, that photocomposition became practical.

Photocomposition is called *cold type,* a logical differentiation from the *hot metal* of linecasters.

The first of such machines was Intertype's *Fotosetter.* This is a conventional Intertype with a camera device replacing the casting mechanism. It uses the principle of circulating matrices. Through the wide side of the mat a hole. is bored, and into it is inserted a piece of black plastic with the negative image of the character in reverse. This takes the place of the mold in the conventional matrix.

A line of matrices is assembled and justified just as in hot-metal casting. But now each matrix is lifted so that a beam of light can project through the film and produce a picture of the character on photographic film or paper. After photography, the matrices are distributed, the film is moved up, and the second line is photographed.

An early weakness of the Fotosetter was the justification system which added space evenly between letters as well as between words to fill out a line. This has been corrected in newer models.

By exposing the character negative through different lenses, it is possible to produce from 4- through 36-point type from only two fonts of matrices. The Super Display model extends the range to 3-point and 72-point. Mixing is done as in hot metal.

Ruling matrices provide horizontal lines in tabulations; vertical rules are *scribed* (scratched through the emulsion) on the film. Scribing is a favored method of ruling in any platemaking process.

An advantage of the Fotosetter is its use of Intertype mechanisms with which hot-metal operators are already familiar.

Meanwhile a group of French inventors obtained American backing and began manufacture and sale of the *Photon* machine. This machine abandoned the principle of the circulating matrix and, with it, its inherent speed limitations.

The Photon carries its negatives of characters on a *matrix disc,* which spins continuously at 10 revolutions per second. It carries 16 complete 90-character alphabets. The keyboard resembles that of an electric typewriter with additional controls at flanking consoles.

When the operator hits a key, a beam of light from a *stroboscopic* flash bulb illuminates the selected negative at the precise moment it orbits in front of the lens. Because the strobe flashes for only .000004 second, it freezes all motion. Rated speed is 8 to 10 characters per second, with line lengths up to 54 picas.

By using various lenses, type sizes from 5- through 72-point can be produced.

The Photon is a single U-shaped unit with keyboard linked directly to the photographic apparatus. There must be an intermediate link, of course, to provide for justification. This is an electronic *memory system* that stores instructions from the keyboard until the entire line has been set and the proper word-spacing determined. If the operator makes an error, he can erase the entire line. Or he can backspace to the error character and replace only it with the correction.

As the operator sends signals to the photographic unit, he also produces a normal typescript, *hard copy*. This enables him to see exactly what he is setting and reduces errors significantly. The machine can also be operated by perforated tape or cards. Data for a directory, for instance, can be punched into conventional business-machine cards for filing and sorting; the Photon can convert this coded information into type.

The *Linofilm System* is manufactured by Mergenthaler Linotype Company. It varies in several principles from the other two photo-setters. It is a two-unit machine; the keyboard is separate and independent from the photographing units. At the keyboard, again an augmented typewriter version, the operator produces perforated tape plus hard copy. This tape actuates the photo unit.

Linofilm carries its negatives on a *grid* of one alphabet. It remains stationary behind a group of *lenslets,* one for each character and each covered with a tiny shutter. Each lenslet is focused on the identical spot; were they all to be exposed at one time, images would pile up on each other. But the shutters remain closed until the tape signals a specific character; its shutter opens, allows a strobe beam to shine through the negative and onto the photo film or paper. A moving mirror directs each image to the proper position on the film.

Linofilm sets type in sizes from 6 to 36 points, in line lengths of 42 picas, at the rate of 6 ems per second—15 lines of 12-point, 18 picas wide, per minute.

A third machine in the Linofilm system is the *composer.* Right-reading negative material from the Linofilm or elsewhere is enlarged, up to six times, or reduced, down to two-thirds, and positioned according to an overlay dummy. The result is a complete layout, up to a full newspaper page, on photographic paper. This process is analogous to making up a form in hot metal but mechanized to such an extent that substantial economies may be realized. A major advantage is that the make-up man is freed from point-size restrictions. If he wants to fill a given line-length, he can do so by manipulating the size of the type to fill the exact area, whether the result is 96-point type or 107½-point type.

Tape operations give to the Linofilm the advantages of automation discussed in connection with TTS.

Another tape-operated phototypesetter is the *Monophoto,* the photographic equivalent of the Monotype. It uses the same principle as the hot-metal version, except that the matrix case now holds negatives and is called the *master negative case.* Just as the hot-metal case shifts to bring the Monotype matrix over the casting box, so the negative case shifts to bring the proper character negative into alignment between light, lens, and photo paper. The Monophoto sets lines up to 60 picas and in sizes from 6- through 24-point.

The Monophoto produces type on photographic film; the other three machines on film or paper. As the original image in all machines is a negative, the machines' products are right-reading positives. But a simple chemical reaction converts them into right-reading negatives. Thus the proper copy for letterpress, offset, and gravure platemaking may be produced without the intermediate step of photographing pasteups to obtain negatives.

Cold-type typography is of high quality. All standard faces are available. Kerning is no problem whatsoever. Widths of type body or matrices have no bearing on where a photographic image can be placed. So spacing can be manipulated in ways utterly impossible with hot metal. Scripts can join without any break.

A major advantage is that, in many processes, the film output of phototypesetting machines can be used directly to produce printing plates, thus eliminating the need for the platemaker to make a negative. The fewer the reproductive processes, the higher the fidelity.

Newspapers are major users of the phototypesetters discussed, although magazines, book compositors, business-form manufacturers, and map makers also use cold type advantageously.

Most newspaper use is for advertising or for Sunday magazines, where deadlines are not too pressing and where type is handled as simple blocks. For the time being at least, news columns are best made up by manipulating linecaster slugs.

Newspapers make up ads by pasting up, as for offset plates; by placement of original photographic material on the Linofilm composer or by utilizing a *make-up guide* on the Photon; or by *metal paste-up*. In the latter method, all elements in several ads are engraved on a single flat. They are sawed into individual blocks and positioned and pasted onto a metal base. Although, on the face of it, metal paste-up may not seem to be advantageous, newspapers using the method report excellent results.

Just as hot-metal compositors have a Ludlow to cast large display type, so the cold-type operator has a source of photographic type beyond the range of the keyboarded machines we have considered. These display machines share a common principle: They produce images from negatives which are carried on pieces of film or plastic. In the simplest of such machines, the *ProType,* the operator slides a rectangular piece of film into position by hand. A grooved track provides horizontal alignment; a guide line on the film indicates proper letter- and word-spacing. This machine uses a film or paper that is sensitive only to fluorescent light, which permits the operator to work under incandescent or natural light.

The process is mechanized to a greater degree in other machines where the operator manipulates knobs and levers to select and expose the negative character.

In the *Headliner,* characters are carried on a disc and brought into position by dialing. The product, on film or paper, is in the form of a single line of type. The *Typro* can set several lines on a single piece of photopaper. *Alphatype, Hadego, FotoRex,* and *StripPrinter* are other cold-type display setters.

The wide selection of self-adhering plastic letters such as Artype and Craftype is technically cold type. These are available in all sizes, but they are customarily used to produce only a small quantity of copy, a word or a line or two. The process is too slow to be economical for a large amount of composition.

The cost of these cold-type display machines is relatively low, so their use is wide. Art agencies, advertising departments, and publications can use them to advantage. But there is a convenient and inexpensive source for photographic display type in the *photolettering* services. These commercial houses sell such type by the word and the buyer has the resources of extensive type libraries with no investment on his part.

By using various lenses, photoletterers can distort type into almost countless variations of the original.

Temptation to utilize extreme potentials of photolettering is acute. The designer must constantly keep in mind that legibility should never be sacrificed to the design value of type. Fads sweep through the graphic arts like weevils through a cotton field. Most fads, fortunately, have a high mortality rate. This is fortunate because many are poor typography. *Stacked type* is a plague that has endured far longer than we might have hoped. In this style, there is no interlineal spacing; one row of type butts up tightly to that above or below it. The beauty of such arrangement as pure design is debatable; there is no question about its legibility—it is nil.

The simplest way to "set type" for the platemaker is on an ordinary typewriter. Justification can also be achieved. The typist draws the righthand margin and types the copy as close to that length as possible. If the line is short, he fills it up with periods or asterisks. If long, he types the number of excess spaces in the right margin. Then the copy is retyped. Should it be, say, four spaces short, these are inserted between words in addition to the normal word spacing. If the line is long, the necessary amount of word spacing is reduced from a full to a half space. Even regular typewriters allow this manipulation; those with space and backspace in half-unit increments make the job easier.

Several makes of electric typewriters have this feature plus that of *proportional spacing*. In a standard typewriter, each character, be it an i or an M, gets exactly as much space as any other. The effect is that the i or l looks like a utility pole in the middle of a hayfield while the wide letters are cramped. Proportional-spacing machines provide usually four different spaces. This is an improvement even though it cannot match the spacing of a Linofilm, for instance, which provides increments in eighteenths of an em, or of hot metal where each character gets exactly its proper width with no relation to restriction of increments.

The advantage of justified lines is usually considered worth the time and effort of the second typing. The *Flexowriter* and *Justowriter* mechanize justification by producing a perforated tape at the keyboard which, in turn, actuates a second typewriter. Equipment cost is higher than for a single conventional typewriter, but savings are high enough

1 CAMERA modifications *4 CAMERA modifications*

2 CAMERA modifications *5* CAMERA modifications

3 CAMERA modifications

Fig. 92. Variations of letterforms by photographic manipulation. "Floating" shapes (right) were produced by a Statmaster and shown courtesy Statmaster Corporation. These modifications are by Lettering, Inc., used by its courtesy. 1: normal letter form; 2: larger letters condensed 25 per cent; 3: smaller letters extended 33 per cent; 4: normal letter italicized to 20-degree slant; 5: backslanted 20 degrees.

so that many weekly newspapers use this method for "composition."

The *Varityper* and a new *IBM Selectric* typewriter add versatility. They place their type, not on the end of permanent key bars, but in an individual element that can be changed in a matter of seconds. Thus a large selection of type faces is available for every keyboard.

The inherent disabilities of a typewriter still keep such "composition" at a level scorned by many typographers. The problem of proper fitting of characters has not been wholly solved by proportional spacing. If it were to be completely solved, the cost of the machine probably would no longer be competitive against hot metal composition.

New Art Forms Through Reflective Photography

There also seems to be an innate inability to produce a type face with sufficient body or weight on a typewriter. The result, up to now, is that such type looks weak and spindly.

The ATF *Typesetter* strikes a medium. Again the keyboard produces tape. This actuates a photo unit which utilizes the disc of vinyl plastic that carries the negatives of two fonts, both in the same size. Discs do not spin as Photon's but turn to proper position, at a rated speed of 200 characters per minute. Maximum line-length is 7½ inches. Discs can be changed easily, like changing records on a phonograph. The product is right-reading positive type on paper or film. The Type-setter costs considerably less than other straight-matter phototype-setters.

The problem of correcting cold type is a vexing one. Usually the entire error line is reset and pasted over the original. Sometimes a single word or even letter can be pasted over the error but this is too small to handle conveniently.

Errors in film are harder to correct; for now the error line must be removed before replacement. Fotosetter uses a *line-strip punch* that cuts out a rectangle bearing the error line. Correction lines are cut to the same dimensions. By means of *register holes* punched in the side of all Fotosetter photographic materials, the correction line is inserted into proper position while held in a vacuum box and then affixed by transparent tape. The Linofilm system has an automatic corrector. After the operator has matched error and correction line, again with register punches, the original film is sliced off just above the error line; the correction film is heat-welded into place; the error line is cut off and the next correct line is welded onto the correction.

Proofing of cold type is done as that for offset plates—Vandykes, blueprints, etc.—and by office copying machines such as *Bruning, Ozalid,* and *Diazo.*

A unique process, *Brightype,* was developed by the Ludlow Typograph Company. It provides cold type from hot metal but eliminates the proofing process.

The form is composed and locked up as for relief printing. After it is sprayed with liquid lampblack, a rubber pad—which looks like a classroom blackboard eraser—polishes the face of the form. This removes the black coating from—and from only—the printing surfaces. The form is then photographed; the result is a positive image on film.

The image is often sharper than that produced by proofing and typographic elements can be re-used without showing signs of wear.

It is in the area of cold type that the greatest strides will undoubtedly be made in the next decade or two. The potential market is vast and free industry needs no greater incentive than that to achieve new and economically sound equipment, methods, and techniques.

SUGGESTED READINGS

Wide commercial use of photocomposition is so comparatively recent that no definitive work on the subject has yet been published. The best available information is in materials prepared by the manufacturers of such equipment.

A wealth of information on almost every phase of the graphic arts is contained in the eight annual *Production Yearbooks* (New York: Colton) and in the *Penrose Annuals* (New York: Hastings House, Publishers, Inc.). Information on developments in typography and production are well reported in the following magazines: *Inland Printer/American Lithographer* (Chicago), *Western Printer & Lithographer* (Los Angeles), *Canadian Printer & Publisher* (Toronto), *Printing Production* (Cleveland, Ohio), *Advertising & Sales Promotion,* formerly *Advertising Requirements* (Chicago), *Graphic Arts Buyer* (Philadelphia), *Print* (New York), *Printers' Ink* (New York), *Productionwise* (New York), and *Printing Magazine* (Oradell, N.J.).

18

Paper

THE WRAPPING OF CULTURE

Paper is more than "the wrapping of culture"; it is an indispensable tool of civilization. Some night when you are unable to sleep, instead of counting sheep start counting all the paper that you use in everyday life. The alarm will go off before the list is complete; it ranges from the tissue at your bedside table to clothing and averages 500 pounds per American annually.

Paper, like its name, derives from *papyrus*, the writing surface developed by the Egyptians about 3000 B.C. Papyrus was not truly paper; it was made by weaving the stalks of a reedy plant, pasting them together with fruit juices, then pounding the sheet to the proper thickness and smoothness.

Real paper was first made in China by Ts'ai Lun early in the second century. He floated vegetable fibers—inner mulberry bark and bamboo —in a bath of water and allowed them to settle and dry into a sheet. Six hundred years later, when the Arabs conquered storied Samarkand deep in central Asia, their prisoners included two Chinese paper-makers. Via North Africa, the art of papermaking came to Europe, reached England in 1494, and took until 1690 to come to America.

Technically, paper is a web or mat of vegetable fibers—cellulose. All growing things contain this fibrous substance but cotton and wood are the main substances used for papermaking today. Some special papers are made of rice, corn straw, or grasses and constant experimenting goes on to seek new raw material. Current experiments with wheat are showing promising results. But, as forests replenish themselves faster than the woodsman fells them, wood remains an excellent source of cellulose.

Paper remained an expensive product for several centuries because it was made slowly, sheet by sheet. Mechanization came to the industry with the invention of a papermaking machine in 1798 by Nicholas Louis Roberts, an employee of the famous Didots. But he sold the patents to the Fourdrinier brothers of England, and it is their name that commonly designates all such machines today.

Paper is an essential ingredient in all printing. Its color, surface, and physical characteristics are as important as the shapes ink places on its surface. Because of this, the designer must have at least a cursory knowledge of paper. Actually that is all he can expect to obtain; the subject is so complex that only a specialist can hope to master most of it in a lifetime.

To oversimplify the manufacturing process: Wood or cotton rags are ground or *cooked,* with chemicals, into pulp. The fibers are beaten in water to soften them and to extract a gelatinous substance that causes the fibers to cling together. This creamy soup is further diluted with water which makes up 90 per cent of the mass.

This solution is strained through microscopic slots onto an endless conveyor belt made of a finely woven screen, with 60 to 80 horizontal —and the same number of vertical—wires per inch.

The fibers all tend to float parallel to each other; this gives the *grain* to paper. Short fibers, such as those produced by grinding wood or cooking it with caustic soda, provide the smoothness necessary for good printing. Long fibers, from pulp cooked with sulphites or sulphates, give strength. The skill of the papermaker is demonstrated in the way he mixes the two lengths.

Papermaking machines are behemoths. They are several hundred feet long, depending upon how many drying rollers they have, and produce paper from 6 to 20 feet wide in continuous rolls. The screen conveyor is up to 50 feet long. As the paper mash moves onto the screen, water drains off by gravity and by vigorous sideways shaking that throws out the water and causes a lateral interweaving of fibers which increases paper strength. Paper at this stage looks like a thoroughly wet piece of blotting paper.

By this time water represents about two-thirds of the mass. By squeezing, blotting with felt rollers, and applying heat, the paper is finally reduced to only 7 per cent to 10 per cent water content, its final form, and is wound onto rollers.

There have been several other steps during the process. Some will be discussed as they effect differences between kinds of paper; others can be safely left to the papermaker.

Watermarks, if any, have been produced by a *dandy roll,* a wire-cloth roller, just after the paper has left the screen. The design is impressed into the very wet paper as it receives its first surface pressure.

Extra materials are added to paper pulp to perform specific functions. *Sizing* helps hold the fibers together, makes book paper repellent to the dampness which might cause pages to wave or wrinkle, and reduces the absorbency of writing paper so the ink doesn't blur or feather.

Loading agents, or *fillers,* are mineral substances added to fill the spaces between paper fibers and to give solidity and a smooth surface.

Similar mineral smoothing materials are used to make *coated paper;* one or both of its sides are surfaced very smoothly for better printing. Although "coated papers" usually refers to glossy stock, dull or semi-dull finishes are also available and are often used because eliminating glare is easier on the reader's eyes.

Calendered, or *machine finish,* is produced by running the paper between smooth metal rollers that press and polish it. In *super-calendering,* pressure, steam and friction "iron" the paper to glassy smoothness, just as a housewife irons a shirt.

Four major divisions of paper commonly used in printing are *news-print, book, writing,* and *cover stock.* Many others come to mind instantly—kraft paper for heavy wrappings, cardboard, oiled paper, tissues, for instance—but these are handled by specialized printers, if they are printed upon at all. The paper used for a printing job is the *stock,* and that word is used constantly as a synonym for paper.

NEWSPRINT

Newsprint is the cheapest paper used for common printing. It must be stressed that price does not necessarily make a "poor" paper; if it does the job it is supposed to, paper is "good." Newsprint does that. It furnishes an adequate printing surface that satisfactorily takes type and halftones in 65- or 85-line screen and 150-screen in rotogravure. Its color, though grayish, is bright enough to lend reasonably good legibility.

Its permanence and strength are low because of its high content of short wood fiber and large proportions of filler. Because the whole log is ground up to make newsprint, vegetable resins and gums remain in the paper, causing it to yellow and discolor. Newspapers overcome the short life of newsprint by microfilming pages or printing a few copies, for permanent records, on rag content paper. A newspaper is not reread so often that its brittleness is a grave disability.

Roto paper is a smooth-finish newsprint.

Newsprint, in addition to its common use, is chosen for handbills and other advertising material of a very ephemeral nature.

BOOK PAPERS

Categories of book papers are as varied as those of type faces; many stocks have characteristics of more than one classification. Yet we must have some pigeonholing in order to discuss them logically. Arbitrary but useful subdivisions are *texture*.

Antique is a loose term applied to papers that are soft, comparatively rough surfaced, and *bulky*, relatively thick sheets in relation to its weight. Antiques, as the name indicates, resemble paper used in the early days of printing.

Text paper is high-grade uncoated antique, often with considerable rag content—cotton fibers—for greater permanence. *Vellum* finishes are in this same broad grouping.

Eggshell antique is named for the texture of its *felt side* which strongly resembles that of a shell.

We must digress for a moment to define "felt side" and its opposite, *wire side*. As the paper moves through the papermaking machine, that side which rests on the wire conveyor receives a faint pattern of the mesh. The top side, which has been pressed only by the felt rollers, is smoother. For printing on only one side, as on a letterhead, the impression is made on the felt, or the *right*, side, that from which the watermark, if any, can be read.

A common differentiation for antique paper is *wove* or *laid*. The first is so named because the textures of both the screen and the felt are combined to create a comparatively smooth paper that looks like a woven fabric. Laid stock purposely resembles handmade paper. A special dandy roll creates an over-all watermark somewhat like a Venetian blind. Horizontal parallel lines, equivalent to the blind's slats, are the *wires*. These are broken by blank vertical lines, equivalent to tapes in a blind, the *chain*. Laid stock is not only a little rougher than wove, there is also a more marked difference between the felt and wire sides, and therefore it is commonly used for letterheads, which require printing on only one side.

Offset stock is smooth, uncoated, and sized with extra care to minimize the effect of the dampening agent of an offset press.

English finish—E.F.—is given its smooth surface because its relatively high content of clay filler is heavily machined. The clay filler gives a rather suede-like finish; it can be detected by the slight pull as fingertips are brushed across the surface.

Super-calendered stock—just plain *super* to most printers—is given a very high finish by running it through a separate machine which continues and intensifies the results of calendering rolls on the Fourdrinier. Super is the slickest of the uncoated books.

Coated stock goes through a supplementary process whereby a substance consisting of clay, whitening agents and casein glue surfaces the paper. Coated finishes range from *dull*—very smooth but not glossy—to the extremely high luster of *enamel* which has been super-calendered.

WRITING PAPERS

Writing stock subdivides into three groups. *Flat writing* is a calendered, well-sized paper of wood pulp. *Bond*, the most important group, usually contains varying percentages of rag content and is often sized with animal gelatins. The sizing gives not only the proper surface for writing but also contributes to the *rattle*, the crispness and snap that distinguishes good bond.

The finest bonds, made entirely from new cotton or linen rags, closely resemble the stock of paper money. Bond gets its name because it was first developed for printing bonds, stock certificates, deeds, and other documents which require maximum durability. Bond is closely associated with quality in the public mind.

Ledger, the third writing category, is smooth-surfaced for ease in writing, specially sized to resist erasure, and made with long fibers to facilitate folding. Often it has high rag content. As its name indicates, it is largely used for ledgers and other records, but has many other uses, often for letterheads, and—of special interest to designers—for line drawings and for making dummies.

COVER STOCK

Cover stocks are made in the same way as book and writing stocks but are usually considerably heavier to withstand the wear that their name indicates they will receive.

Cover is available in a very wide range of colors and finishes, ranging from laid and wove through velour, imitation leather, and fabric, to paper faced with foil.

FINISHES

All papers can be finished in a variety of textures, but offset is used in the widest range of finishes because the printing process of that name can print on irregular surfaces.

Cockle finish has surface ripples caused by shrinkage under little or no tension during drying. It is popular in writing paper. *Pebble* and *ripple* finishes are placed in the paper by textured rollers in the manufacturing process. *Stucco* and *fabric* are other popular textures.

Ivory finish is produced by calendering between rollers coated with beeswax. Its tactile effect is like that of the substance that names it.

Deckle is the irregular, feathery edge produced by contact with the walls that confine paper pulp during manufacture or by jets of water or air. Handmade paper is deckled on four sides; machine-made, on two. Imitation deckle is produced by sawing, cutting, tearing, or sandblasting finished paper.

There are a few of the myriad papers that we ought at least nod to in passing. They mostly concern designers who specialize narrowly.

Bible or *India paper* is extremely thin but strong, opaque, and permanent. It is used for printing, in addition to Bibles for which it was developed, any book with so many pages that bulk becomes a problem.

Cardboard is a thick, heavy paper made by pasting together several *plies* of cheap filler with one of coated or calendered paper on the outside.

Bristol board is a thin—.006 inch—cardboard with an excellent surface for printing, writing, or drawing. Often several sheets are pasted together to create two- or three-ply or even heavier boards.

Kraft—German for "strong"—is usually identified as familiar brown butcher paper. It is also called *sulfate* from the manufacturing process that uses caustic soda to cook pitchy woods such as pine. This produces the longest of all chemically refined pulp fibers and gives unusual strength to the paper. Therefore kraft is often used to reinforce other papers. Although it is most commonly unbleached, it can be manufactured in colors suitable for gift wrapping.

Manifold is commonly known as *onionskin*. Strong and durable, it accepts carbon-paper typing well and its low bulk is an asset where many records must be kept. Onionskin is used for airmail stationery.

Safety paper is made by adding certain chemicals to the pulp, by bathing finished paper in chemicals or by printing an allover design in special inks. These methods make the paper sensitive to erasure, bleaching, or other attempts to delete or change the writing on checks, money orders, tickets, or other negotiable papers.

Blotting paper, made without sizing, is soft, absorbent, and bulky. (Incidentally, white blotting paper shows clearly the difference between wire and felt sides.) Blotting paper to which a harder-finished paper has been pasted is known as *porcelain*.

The buyer of printing and the designer of printed jobs must specify the paper. He is usually concerned with the weight, finish, and color, but there are other factors he cannot overlook.

Opacity, the quality which prevents *show-through* of printing from one side or leaf to the other, is important. Bulk and weight must be considered, the first in relation to ease of handling and storage, the latter in regard to cost of mailing or shipping.

Color is, of course, a basic element of the over-all appearance. Wide ranges are available and that choice is made by the artist who designs the piece.

Color of paper is as useful as color of ink. When colored stock is used, its selection must be preceded by careful thought. There must be enough difference in value between paper and ink so that the type will be strong enough for readability. Especially small faces, or those with very thin hairlines, can lose readability dangerously on an unsuitable color stock.

Always the ink should be of strong value. Black is best for printing on colored stock but other deep colors can be effective.

Two-tone coated papers have a different color on front and back. Their use, especially when folded or cut in unusual fashion, gives a multicolor effect with only one trip through the press.

Sizing is important, especially as it affects the receptivity of paper to moisture.

This is particularly important in offset printing where the stock is acutely exposed to moisture during the printing process. But in any printing process, excess moisture in the storeroom can create curled or wavy paper that is difficult to feed through the press or on which it is hard to produce an even impression.

Addition of moisture can have an unhappy increase in weight. Large catalogues, such as those of Sears, Roebuck or Montgomery Ward, are printed and stored in humidity-controlled rooms; the increase of 1 or 2 per cent of moisture in a million or more books can add hundreds and thousands of dollars to postage.

Paper can never be entirely free from moisture because it would then lose pliability.

The *grain* of the paper must be considered, especially for folding. It has been seen how the cellulose fibers in paper float endwise during the manufacturing, just like logs floating down the river. When paper is folded against the grain, these "logs" are broken and the folded edge is harsh and irregular. The heavier the paper, the worse the results of folding against the grain.

For many kinds of printing, especially color offset, the relation of the grain to the direction in which the paper is fed into the press has a distinct effect on the quality of registration and impression. This must be considered when planning how the stock is to be cut out of the basic sheet.

Direction of the grain can be determined by three methods. The first is to tear or fold the paper; it tears more easily and folds more cleanly with the grain. Often, however, the difference is too slight for anyone but an expert to detect.

Sized paper can be wet on one side only and immediately it will curl into a semi-cylinder whose long axis runs with the grain.

The *strip test* can be used for any paper, sized or not. Two strips, about ½ inch wide and 6 to 8 inches long, are cut from the stock, one in each direction. They are held, horizontally and side by side, at one end. One strip will droop considerably more than the other. This is because in it the grain runs sideways and allows the strip to sag, while

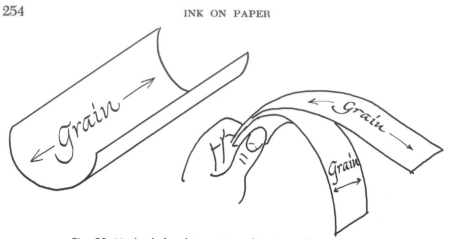

Fig. 93. Methods for determining direction of paper grain.

on the other strip the fibers run lengthwise and give more support.

The advice of the pressman can always be sought before an unusual stock is selected. He is well able to judge whether a stock is best adapted to the specific needs of the particular job and printing process. It is wise to leave many technical decisions to the pressman; but the designer should know the basic strengths and liabilities of those papers which he most frequently uses.

Newsprint is good for letterpress and gravure, but because of its readiness to accept moisture it cannot be lithographed. Its ability to take line and halftones in proper screens has been noted. A good range of colored news inks has been developed and newsprint itself comes in a few colors. The growth of comic books has opened this art form to advertising and instruction; newsprint thus becomes a more useful tool in many areas of communication.

Adaptability of antique papers depends so much upon texture that generalizations are hard to come by. Generally they have a natural affinity for Old Style Roman type and for line cuts in letterpress. They will accept coarse halftones—65- to 85-line. Sometimes solid tint blocks are printed to smooth the surface and over them finer screens or type can be used. But it is never wise to force a medium to do a job which it is not supposed to do. It is far more honest, and results are happiest, when any material can use its true resources.

Antiques—indeed, any textured paper—are well suited to offset if properly sized and add interest and appeal to printed jobs. Gravure also easily adapts to textured surfaces.

Offset stock is comparable to the antiques for letterpress work; for offset litho, it is ideal; for gravure, its hard surface may create problems.

English finish takes up to 120-line halftones by letterpress and is well suited to intaglio and planographic printing. Transitional and Modern Romans, Sans, and Gothics are its most compatible types. Its easy-on-the-eyes glossless surface makes it a favorite for a wide range of printing.

Super-calendered stocks will easily take up to 133-line, so fine that the human eye is unconscious of the screen. Often super is equivalent to coated stock with the added advantage of lighter weight.

Coated stocks will take up to 150-line screens and, in some cases, as fine as 200. It is ideally suited to Modern Romans because the fine hairlines print sharply and cleanly. Coated stock gives extra sparkle to the thinner inks of offset but it is seldom used for gravure.

Writing papers are generally difficult to print on by letterpress, although as countless letterheads testify, they will accept type and line. The better the quality of bond, the more difficult letterpress printing becomes. It is necessary to use inks that dry by oxidation rather than by penetration, which is difficult or impossible with the hard surface of bond. Letterpress halftones should not be attempted on bond. But offset gives excellent quality on this paper and it is common to combine the two processes: letterpress for type, offset for illustrations. Copper and steel engravings are ideally suited to bond.

Ledger accepts offset beautifully and accepts letterpress better than bond. In many cases ledger will give the same effect of quality associated with bond and without the cost and many of the problems of high-grade bond.

Because the range of cover stock is so vast, any statement about its adaptability to printing must be made with reservations. Generally covers will not take letterpress halftones, although there are exceptions, but will accept offset screens. Covers are often designed for special functions. Thus catalogues which must take heavy usage or those which will be used by people with greasy or dirty hands can be covered in extremely tough or grease-resistant stock.

Paper is sold by *weight*. That is about the last simple statement that can be made on the subject. For, as in so many printing terminologies and systems, things get complicated from here on in. A printer is not interested in buying 87 pounds of bond; he wants enough for 5,000 letterheads. So there must be a combination of weight and *count*.

To add confusion, there are still two systems in use.

In the first, paper is designated by size and *substance*. The latter is the weight of 1,000 sheets of paper in the basis size. So an antique designated 25×38—$70M$ weighs 70 pounds per thousand sheets in that size. (Printers use the Roman numeral M for "thousand"; when written, it carries a horizontal stroke through its middle.) If one of the dimensions is underscored it shows that the grain runs lengthways on that dimension.

But all papers are available in other than base sizes. To convert odd weights and/or sizes to standard, we use the formula:

$$S : B = S' : B'$$

S is the square-inch area of the basis size; B the basis weight. S' and B' are the same factors in the non-standard sheet. While this formula is simple and accurate, it is far better to ask a paper salesman to read the answer off a conversion chart he always carries with him— or to give you a spare copy of it.

An older system, but still in use, is based on the *ream,* 500 sheets. When the printer talks of "60-pound stock," he means that is its weight in 500 sheets, only half of the "substance weight." It is well worth defining terms before you get too involved in discussing paper purchase or selections.

The basis size varies among various categories of paper. Thus a single sheet of basis-size 100-pound cover stock will not weigh as much as a basic sheet of English finish of the same weight, for cover is based on a 20×26 sheet, E.F. on 25×38.

Another confusing practice of paper merchants creates the pleasant paradox that often you can buy more paper for less money than a smaller quantity costs. Flat papers are packaged in several standard quantities; if you buy less than this amount—a *broken-package lot—* you pay a *penalty* of as much as 25 per cent for the extra effort of opening the original package, rewrapping it, and storing the remainder in a less convenient form.

For a round-figure example, let us assume that you can buy 1M sheets of cover for $20 at package price. If you bought only 900, you would pay $18 plus a penalty of $4.50, a total of $22.50. By buying the extra hundred sheets for $20, you save $2.50. This anomaly often makes it practical to print extra copies of a job if they can be distributed usefully; paper savings may well be greater than the cost of the extra presswork.

The most important thing to remember about paper is that its use is far more important than details about its manufacture or characteristics. The choice of proper paper can effect savings in press and bindery work, in distribution and storage, as well as lifting any job from mediocre to outstanding.

SUGGESTED READINGS

Ainsworth, John Haworth. *Paper, The Fifth Wonder*. Kaukauna, Wis.: Thomas Printing and Publishing, 1961.
Hunter, Dard. *Paper Making*. New York: Alfred A. Knopf, Inc., 1947.
Norris, F. H. *Paper and Paper Making*. New York: Oxford University Press, Inc., 1955.

19

Ink

THE LIFEBLOOD OF PRINTING

The first "inks" were juices—of fruit, vegetables, or sea creatures. Later writing fluids were actually *paints,* pigments of mineral, animal or vegetable matter in various solvents. The first true printer's *ink* was boiled linseed-oil varnish with carbon black. When printed, the pigment was well varnished onto the paper and it is still a delight to see how brilliant and legible are the earliest books printed.

Ink is, with paper, the flesh and blood of a printed piece and thus must be selected with as much care as the type, illustrations, and paper. Many factors in the selection of ink are highly technical and are best left to the pressman. But every graphic designer must be familiar with some basic characteristics of ink in order to base his part of the selection on sound logic.

Ink consists of three components. The *pigment,* minerals or metals, gives ink its color. The *vehicle,* or *solvent,* converts the powdery pigment into a liquid that can be easily distributed over a printing form and deposited onto the paper. The *binder*—oils or mineral compounds —causes the ink to dry rapidly enough so it will not smudge.

Ink dries by one of several processes. Oil-based inks dry by *oxidation,* which solidifies the vehicle. Oxidation is speeded by subjecting the printed sheet to heat. The paper may be passed through a gas flame (a process that requires care lest the paper catch fire) and then over chilled rollers. It may be wrapped around a steam drum. It may be passed under heat lamps.

Inks with alcohol or petroleum solvents are dried by *evaporation*. Heat, applied by any method, evaporates the vehicle in less than a second. (It is interesting to note that rotogravure plants, which use petroleum vehicles, have recovery systems so that the evaporated solvents can be distilled and reused.)

Selective precipitation is used on medium- and low-quality printing. Many vehicles contain resin as part of the vehicle. These are subjected to a spray of water or steam which causes the resin to come out of solution while the rest of the solvent is absorbed into the paper.

Absorption is used in newspaper printing and is not actually drying. The ink (so thin it is transported by tank truck and pipes) is absorbed by the inner fibers of the paper. There it remains, still damp, during most of the transitory life of the newspaper—and smudges off on the fingers of the reader.

Consistency of ink varies by the printing process used. Letterpress requires a fairly *tacky* ink that will not run into the counters of type or the etched depressions in engravings. Offset ink must be greasy so that the dampening agent repels it. Because it is deposited in a very thin layer and without pressure, its pigment must be strong. Gravure ink must be very fluid in order to fill the tiny wells, and therefore its solvent must be highly volatile so the thin ink will dry rapidly enough. In fact, its volatility is so great that the ink fountain on a gravure press must be enclosed.

Aniline ink is widely used for printing food wrappers, bags, and cellophane. It has given its name to a rapid and simple method of lower-grade letterpress work. Aniline, a dye, is carried by resin-alcohol vehicles that dry rapidly, a necessity when printing on impervious surfaces such as metallic sheets or plastics.

Silk screen uses both inks and paints, transparent and opaque. Variations are many, and each ink must be carefully chosen for the particular function of a specific stencil.

The planner of printing should be aware of the many special inks that are available: glossy and dull and many intermediates, non-scratch and non-rub, rain- and paste-proof for outdoor posters, with special vehicles and binders for printing on any kind of surface from fabric to glass.

Inks used for food wrapping must have many special characteristics.

They must conform to federal pure-food specifications. They must be odor- and taste-proof to avoid contaminating the food and colorfast to avoid discoloring the contents. Ink for butter and oleo wrappers must be impervious to grease. That used for frozen-food packages must be resistant to marked temperature changes.

There are inks that change color under varying atmospheric pressures; they are used for souvenir weather predicters. There are invisible inks that appear when the paper is wet or exposed to black light. There are perfumed inks (for writing billets-doux or printing newspapers). There are slow-drying, fast-drying, and instant-drying inks. The fabrics that make most dresses and draperies are printed in *textile inks*. Leather and wood require special inks. Electrical circuits in radios, television sets, bombing computers, and countless other appliances are literally printed, with electrically conductive ink.

One of the newest inks is that sold under the trade name of *Day-Glow*. It is so bright that it seems to have a fluorescent quality.

Even that old stand-by, black ink, has many variations. It has various degrees of, or lack of, gloss; it has different textures when dry; it has different hues, blue-black, brown-black, and red-black to obtain special effects.

Inks used in process colors must be used according to color specifications of the platemaker as has already been noted. Flat colors come in a wide spectrum. When the exact shade of merchandise is to be shown in flat color, it is not uncommon for the printer to send a sample of the merchandise to the ink-maker, who mixes a batch to the exact color required. When a new color is to be featured by the fashion world, clothing and accessory manufacturers work closely, and well in advance, with the ink-maker who concocts sufficient quantities of a new ink so that the advertiser in newspapers or magazines knows he can show his merchandise in the new "shrimp pink," which is the rage this season, instead of the "flamingo pink," which was popular last year.

But the printer must often mix his own inks to the customer's specifications. As he mixes, he painstakingly notes the addition of even the smallest ingredient. His "recipes" are carefully recorded and are usually kept attached to the sample printed sheet so that he can match the mixed color exactly should additional press runs be required.

In mixing for a tint, the printer adds color to white inks; for a shade, he adds black to the color.

Fortunately, the designer need not know all about the composition or physical properties of ink. But he should have a collection of ink catalogues for constant reference. Not only will they show the wide variety of optical effects possible through the use of ink, the rainbow-bright pages of ink catalogues make wonderful browsing material.

Inks can be used with other substances to create special effects. *Thermography* is an inexpensive simulation of intaglio engraving. Printing is done with an ink of high tenacity and dense pigments. While it is still wet, it is dusted with a powdered resin. That which does not adhere to the ink is blown away. The job then passes under heat which causes the resin to melt and fuse, producing a raised surface like an engraving.

Bronzing is the application, by adhesion only, of a fine metallic powder to ink. This gives a brilliantly glossy effect impossible to obtain with ink alone. Bronzing is also used to insure absolute opacity on glassine proofs used in gravure platemaking. (The designer is wise to consider the use of metallic colored inks charily. There are some which carry enough pigment to give a full-bodied impression. But many gold inks, especially, are so weak they require several passes through the press for even a passable sheen.)

INKLESS PRINTING

Some printing is done without ink. *Embossing* is producing a raised surface on paper by forcing a male die into the back of the sheet, pressing it into a female die. *Blind embossing* uses no ink, but embossing can be done in an operation that also deposits ink.

Another inkless printing method is the newest process, first shown as recently as 1948. This newcomer is *xerography,* from *xero,* dry. It uses static electricity to create a pattern on paper and to hold powder, instead of ink, onto that pattern.

As this book was being written, Radio Corporation of America, which had recently expanded into the field of written as well as spoken and visual communication, was field-testing a process which is similar to xerography in its use of static electricity. Charged metal plates are exposed directly to original copy. The opposite polarization of the exposed areas attracts sub-microscopic particles of a trade-secret substance. This is then baked into an acid resist before etching into a relief plate, without the need for the intermediate step of an engraver's negative. If a negative—as from the cold-type process—is used, the new method still promises advantages. In photoengraving, pre-sensitized plates deteriorate with age. Sensitizing just before exposure to the negative takes inconvenient time. The new method prepares a polarized plate in a matter of seconds and eliminates messy or short-lived fluids.

SUGGESTED READINGS

Wolf, Herbert Jay. *Printing and Litho Inks.* New York: McNair-Dorland, 1949.

20

The Bindery

PACKAGING THE WRITTEN WORD

After a piece of paper has been printed, its effectiveness depends on the way in which it is presented to the reader and how he uses it. This "packaging" is done by cutting, folding, fastening, and covering the paper; this is the function of the *bindery*.

Most of our printed matter is packaged as a *book* or some variation thereof. This is such a familiar form to us that often we fail to realize that there are "books" other than the kind we use.

The name comes from the Phoenician city of Byblos, whose merchants bought papyrus in Egypt and sold it throughout the Mediterranean basin. The Greeks transmuted the name to *biblos*, "book," and the most famous of all books is called just that, "The Book," the Bible.

Books were once just long strips of parchment, papyrus, or paper wound onto two wooden rolls. The reader rolled the material off one spindle and onto the other as he read. The sacred writings of Judaism, the Torah, are still preserved in scrolls for ceremonial occasions.

In the South Pacific a book may be a tall stack of bamboo boards, kept together by loose cords that pass through parallel holes in the wood.

A very few of our books still retain the traditional *portfolio* design, a series of loose leaves stored in a specially made box.

Conventional books are too familiar to need description but it should be pointed out that when a letter or an advertising piece is folded, it forms a small book. To learn how to manipulate printed pages most effectively, we can do no better than to consider each of the functions of the bindery.

CUTTING

The first bindery job is *cutting*. Most paper is made in sheets far larger than the customary printing sizes. Before or after printing, these large sheets must be cut to the proper dimensions. In specifying this process the graphic arts buyer can effect substantial savings or create monumental waste.

As has been seen, paper is manufactured in almost endless sheets and wound into rolls. These are then cut into flat sheets, some roughly as large as 4×5 feet.

Basic size for book stock is 25×38 inches; writing, 17×22; cover, 20×26. Although larger sheets are usually available, they are all in multiples of these sizes unless a special *make order* has been manufactured to special specification. This is done, of course, only when the quantity is sufficient to retain the economies of standardization.

When a printing buyer specifies a sheet, he is charged for the total amount of paper including that wasted in cutting down to his size. To *cut without waste* is a skill that must be learned early. Cutting depends on three factors, only one of which is variable: specified size of the printed job, press capacity and *imposition,* size of available paper stock. The latter two usually cannot be changed, but by modifying the first, waste can be minimized or eliminated.

Some jobs, as a letterhead, for instance, can go through the press one small sheet at a time. Any page of a book or booklet must be printed with an opposing page against which the first page is folded. Actually, all except very small books are printed on far larger sheets, with as many as 64 pages or more at a time. When such a sheet has been folded into pages, it is called a *signature.* (With the misuse of terms so common in the graphic arts, the printed, but not yet folded, sheet is sometimes called a signature, too.)

The obvious advantage of printing many pages per sheet is to reduce the length of the total press run as well as to simplify later bindery operations.

The capacity of the press determines just how large each signature will be, so does the number of pages in the book. For a 70-page book, for example, the pressman would run a 64-page signature plus an additional one of eight pages. Two pages in the last signature will be blank but they are necessary to fold the printed pages into the book. Or the press capacity might dictate two 36-page signatures, again with two pages blank.

Consider a simpler printing job to see how waste can be avoided. Assume a 4-page folder, each page 6 × 9 inches. This must be printed on a 9 × 12 sheet containing two pages. Perhaps the original sheet must be even larger to provide room for the grippers on the press or for trimming, especially when there are *bleed cuts.*

(*Bleeds* are cuts that run off one or more sides of the paper. They require an extra ⅛-inch margin of paper which is trimmed off after printing. In planning bleeds, attention must be given to their position. Should a bleed run off the edge which the grippers grasp on the press, additional margin must be provided. This adds to waste.)

Book stock is available in 25 × 38-inch sheets. Some printers use what they term the *gozinta system.* They divide the job size into the stock size, one dimension of the job into one of the stock, then the other job dimension into the second stock measurement.

Dividing 12 inches into 38 inches, shows that the printer can get three lengths of the job from each length of stock and have only 2 inches left over. He will probably need this much for trimming so he doesn't consider it waste. Then, dividing 9 inches into the width of the paper, he finds that he can get two pieces crosswise for a total of six pieces from each sheet of stock. But now he has real waste, a 7-inch strip across the whole 38-inch height, as shown in Figure 94, left.

So he tries again. He divides 12 inches into 25 and finds he can cut two sheets crosswise. Then, 9 inches goes into 38 four times. Now he has left over a 1 × 38-inch and a 2 × 24-inch strip, just about the amount needed for normal trim.

By cutting the original sheet advantageously, he gets eight desired pieces instead of the six that the first method produced. Because he had to pay for the entire stock sheet, he thus saves 25 per cent of the paper cost.

Suppose this same job had been specified for 7 × 9½-inch pages. That would require 14 × 9½-inch pieces. Using the same division method, 14 goes into 25 once, with 11 inches of waste, and 9½ goes into 38 exactly four times, without trim margins, for four pieces per

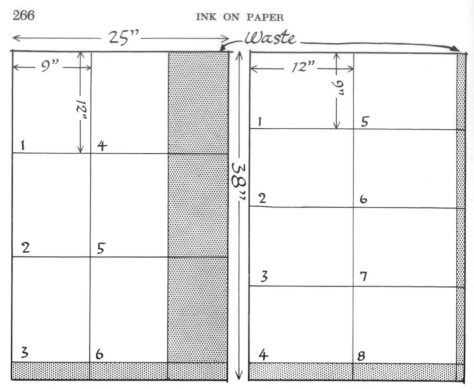

Fig. 94. Diagram shows how proper cutting, right, can minimize waste.

sheet. The other way: 14 goes into 38 twice with a 10-inch waste, and 9½ goes into 25 twice, with 6 inches of waste, and a total of four pieces per sheet again.

In both instances, 44 per cent of the stock is wasted. This would add an unconscionable burden on paper cost. It is apparent, then, that by reducing the size of the printed page only a trifle—from 7 × 9½ to 6 × 9—substantial savings can be made without destroying the effectiveness of the printing job.

The good designer will determine what size stock is available and try to design his job to cut without waste. Working with standard sizes, he knows automatically those dimensions which cut advantageously. He is also assured that the proportions of such cut sheets will be harmonious; that is why standard paper sizes were established at those particular dimensions. Figure 95 shows practical sizes that can be cut from standard sheets.

Sometimes the problem does not work out as neatly as these examples. For instance, after waste has been reduced to the minimum, it

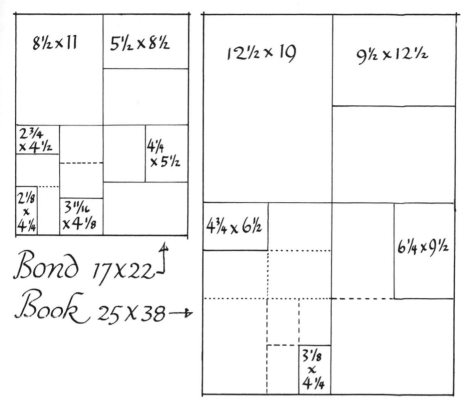

Fig. 95. Common page sizes that cut without waste from standard sheets of paper.

may be possible to cut one or more sheets in the opposite direction out of the original trimmed-off paper. But the principle of division is still valid.

With some paper the direction of the grain becomes a factor. If the press must be fed, or if the job must be folded, *with the grain,* this will effect the cutting-out pattern and must be considered in planning. Sometimes the watermark, too, must be taken into account. Is it imperative that it read right or can it be ignored? In writing stock, where watermarks are most common and most important, they are placed so that standard letterheads can be cut without waste and yet have the mark read properly.

It is wise for the beginner, with any problem, or the experienced layout man with a more complicated one, to draw a rough sketch as he works the solution. Visualization often enables maximum utilization.

There are times, of course, when waste stock can be used for other jobs. Often one or several smaller pieces can be *ganged* with a larger one and run through the press at the same time for the same or different customers.

Often it is possible to obtain striking effects by cutting at other than right angles. This is especially effective when two colors of ink are used, one on each side, or when a two-toned paper is used. Figure 96 shows how a piece of paper is cut with the upper edge at an angle. In an accordion fold, the back of the paper makes each alternating triangle at the top. Variations on this method are many.

Although the process is done on a press, *die cutting* is so closely related to bindery cutting that it should be considered here. *Dies* resemble cookie cutters. They are made of thin, sharp-edged steel strips that can be formed into countless patterns, simple or quite complex. On a platen press, the die takes the place of the printing form. A mirror die may be placed in the platen to assure a clean cut. Envelopes and boxes are made this way.

By die cutting, it is possible to make the piece of printed paper, or a whole booklet, assume an appropriate form. Or a *window*, of any shape or size, can be cut into one page to show printing on the third page. In such cases the third page must be so designed that the exposed portion harmonizes with the front-page pattern as well as that one on the page on which it is printed.

Figure 97 shows several pages from a handsome booklet that announced *Show* magazine. A large circular hole was punched through the entire booklet. On the cover, the hole made the *O* in *SHOW*. On inner pages it made one lens of binoculars, the halo around a light bulb and similar circular shapes.

Dies are available in a great many standard shapes and sizes. Rectangles, circles, ovals, and stars are favorites. Standard dies are inexpensive. Special dies can be made to almost any desired shape;

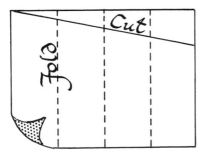

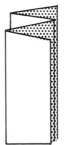

Fig. 96. Cutting paper at angle before folding gives interesting effect.

Fig. 97. Simple circular diecut is used as decorative element on every page of this booklet. (Courtesy *Show* magazine)

while they are expensive, cost is a relative standard; often a special die is an excellent investment.

Simple dies can be used on regular platen presses, but most often such cutting is done on special, heavier versions of platen presses.

Scoring is the process of creasing paper or cardboard to facilitate folding with less cracking or breaking. The *score* is impressed into the paper by plates or rollers consisting of a raised metal tongue that presses the paper into a recessed groove on a metal surface behind the sheet. The score marks the line on which the paper will be folded. A common example is the box used by clothing merchants. Boxes are shipped flat, then folded by hand as needed.

Scoring may be done as simply as by raising a plain rule a little higher than type-high. The crease is not deep but is adequate for light stock. If the fold is a permanent one, as that on a 4-page folder, scoring may be done during the printing process. The line printed by the scoring rule will not be visible on the fold. But most scoring is done with blank, uninked elements.

Perforating is done by a mechanism attached to a press or a separate machine. Check and receipt books are common examples of perforating, while in advertising it is frequently used to make it easy for the reader to detach a coupon or return postal card.

The most common perforation is a line of small holes although there are variations, such as *serrated* incisions.

Scoring and perforating are commonly considered bindery operations although they may be done during the printing operation. *Numbering* is often grouped with the other two processes, but it is definitely a printing, not a binding, operation.

Many jobs—checks, receipts, tickets, etc.—require consecutive numbers which are imprinted by a *numbering machine*. This mechanism is contained in a type-high unit that is locked into a printing form just as a piece of furniture might be. Pressure of the printing impression moves the next number into printing position, just as the numbers on an automobile odometer rotate into view.

Numbering machines can be set to move up one or more numbers after an impression. If a printer were producing a checkbook with four checks per page, he would set his first numbering machine to imprint #1 on the first page, #5 on the second, and so on. The next machine would begin at #2 and move to #6 for the next sheet, etc.

Tipping-in is a bindery operation that can be done by hand, by a special machine, or by an attachment to a press. This is simply pasting a single sheet, a *tip,* into a book or magazine, or onto another page. Often inserts of pre-printed material, or on special stock, are pasted into books or magazines. It used to be a common practice to produce illustrations for books by lithography, then tip them onto a blank page of a letterpress book. This method is still used, especially for books of art reproductions, but one-color reproductions are commonly printed by the same form that contains the type.

FOLDING

Origami is an ancient Japanese art form that has had recent revival and popularity in the United States. An amazing variety of three-dimensional objects are created by folding a single piece of paper. Graphic artists especially find it fascinating; it challenges their creativity and utilizes a common material that is always in abundance in any of their working places.

While it is not necessary to master paper folding to this advanced degree, every designer and printer should know how to enhance the effectiveness of a printed piece by proper folding.

The simplest fold is to crease a piece of paper down the middle and thus convert it into four pages. A series of such folds can be inserted into each other to create a sizable booklet. (The designer must remember, when using this method, that eventually the inner set of pages will protrude considerably past the outer ones. So he must leave a generous margin for trimming.)

Booklets as large as 80 pages are folded from a single sheet of stock and pages are cut open after binding.

The double fold of a regular business letterhead gives six "pages." If the second fold is made in the same direction as the first—instead of backwards to form an enclosure—it is an *accordion fold*.

There are some 40 or 50 standard folding patterns, all of them possible on automatic folding machines. A few of them are shown in Figure 98 and it is easy to see how these can be expanded upon.

Paper grain is a decisive factor in all folding and must be considered as early as in the first rough dummy.

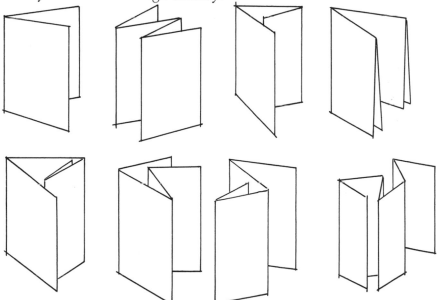

Fig. 98. Few of many folds that can be produced mechanically.

FASTENING

Fastening is the part of its work that gives the bindery its name. *Binding* paper together into a convenient and durable book or booklet is an important function.

If we consider the ways in which a book may be bound, we shall also learn those methods acceptable to booklets.

Books are usually bound so that pages are vertical rectangles. But occasionally, most usually for advertising booklets, they may be fastened along a short side to open horizontally.

The simplest binding is *padding,* which is commonly seen on scratch pads. A suitable quantity of single sheets is squeezed under pressure. An extremely flexible adhesive is brushed onto one edge. When dry this holds the sheets into a quite permanent pad from which a single sheet may easily be removed.

This method is used to bind inexpensive paperbacks. They are printed in signatures and are padded after being trimmed into single sheets. Around this pad is placed the one-piece wraparound cover, which also adheres to the adhesive. Sometimes a loosely woven fabric is placed between the pad and the cover to add a little strength, or the edges of the pages may be striated to absorb more adhesive. Books bound this way—in *perfect binding*—open flat but, when the adhesive becomes brittle, after two or three years, pages tend to fall out.

The simplest permanent fastening is *saddle wire,* or *saddle stitching*. If the binder took our first folding example, two pieces of paper, each creased to make four pages, and slipped one inside the other, then fastened them with a long-armed paper desk stapler in the fold, he would produce a perfect example of saddle wiring. Commercially, the folded sheets rest on an inverted V of metal and a machine stitches them together, cutting each "staple" from a coil of wire.

Saddle stitching is suitable for books from eight to 32 pages. Beyond that number the book will gape open and the inner pages will be noticeably narrower than the outer. But the book lies flat for easy reading; inner margins may be quite narrow; bleeds may run across the fold.

Usually two stitches are used on smaller books. For larger pages, three or more may be required. The number, and the size of wire used for staples, depends on the page size, thickness of the book, kind of stock, and the kind of usage it will receive. Many magazines are wire-

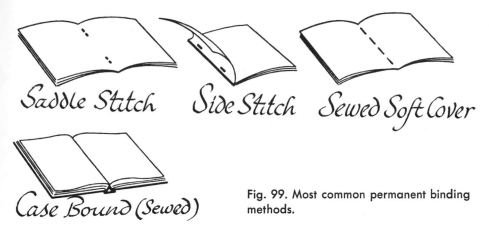

Saddle Stitch   Side Stitch   Sewed Soft Cover

Case Bound (Sewed)

Fig. 99. Most common permanent binding methods.

stitched and it is annoying to have the centerspread part company from the rest of the book on the first reading because the paper has torn away from the staples.

Now if the binder takes those original two folded pieces, again one inside the other, and staples them at the fold but from the outside, and sideways, he produces an example of *side wiring* or *side stitching*. This method is simple and inexpensive. The cover is usually pasted on in one piece, front and back. This creates a *backbone*—which saddle stitching does not provide—that may be printed on for identification.

Side wiring can be used on books up to about a half-inch thick and up to 9×12 pages. Unless it is very large, a side-wired book will not lie flat. Inner margins must be wide enough to compensate for that strip which is invisible under the staples.

Sewed soft cover books are gathered in signatures, usually of 16 pages, which are sewn down the fold as in saddle stitching. Now, however, thread replaces the staples and the stitches are many and even, just as in a garment. Each signature is tied, in loops from a continuous thread, to the one over and under it. This process is more expensive than the previous two but it has many advantages. It is strong. It can be used for any size books, up to the largest. It lies flat when opened, and thus the inside margin can be small and bleeds can be used through the gutter. It has a backbone, of course, which may be printed. The cover is glued on, as with side stitching.

The book you are now reading is an example of *sewed-case binding*. Again, signatures are sewn together as in the method just examined, with all the enumerated advantages. But now the cover is made separately. Fabric, paper, or leather is pasted onto the *boards,* two stout pieces of cardboard, with the edges overlapping and turned over on all the outer sides. The backbone, with no board behind it, is sturdy but flexible to protect the sewing. Tough paper, the *end papers,* is then glued—tipped—to the outside signatures and pasted to the boards. The result is a cover of great durability that can be decorated in many ways. The simplest is printing, the most elaborate, hand-tooling of leather, perhaps with gilt added. End papers are often decorated, too.

Stamping into leather or fabric of fine binding is done with special foundry type or Linotype slugs. Type-high for these is .950 and the shoulder or neck of the characters protrudes .075 inches above the shoulder, .032 more than on regular slugs. This type is impressed upon extremely thin gold leaf or metal foil into the leather. Brass dies are used for trade book cover printing.

Books bound in these four methods are permanent. But for many uses, books must be bound so that pages can be added or replaced. These are *loose-leaf* books and they are of three general kinds.

The most common form is the simple *ring binder* such as students use for class notes. Pages lie flat when opened and inner margins can be small. This is the best binding when pages must be changed quickly and frequently.

Binding posts are like staples in side stitching except that they are metal "bolts." Posts are inserted through pre-punched holes and a flat nut is screwed on the end to prevent the post slipping out. To change pages is possible but it requires unscrewing the top, sliding the pages off and sliding them on again with care. Pages do not lie flat and the exposed ends of the posts preclude handsome covers. This binding is used on journals and ledgers where changes must be made, but only on occasion.

Tongue covers are used to hide binding posts. Here the covers—front and back are separate—have a short extension through which the post fastens and then the cover itself is folded over to hide the post. Except that the cover is more attractive, this binding has the same assets and liabilities as that with naked posts.

Mechanical bindings that have become popular in recent years are *plastic* and *spiral.*

Plastic bindings are *combs.* They have many short wide teeth fastened to a wide backbone. The teeth are inserted into pre-punched slots and the whole comb encircles tightly into a cylinder. In spiral binding, a continuous length of wire or plastic spirals through pre-punched holes.

Mechanical bindings have many advantages to outweigh some obvious disadvantages. Books need not be run in signatures, each 2-page sheet can be fastened separately. This is a great advantage in color work. Color pages can be ganged and printed without regard for their ultimate position in the book and thus press runs can be reduced though hand-gathering is then required. Odd-sized pages can be inserted, again by a manual operation. Margins can be small; the entire page is always visible.

Mechanical bindings are generally rugged and therefore are good for catalogues and other books that must constantly be referred to. The book lies perfectly flat.

Plastics and spirals come in a wide range of colors and handsome effects are possible. Comb backbones can be printed on.

The main disadvantage is that mechanical bindings do not convey the impression of quality that sewn books do. New sheets can be combed into plastic binders but this is a painstaking job and the added sheet does not hold as well as the originals. Pages cannot be added to spiral binding. But in both cases pages may be torn out without affecting the remaining ones.

Spiral binding requires stiff covers; combs do not. Facing pages will register perfectly in combs; they cannot in spirals. Spiral bound books will fold over on themselves for ease in reading (and also in writing; that is why stenographers' notebooks are so often bound this way).

Variations of these mechanical bindings are flat metal or plastic *rings,* comb teeth without the backbone; *wire loops* at close intervals, which resemble spirals; metal rings riveted to a backbone; *overwire,* a spiral hidden by a separate cover.

Much of the function of covering has been discussed. The simplest form is a *self-cover,* which is the very same paper as the rest of the pages.

Then comes the simple *stock cover.* This is a four-page single fold of cover stock, which is just placed around the outer pages and bound by the same stitching that holds the pages. Sometimes heavy paper is folded to double thickness for a cover before stitching. Covers for mechanical binding are single sheets, front and back, and so two different stocks can be used.

Note that cover stock has a different basic size than book stock. This is to allow the cover to extend beyond the pages for protection.

The choice of binding and cover stock should be made on a purely functional basis. Normally it would be foolish to case-bind an advertising piece. This has been done, though, when the value of making an impression outweighed the extra cost. It would not be wise to side stitch a dictionary; outer pages would be torn off, inner pages would have deeply hidden inside margins.

The choice of cover material is also based on function. Cookbooks and reference books used in a garage must be impervious to grease. Dark covers hide black fingerprints. Fine books deserve handsome bindings.

With the extremely wide selection of cover stocks, it is possible to create the important first impression and to carry out the basic feeling of the contents. In color, covers can contrast or blend with the paper or ink inside. A catalogue for a sporting goods dealer can resemble wood so closely it is often difficult to detect the difference. For a jeweler, a cover can simulate mother-of-pearl or gold.

Sometimes unusual materials can make covers. Wallpaper is often striking. Metal foil or fabric is often usable. (Aluminum foil is pasted on paper, on one or both sides, and gives striking effects. Special techniques must be used to print on this metal but the end result is often well worth the extra effort.) Genuine wood or veneer, sand- or emery-paper or -cloth, butcher or gift-wrapping paper, anything which combines flexibility and durability can be used for covers. Human skin was used for fine books long before the Nazis gave this binding notoriety.

Cutting, folding, and binding is the packaging of printing. It is as important as packaging is to the purveyor of soap powder, soft drinks, or diamonds. Precious stones are not sold in kraft bags; good printing should not be presented to the reader in any way other than that which will make the message more easy, convenient, and pleasurable to read.

The bindery is an important ally to the graphic designer; he should learn its potentials well.

SUGGESTED READINGS

Groneman, Chris. *General Bookbinding*. New York: Taplinger Publishing Co., Inc., 1958.

Stanley, Thomas Blaine. *The Technique of Advertising Production*. Englewood Cliffs, N.J.: Prentice-Hall, Inc., 1954.

21

Planning Printing

ECONOMICS AND THE BUDGET

Graphic arts developed for economic—rather than esthetic—reasons. Demand for multiple copies also required not only fast, but economical production. The economics of printing are still a major influence on all graphic arts design and methods.

Printers estimate their work as composition; makeup and stonework, which are often lumped as *lock-up;* makeready; presswork; and binding. To this is added the cost of paper and plates and often the cost of envelopes, stuffing, addressing, and postage.

In analyzing each process in the hope of effecting economies, functionalism must be the constant criterion. Opportunities abound for false economy. Putting out a handbill for the corner grocery, the printing buyer would choose newsprint and save several dollars from the cost of rag bond. If he is advertising diamond tiaras, newsprint would not be an economy at all; he would lose the aura of quality which is necessary to sell high-priced merchandise.

Always he must ask himself, "What is the function of this printed piece?" and only then can he determine how he can reduce cost without reducing effectiveness.

We have already discussed the economy of cutting paper stock without waste. The kind and weight of paper depends on the function of the job; if minute detail must be shown by letterpress, it is economical to choose a high-gloss stock, no matter what its price. If printing is on only one side of the paper, opacity becomes a minor factor, and so on.

Paper is a decisive factor in postage costs, especially when large quantities are involved. It is wise to prepare a dummy of the finished job, using the same stock and binding and placed in the same envelope that will be used for mailing. If, on weighing this package, you find it has just edged over into the next postage bracket, you might save tidy sums by making the pages just a trifle smaller, even though that does mean more paper waste.

Just as a job should be planned to utilize standard paper sizes, so it should fit into standard envelopes. Special sizes or styles can be made to specification but, unless the quantity is very large, costs mount prohibitively. There are sufficient standard envelopes so that it is a mighty rare job which cannot be designed to use one of them. (The tall slim shape of many contemporary greeting cards, especially the "sick" kind, results only because their original designer wanted to pick a standard envelope and decided a No. 10 would give striking contrast to shapes then more common.)

That No. 10, called *official*, is the common business size; $4\frac{1}{8} \times 9\frac{1}{2}$, it takes a two-fold $8\frac{1}{2} \times 11$ letterhead. *Commercial* sizes—*No. 6* envelopes, $3\frac{3}{8} \times 6$, or *No. 6¼*, a trifle smaller—take invoices or small letterheads.

Growing in popularity are *baronial*, $4\frac{1}{8} \times 5\frac{1}{8}$, and *monarch*, $3\frac{7}{8} \times 7\frac{1}{2}$, which were once exclusively social correspondence.

Other standards that have wide use are the 6×9 and 9×12 *catalogue* envelopes and, in the same size, *clasp* envelopes. These open at the narrow dimension. *Postage savers* have a deep, ungummed flap on one side so they can be opened for postal inspection and go at rates lower than sealed first class. *Window* envelopes in many sizes and styles save addressing time and also enable a modicum of personalization in direct-mail advertising.

Selection of an envelope should be an early, not deferred, decision. Cases are far too numerous when a printing job has been completed and only then did the user discover that a special envelope would be required or else the piece would rattle around in a standard size far too large.

What can be done to avoid waste in composition? The manuscript should be perfectly clean. It is far less costly to have a stenographer retype a manuscript than to tie up, and pay for, a man and a machine while the Linotype operator deciphers a mass of changes scrawled between lines.

Linotype time can be saved if all instructions are written plainly and unmistakably. Ganging-up copy speeds operations, too. Put all 8/9-14 pica copy together, then that set at 11 picas, 27 picas, etc. Then keep all your 12-point together. All headlines should be grouped by face and size. This avoids the necessity of the operator thumbing through the copy or changing magazines too often. This ganging must be done with intelligence, of course. It's false economy to set a one-line 14-point Italic subhead separately and make the stoneman look through a dozen galleys of body type to find where to insert it.

Type should be chosen to provide the proper duplexing. It wastes time to have to set boldface on a second machine because your basic body type is duplexed with Italic instead.

Make-up is speeded by an accurate and complete dummy. While pages are designed in units of facing pages, they are not made up in that way. In a 16-page booklet, for instance, page one and page 16 are printed side by side as are pages 2 and 15. Often it is necessary to submit dummies in facing pairs if certain elements must align with each other. In this case a smaller rough can be prepared to show *imposition*. This is the placement of pages on the press. It is fairly standard although it may vary under special circumstances. This is discussed later at more length.

Remember that instructions to the typesetter must all be marked on the copy; those for the make-up man on the dummy.

Pictures must be accurately scaled and indicated. It comes as a shock—not a mild one, either—when the make-up man has justified a form, leaving blanks for the cuts, and then finds that the engravings delivered at the last minute are too big.

There is little that can be done to affect makeready other than to buy composition and engravings from sources of high standards. Cheap engravings may be cheap because they are mounted carelessly on poor blocking material. Then the dollar saved on them is erased by two dollars worth of makeready time as the pressman attempts to bring them to uniform type-high.

There are some techniques of presswork that can effect substantial savings. Printing may be *sheetwise;* one sheet—although it may contain several or many individual pages—is printed on one side, allowed to dry, then printed on the other. Or it may be printed *work-and-turn*. Figure 100 demonstrates this technique.

The front form (A) and the reverse (B) are printed at the same time, side by side on one double-size sheet. Then the paper is turned lengthwise. The printed side A now lies, face down, under form B. After B is printed there, the printer need only to cut the paper on the dotted line to have a completely printed job. He gets one whole piece with each press impression. Note again that this piece may be a single page or a complete signature, depending on the size of the job and press.

Work-and-turn, *w&t*, has many advantages. With quick-drying ink and a fairly long run, the first piece can be *backed up*, printed on the reverse side, as soon as Piece No. 10,000 comes off the press. There is no additional makeready; the process continues without pause. No changes are necessary on the grippers or side guides on the press.

Work-and-tumble is the variation in which paper is turned sideways before backing up and then is cut lengthwise to get the two separate pieces. One disadvantage of work-and-tumble is that the gripper edge of the paper is changed, unlike the work-and-turn process. This means extra adjustments on the press because paper cannot be cut in a perfect rectangle, the drag of the knife produces deviation from right angles. Even with this extra work in adjusting for the difference in gripper edges, work-and-tumble often has economic advantages.

A two-color effect is obtainable by the simple expedient of washing up the press and changing inks before backing up. Thus half of the job would be printed with A in blue and B in red, and the other half with A in red and B in blue. Not every job lends itself to this treatment, of course. But often the color for any given form does not much matter; the over-all effect of two colors, no matter on what pages they may appear, may be desirable and functional.

Another way of obtaining two colors with one press run is the *split fountain*. The ink fountain and the inking roller are divided so that the form is inked in two or more colors for each impression. This means that the form must have some division there, too, for any typographic element that passed under the separation would be uninked in a thin strip. Sometimes two colors are placed in the same, unsplit fountain. The colors remain true at opposite ends and *blend* together in the middle. The longer the run the wider the area of blending. Neither of these methods can control color critically but both have advantages

Fig. 100. Schematic of work-and-turn process. After first impression, sheet is turned sideways, keeping same edge of paper at grippers. After second impression, sheet is cut along dotted line.

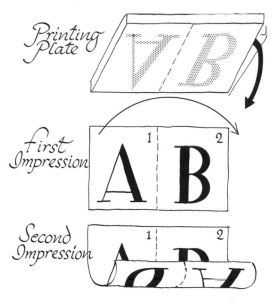

similar to those of work-and-turn with two colors. Split fountains and blending can be done only on presses that have fountains; platen presses with their ink plates cannot be used.

Interesting effects can be obtained with single runs by utilizing colored inks on colored paper. Blue ink, applied full intensity or screened in various degrees, will produce pleasant effects on a light green stock, for instance. Two-tone papers give a multicolor effect to a single-color job, especially with unusual folding or cutting.

Utilizing the imposition scheme can reduce color cost when it appears on only some pages. Figure 101 shows the imposition scheme for a 16-page booklet, printed sheetwise. If all color can be placed on one side of the sheet, it need go through the press only three times, front and back in black, front *or* back in color. The designer must lay out his pages in such a way that he does not bleed cuts at the gripper edge.

Press time can be reduced by printing more than *one up* and by *ganging*. One up means printing from a single form, sheetwise or work-and-turn. By making duplicate plates we can print the same form twice in one impression; this is *two up*. Depending on size, jobs may be printed with any number up, sheetwise or w&t. For large quantities the cost of duplicate plates is trifling compared to press savings though extra cutting costs do decrease savings to some extent.

Ganging is printing several forms on the same sheet with one impression. A letterhead may be ganged with invoices, memo sheets, billheads, and invoices, for instance. Any one of these items may be printed two or more up to establish the proper ratio of printed pieces. Odd areas, which otherwise would be trimmed to waste, can be utilized for small advertising pieces as envelope stuffers. All these pieces will be printed on the same stock, of course. Often the economy of gang runs makes it feasible to use higher quality paper for some of the items than would be practical were they printed separately.

Mail-order printing firms are able to offer extremely low prices on standard items by ganging dozens of letterheads and scores of business cards, for many different customers, into one run.

Binding economies can be built-in in original dummies. Suppose you have a halftone or headline that runs across the gutter from page 6 to 7. A look at the imposition scheme shows that the sheet must be folded precisely along the horizontal line that divides the two pages. If the fold is off only 3 points, the cut on one page will be lowered that much and on the other raised the same amount so that registration will be off by 6 points. If the fold between pages 10 and 7 is off, a portion

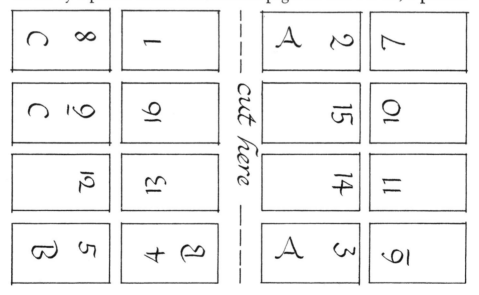

Fig. 101. Imposition scheme for printing 16-page booklet in one impression. After printing by work-and-turn, sheet is cut down middle. First fold brings A on page 2 upon A on page 3. Second fold brings B's face to face and third fold matches up C's.

of the cut on one page may be hidden under the stitching or it may be moved away from the gutter, leaving a blank strip. In any of these instances, the two halves will not match properly. The only way in which to assure necessary accuracy in the folding operation is to reduce the speed of the folding machine. This increases the time, and cost, of the operation.

So it is wise to minimize such close folding-registration. When this is impossible, care must be taken that within the gutter area there is no fine detail that might be destroyed when registration drifts.

Most of these economies can be effected in all printing processes but there are some that are inherent in each method. This is one of the factors that determines the choice of basic processes.

In the public mind offset is inexpensive, roto expensive, just as newsprint and bond are instinctively evaluated. This is not necessarily so. No process is inherently inexpensive or otherwise. Printing is custom work, each job tailor-made. So each job determines what process is most functional, and hence economical, under any set of circumstances.

If you keep in mind the effect of variables, you can arrive at some rules of thumb.

Basic considerations are five.

Composition: Is the type standing for a reprint? If so, you eliminate composition costs by letterpress. If it is a reprint but the type has been thrown in, do you have a copy of the old job that is good enough to go before the camera? If so, offset would be indicated. If you have to set new type is there an advantage in having the form remain standing so you can make minor or recurring changes? Tariff schedules mentioned earlier come in this category and letterpress is the cheapest way of printing them.

Paper: Will halftones be used on coated stock? No problem; letterpress or offset can both do the job. But if the paper is rough, you must go offset.

Art work: Are photos, drawings, or paintings completed already? Or in your files? To which process are they best adapted? If you have a commitment to an artist, what technique do you want him to use, or in which medium does he do his best or most distinctive work? Which process will best reproduce this?

Length of run: Will the job be comparatively small, 500 to 5,000, with many pictures? Offset is probably best. With many pictures and a very long press run, gravure is indicated.

Press speeds: How much time will your job require for printing? This determines press costs. Gravure presses are generally fastest, offset next and letterpress third. If you want the speed of rotary letterpress you must make curved plates.

Press speed is indicated by *impressions per hour*. The quoted speed must be discounted to get true production speed. On small presses, cruising speed is 40 per cent less than maximum; on large presses 30 per cent. A press cannot operate at maximum speed all day long any more than your car can travel 100 miles per hour all the way from San Francisco to New York.

Letterpress is indicated for: work on tight deadlines—no other process can go from copy to printing as quickly; short runs—100 to 25,000—with all type or few cuts; reprints of standing type, especially in complicated forms; finest detail possible in halftones; good, even black tones with a crisp effect; long runs of halftones on coated stock; envelopes in runs up to 10,000.

Offset should be considered first for: runs up to 10,000 when the ratio of illustrations to type is high; reprints when good camera copy is available; ruled work; halftones on rough paper; envelopes in long runs that are printed before they are cut and formed; soft illustrations as vignettes, washes, fine stipple, and crayon.

Gravure has natural advantages for: long runs—above 25,000—with relatively many pictures; fine details and color on lowgrade paper; jobs which contain little type; reproduction of fine art work without an apparent screen.

No one can argue with these basic assumptions but not even these apply all the time. The economics of the individual printing plant enter now.

Suppose a plant, by any process, prints several publications every month. The *Gadgeteers Journal* is off the press by the nineteenth of the month but the *Forbisider Bulletin* isn't scheduled until the twenty-first. Leaving the press stand idle is sheer waste; overhead, depreciation, and wages continue. It is wise to take a one-day job at 6 per cent profit instead of 8 per cent, and keep the press running.

Or suppose you have a 4-hour job that does not have to meet a tight deadline. And suppose the printer also has an 8-hour job to get out. If he does yours in the morning, he has to split the longer run between this afternoon and tomorrow. This may mean additional wash-up time or complicate storage of the incomplete job under humidity control. It is advantageous to him, and to your price, to do your job tomorrow.

Or suppose his bindery is occupied by a big job. It is better to keep your forms lying unprinted than to store printed sheets while they await binding.

Or the printer may say, "Look, you've got a simple spot color on this job. If you can wait a couple days, I'll have orange in the fountain for another job and can put yours on without extra washup."

In all these cases, the ability to adjust your schedule may mean savings. That is why cliff-hanging deadlines should be eliminated: A rush job or a missed deadline produces chain reaction.

Let us suppose that you have a job that just has to get out by Thursday or you will lose your job—and maybe your life. The printer will accommodate you. He takes his compositor off another job to work on yours. He schedules yours onto the press or bindery ahead of the one that would normally be there. Your job is completed during normal working hours.

But, to meet delivery dates on the displaced jobs, the shop must work overtime. Who gets charged for this time-and-a-half? Not innocent Customer X—you do!

Unfortunately, so many printing orders are marked *RUSH* that these get only normal treatment. In order to warrant even a second glance, a job ticket must be marked *CATACLYSMIC! ! ! !* The buyer who sets a realistic delivery date and gives the printer maximum time to meet it will always be rewarded with a better job.

For two factors are invisible but essential in any printing process: time and craftsmanship. You can't buy time; if you try to cheat the clock a little on the press, you may find your spoilage mounting because the ink hasn't dried completely and there is a lot of set-off. *Railroading* copy through the composing room lowers quality; the comp will have to let loose word spacing go through because he just doesn't have time to go back and manipulate spacing by hand.

Craftsmanship cannot be measured by the arbitrary figures of estimate, bid or bill. But it is the final difference between mediocrity and excellence. Good craftsmen—even in shops as tightly unionized as most graphic arts—are rewarded with above-scale rates that are reflected in the buyer's price.

Craftsmanship is linked with time. A good compositor gets type to the stoneman on time, and he, in turn, delivers forms on schedule to the pressroom. A less competent man, then, takes away irretrievable time from succeeding operations and quality inevitably falls.

It is these two intangibles that complicate evaluation of competitive bids and this is why many buyers of printing no longer seek bids on every job.

Again, there can be no hard and fast rules and both schools of thought can muster convincing arguments.

Says one buyer: "Printing is a very competitive business. By letting plants bid on each job, I get advantage of the economic situation in each one. If a printer wants my business badly enough to shade his profit a little, I wouldn't be doing my job properly if I did not take advantage of these savings."

Says another, just as sincerely: "No buyer can expect a job less than cost plus a fair profit. The lowest price is not always the best price; cutting corners to be competitive and still solvent may be done by increasing efficiency, but most of the time it's done by lowering quality. I actually save money by staying with one good printer. He knows my problems and what I like. We save a lot of time in communicating therefore. The printer is a backstop against errors; he knows my line well enough to question me when something doesn't look quite right. If I used a low bidder each time, I'd be working in a new shop with new people most of the time."

When competitive bids are sought, indeed on any job where an estimate is required, detailed information must be given. Paper should be specified by kind and weight, or by a trade name or "equivalent thereof." This phrase, however, might lead to disappointment; products "just as good as" often are not, except by the flexible evaluation of a biased person.

If the printer is to buy plates, this must be specified; so should all details such as delivery dates and *packaging*. It is disconcerting for a stock room accustomed to storing letterheads in packages of 500 to be confronted by 100,000 pieces in a big wooden box. If the printer stores the job for you, he must charge rent—even though the item may be disguised on the bill. Labeling is often important; no one wants to open three identically wrapped packages to find letterheads instead of second sheets.

Spoilage is a factor that grows more important with the size of the run. Even though the percentage drops, numbers get larger. On short runs, 250 and under, allow 10 per cent spoilage for one color, 5 per cent for each additional color and 5 per cent in the bindery. This is cut in half on runs of 500 to 1,000. Between 5,000 and 10,000, spoilage is 3½ per cent for the first color, 2½ per cent for each extra color and 2 per cent for binding. Over 10,000, it is 2 per cent for each category.

Because it is most difficult for a printer to produce a job in exact amounts, contracts customarily specify a leeway of 10 per cent over or under the order. The price is adjusted to the actual number delivered. Spoilage is an important factor in estimating costs and cannot be over-looked.

The wisest procedure is to stick with one printer and to have him bill you on a cost-plus basis for each job. There will be times when emergencies run up the price on a job; but when the printer makes a firm estimate, he must include a sum for contingencies and the buyer pays for unusual costs anyway.

The buyer must have confidence in the efficiency and integrity of his printer. And he must have a general knowledge of average costs in his area. Some buyers put up an occasional job to competitive bidding, both to keep their information up-to-date and their regular printer on his toes. But a close, continued working arrangement between buyer and printer makes a strong team that is more efficient than a pick-up team.

Printers are businessmen; they must have repeat business. Their ef-forts to keep the customer happy will usually result in arrangements that are of mutual economic advantage.

OFFICE DUPLICATORS

Many a printer refuses to recognize office duplication as printing. Not all are true printing processes and they are commonly, often in-accurately, considered of submarginal quality. But, within their capa-bilities, these processes can produce quality dependent primarily on the craftsmanship of the user. At any rate, they do have a definite and useful place in reproduction of the written word.

All methods are called *duplicators*—fluid, stencil, letterpress, and offset.

The simplest *fluid duplicator* is the *hectograph* from *hectare*, "a hun-dred," that indicates the very short runs it is used for. You are probably most familiar with its aggressive purple ink from materials teachers pre-pare on it for class work. Onto a gelatin slab, treated with glycerin, the image is written directly (in mirror form) or by transfer from paper. The plate is not re-inked; each impression removes a tiny layer of the image. Several colors may be used at one time by using different hues in the original ink or pencil.

The principle is mechanized in the *Ditto* machine. The paper master consists of a sheet of high-finish coated stock backed by one of special carbon paper. As the copy is typed on the face of the master, the face-up carbon creates a mirror image on the back of the master. Drawings or signatures done right-reading on the face of the master are also mirror-imaged in the same way.

The master is placed on a drum and reproduced by depletion of the image.

These two methods are inexpensive; materials other than paper cost less than .1¢ per copy. They require only a modicum of skill for passable work. Ditto copy may be prepared and stored for a period of up to a year. Often the method is used to prepare accumulative copy as it becomes available and then duplicate it when material is complete.

The *Mimeograph* (a trade name which is fast becoming as generic as Linotype) is a machine that reproduces copy by forcing ink through a stencil as paper passes under a drum. It is thus related more closely to silk-screening than to the common printing methods.

The stencil is the key to good reproduction. It must be cut on a clean typewriter in good condition and with an even, firm stroke. Electric typewriters, because of their mechanical uniformity of stroke, are best suited to stencil cutting.

Illustrations and ruling are done by hand with a stylus, formed as a loop of wire or a needle with a tiny ball at the tip. By a *shading wheel* or screens, Ben Day-like tones may be added. It is possible to place an image on the stencil by photographic means. This is commonly used for recurring matter such as nameplates on bulletins or simple office forms. Color is possible. Normally the ink feeds from inside a drum around which the stencil is wrapped. An oiled-paper cover may be placed over the inking pad and a fresh pad with another color placed over that. Color may be applied by areas to the fresh pad so that more than one color can be reproduced at the same time or a two-color job can be done as in other processes, by two press runs.

Wax stencils can reproduce up to 400 copies, dry stencils up to 5,000 with care.

Letterpress duplicators become more rare. Type is set into segmented channels as with the earliest rotary newspaper presses. Cuts, electros, or stereotypes are curved or rubber plates are used as wraparounds.

Offset presses have been adapted for office use. Many have ingenious devices such as automatic wash-up and plate changing for specialized work. The plate may be conventional metal or a *paper master,* prepared by typing with a special ribbon. Masters do not have a very long life, but it is possible to run one or more masters off the original and thus the image bearers can be self-reproducing. The improvement of *pre-sensitized* plates broadens the use, not only of office duplicators, but of all smaller offset presses or any offset press in a smaller shop. Presensitized plates are prepared, packaged, and sold like camera film and eliminate time and equipment needed to coat plates in the shop.

The only true limitation on office offset is size and, sometimes, a more rudimentary ink distribution that precludes large areas of solid masses of ink. Color is easy and even some excellent four-color process work is done on these small presses.

Duplicators, except for the hectograph, have rated speeds of 1,000 to 5,000 impressions per hour. They are commonly used for internal distribution of transitory material where quality is not essential, for outside distribution where quality is not of paramount importance, or where informality and spontaneity have virtues. Higher quality is possible on many machines; but a factor in their economics is that semi-skilled personnel is often assigned to the operation and the lack of skill is apparent in the product.

If the criterion of functionalism is consistently applied, common sense will determine which process and technique will produce the best printing at maximum economy.

SUGGESTED READINGS

Auble, J. Woodard. *Arithmetic for Printers.* Peoria, Ill.: Chas. A. Bennett Co., Inc., 1955.

Dalgin, Ben. *Advertising Production.* New York: McGraw-Hill Book Co., Inc., 1946.

De Lopatecki, Eugene. *Typographers Desk Manual.* New York: The Ronald Press Company, 1949.

Melcher, Daniel, and Larrick, Nancy. *Printing and Promotion Handbook.* New York: McGraw-Hill Book Co., Inc., 1956.

Glossary

absorption—process whereby ink dries by soaking into fibers of paper.

accent face—type used for marked contrast to predominant typographic color of page. In newspaper usage, face used for kickers, catchlines, etc., often exaggerated weight of basic head letter.

accordion fold—series of folds in paper, each in opposite direction of previous fold.

acetate—transparent sheet placed over art work to effect mechanical color separation (*which see*) or to carry directions to platemaker.

achromatic—black, white, and gray. Called "colors" but technically they are not.

ad alley—portion of composing room devoted to preparing advertising.

agate—5½-point type; as unit of measuring depth of newspaper page or advertisement, 14 agate lines equal one column-inch.

albumen plate—surface plate; most common kind used for offset lithography.

analogous—color harmony using two colors adjacent on color wheel.

analysis—chemical action of breaking down substance into components, analogous to color separation (*which see*).

anchor corners—make-up pattern—especially on newspaper page—in which heavy heads or cuts are placed in or near each corner of page.

antique—soft, bulky paper with comparatively rough surface, similar to old hand-made papers. Also (capitalized) Gothic letter.

apex—top juncture of diagonal strokes as in A.

aqua fortis—mixture of water and nitric acid.

aquarelle—printed picture on which color is applied by hand through stencils.

aquatone—method of printing combining extremely fine screen on gelatin plates with offset lithography.

arms—elements of letters that protrude from stem as in K and Y.

art—all illustrative material, lettering, and ornamentation prepared by an artist. Original copy for platemaking, especially for photolithography.

art lining—system of aligning letters with long descenders. (See lining.)

Artype—black or white letters on transparent, self-adhering plastic.

ascenders—portions of a letter that rise above the meanline; also those characters themselves, as b, d, f, h, k, l, and t.

automatic typesetting—system in which the keyboard of a typesetting machine is actuated by a mechanical device directed by electrical impulses.

backbone—portion of the binding that connects the front and back covers of a book.

ball—the finishing element on the top of the strokes in *a* and *c*. Also, untanned leather wrapped around pads of wool with which early printers applied ink to type.

bank—cabinet or bench on which is stored type awaiting makeup.

bar—the horizontal stroke in *t*, *H*, and *A* and in many forms of the *e*.

baseline—horizontal line upon which stand capitals, lowercase letters, punctuation points, etc.

Bauhaus—German school of architecture and design that originated Sans Serif letterform.

beak—the serif on the arm of a letter such as *K*.

beard—the side between the shoulder and the face of a piece of type. Also the cross stroke on the stem of the *G*.

beaten proof—stone proof (*which see*).

bed—flat surface of cylinder press upon which type stands during printing.

Ben Day—trade name for a pattern of lines or dots used in photoengraving to provide shading in line drawings, as background for photos or type, or to cut down the tone of type, rules, or solid areas in cuts. Named for the inventor. Patterns are identical with those achieved by Zip-a-Tone (*which see*).

b.f.—boldface.

Bible paper—thin but strong and opaque book paper.

big-on-slug—that quality in a type face which is effected by using maximum of body area for x-height (*which see*).

bimetallic—offset plate combining aluminum and copper.

binder—craftsman who works in bindery, especially those who bind books. Also oils or mineral compounds used to speed drying of ink.

binding posts—kind of loose-leaf binding in which pages are held on metal pegs inserted into pre-punched holes.

Black Letter—Text or Old English, race of type based on letters of early handwritten German manuscripts.

bleed—to place a cut so it runs off one or more edges of the paper.

blind embossing—impressing a design into back of paper so it appears in bas-relief on front side. No ink is used.

blow-up plate—halftone engraving made in small size with fine screen then enlarged, by line engraving, to larger size and coarser screen.

blueprint—photocopy process used to provide proofs for cold type.

boards—stiff material in the cover of a book.

Bodoni, Giambatista—Venetian printer and type founder who designed type face bearing his name.

body—metal block that carries printing surface of a type character. Also regular reading matter of a newspaper, book, or advertisement as contrasted to display lines. Body type is that face in which such material is set, usually through 12-point.

boiler plate—printing material supplied to newspapers in the form of stereotype plates. Also editorial material so printed.

book—a basic category of printing paper.

book system—method of proofreading which requires two marks for every correction. One mark designates place of error; the other instructs how to make correction.

Bourges—(pronounced Burgess), coloring materials, especially thin acetate sheets—keyed to standard printing inks—for preparing art and dummies and modifying photographs.

bowl—curved lines that create circular or semi-circular shapes in letters such as *c*, the lower portion of *a*, the right-hand portion of *b*, etc., and the upper portion of *g*.

box—unit of type enclosed by a border. Modern, or sideless, boxes have border only at top and bottom.

brace—a bracket.

bracketed serifs—those which connect to the stem by a curve that smooths the angle of juncture.

brackets—typographic devices used to set off matter grammatically in apposition.

brayer—roller to apply ink to type by hand.

Bristol board—thin cardboard with smooth surface ideal for drawing, writing, and printing.

broken package—quantities of paper less than normally wrapped amounts. When sold, broken packages carry penalty price.

bronzing—applying metal powder to sticky ink to create metallic effect or perfect opacity on reproduction proofs.

brownprint—photocopy process used to provide cold-type proofs.

Bruning—photocopying process used to prepare cold-type proofs.

buddy system—orientation system of layout (*which see*).

bullet—large period used for decoration.

burin—pointed steel cutting tool used by engravers.

burnish—to increase area of halftone dots by flattening them. Also, to smooth down self-adhering letters and shading sheets.

butted lines—two or more linecaster slugs placed side by side to create one line of type.

c. & s.c.—capitals and small capitals, style of composition in which each word starts with a capital and other letters are in capital form in the height of lowercase letters.

calendered—paper which has been given a very smooth surface by passing it between polished steel rollers during manufacture.

California job case—receptacle in which foundry type is stored and from which it is hand set.

caption—in newspaper usage, display line above a picture; not cutlines, explanatory matter under the engraving. In advertising, any explanatory matter that runs with an illustration.

carbon tissue—gelatin sheet through which a mordant etches a rotogravure plate.

cardboard—stiff, sturdy sheet consisting of several layers of low-quality paper pasted together.

casting box—receptacle in which stereotype flong is placed to cast a printing plate.

center spread—double truck; the two pages at which a newspaper, magazine or booklet is folded. Advertising or editorial matter may occupy that space which is normally devoted to the gutter. (*See* double truck.)

chapter heads—display type that begins a chapter of a book.

characters-per-pica—cpp, system of copyfitting (*which see*).

chase—metal frame into which page form is locked before printing or stereotyping.

Christmas tree—layout pattern in which components project to one or both sides from a vertical axis.

chroma—that quality of intensity of a color.

chromatic—true colors.

circulating matrix—mold, in a brass body, from which Linotype and Intertype cast type. Matrices are automatically returned to proper receptacle for reuse.

clamshell—colloquialism for platen press.

clapper—colloquialism for platen press.

classic—layout pattern based on geometric forms to create rhythm.

claw—projection from stem of *r* and from bowl of *g*.

coated paper—that covered with a smooth layer of mineral substances.

cockle—paper finish with surface ripples.

cold type—that set photographically or by means that do not utilize metal, hot type.

collage—picture or design created by pasting various elements onto common background.

collotype—method of offset printing of continuous-tone copy utilizing an unscreened gelatin plate.

colophon—originally the mark whereby a printer identified his products, now the trademark of a publisher. Also, that part of a book that specifies types used, designer, and/or artist.

color job—printing which uses flat color (*which see*).

color separation—breaking down full-color copy into its component proportions of the primary colors. Also, black-and-white negative which shows amount of one primary color in a full-color original.

color, typographic—devices to alter overall tone of masses of type. Also, apparent tone or density of printed matter on a page as affected by various types, borders, decorations, etc.

color wheel—diagrammatic arrangement of primary and secondary colors as a visual aid in determining relationship and harmony among colors.

Columbian—first printing press invented in America.

comb—a series of prongs connected by a spine, used for loose-leaf binding.

combination cut—printing plate consisting of line and halftone.

combo—combination, a group of pictures arranged into and used as a single unit.

common diagonal—visual method used to determine size of reduced or enlarged picture.

complementary harmony—color combinations using two colors directly opposite each other on the color wheel.

composing room—area where type is set and made up.

composing stick—metal receptacle into which type is placed when set by hand.

composition—typographic material that has been set and/or assembled.

comprehensive—compre or comp, complete and detailed dummy.

connotative—jazz, layout pattern in which regularly shaped areas are suggested but not defined.

continuous tone—photographs or painted pictures that utilize varying values of color.

controller paper—wide perforated tape which actuates casting mechanism of Monotype.

cool colors—those which tend to recede from the viewer, usually greens and blues.

copy—material which the compositor sets in type or from which a platemaker creates printing plates.

copyfitting—determining the area to be occupied by type set from given copy.

copyholder—proofreader's assistant who reads original copy to compare to proof.

counter—areas within and around the printing surface of a piece of type which are depressed to prevent contact with ink rollers and paper.

cover—a heavy paper such as used for covering books and booklets.

Craftint—patterns similar to those of Ben Day which are applied, on thin plastic sheets, onto original art.

Craftype—trade name for letters printed on transparent, self-adhering plastic.

crop—to eliminate unwanted portion of photograph by actually cutting away or indicating, by marginal lines, that platemaker should ignore it.

cross stroke—horizontal stroke of t and f.

cuneiform—early form of writing which contributed to development of Latin alphabet.

Cursive—type which resembles handwriting but with unconnected letters.

cut—photoengraving.

cutoff rule—hairline that marks the point where a story moves from one column to another. Also, all printing lines that create horizontal divisions between typographic elements in a newspaper.

cut without waste—method of reducing large sheet of paper to smaller ones with minimum waste.

cyan—blue-green filter used in color separations (*which see*).

cylinder press—method of letterpress printing in which paper is impressed upon type by a cylinder.

Day-Glow—trade name of ink with extremely high luminosity.

decal—decalcomania, process for transferring pictures and designs onto glass and other materials from specially prepared paper.

deckle edge—irregular, ragged edge of sheet of handmade paper, now produced mechanically.

delete—proofreader's mark, to "take out."

descenders—portion of a type character that drops below the baseline. Also those characters themselves, such as $g, j, p, q,$ and y.

Diazo—photocopying machine used to produce cold-type proofs.

Didot—famous family of French printers for whom is named the system of printer's measurements used in that country.

die cut—paper cut into shapes other than rectangular by means of thin steel blades bent into desired forms.

dingbats—typographic decorations.

dirty proof—one with many typographic errors.

display—type used in larger sizes and smaller quantity to attract attention, as opposed to body type (*which see*). Usually 12-point is smallest size classified as display.

distribution—returning type and other printing material to receptacles for reuse.

Ditto—lithographic duplicator for office use.

doctor blade—metal surface that wipes ink off surface of intaglio plates.

dot etching—method of correcting color separation negatives by dissolving the outer edges of halftone dots to make them smaller.

Doubletone—drawing paper with two shading patterns made visible by application of developing fluid.

double truck—two newspaper or magazine pages at the center of a section or signature that are made up as a single unit. Usually refers to advertising using this space, center spread referring to editorial use.

dragon's blood—resin powder used to protect from acid those portions of a photoengraving that are to remain in relief as printing surfaces.

drop-out—highlight halftone (*which see*).

dry mat—flong for making stereotype matrix.

dry offset—method in which image is offset from rubber blanket where it has been placed by relief printing.

drypoint—method of preparing an etching by incising lines with a cutting tool instead of with acid.

dummy—detailed diagram instructing make-up man how to arrange elements of a printing job. (*See also* rough, comprehensive, mechanical.)

duotone—printing produced by two plates, one in dark ink, the other in light, which produces a third color, usually the only one discernable.

duplex—linecasting matrix that carries two character molds. Also, that character which occupies the secondary position on a matrix.

duplicators—devices for reproducing various forms of printing in small quantity and, sometimes, of low quality.

dynamic—layout pattern which balances elements in an unsymmetrical form. (*See* informal balance.)

editorial—all matter in a publication which is not advertising.

eggshell antique—soft, bulky paper with a finish that resembles the shell for which it is named.

Egyptian—Square Serif.

electrotype—duplicate relief printing plate made by electrolytic process depositing copper on a matrix of original form.

Elrod—casting machine that produces rules, borders, and spacing material in a continuous strip.

em—the square of any type-body size. Unit of measurement for typesetting; a 9-point line 2 inches long, or 144 points, contains 16 ems; a 6-point line the same width has 24 ems. Commonly but inaccurately used as synonym for pica. Em quadrats are called "mutton quads" to avoid confusion with en quad.

embossing—process for raising paper, by means of a die, in a relief pattern. This may be simultaneous with printing ink. Embossing without ink is blind embossing.

em-space—spacing material less than a quad. A 3-em space is one-third of the mutt quad of that face.

emulsion—photosensitive material that reacts to light in photographic processes.

en—half the width of an em of the same font. En quadrats are called "nut quads" to avoid confusion with em quad.

end papers—sheets of sturdy paper that connect the cover to the pages of a book.

English finish—E.F., paper with a suedelike finish produced by a clay coating.

engravings—relief printing plates created by photochemistry.

etching—removing non-printing areas from a relief plate by acid. Also, an intaglio process used to create fine art.

expanded—layout pattern in which an illustration projects in one or two directions from a basic rectangle.

eye fatigue—a factor that determines to a large extent the amount of type a person will read at one time.

face—style or cut of type. Also that portion of a slug or type character which imprints upon the paper.

facsimile—highlight halftone.

fake color—simulation of the effect of four-color process plates by manual modification of black-and-white negatives.

family—first subdivision of type after race. It carries a trade name as identification.

feet—slight projections upon which a piece of type stands.

felt side—right side, that surface of the paper which comes in contact with felt rollers during manufacture, as opposed to the wire side which rests upon the traveling screen.

filler—coating of clay added to paper to give smooth finish.

filter—sheets of colored gelatin used to make color separations (*which see*). Cyan, magenta, and yellow are those most commonly used.

fine arts—that use of the graphic arts to produce original works such as etchings, lithographs, serigraphs, etc.

finial—curve that finishes a main stroke in some Italic faces, replacing the serif of the Roman.

finishing line—thin black line surrounding a square halftone.

first revise—proof pulled after errors discovered in a galley proof have been corrected.

flag—nameplate of a newspaper. Commonly but erroneously called masthead.

flat—group of engraver's negatives exposed and etched as a single unit before being sawed up into individual cuts. Also group of original pictures shot on one negative.

flat casting—making relief plates by pouring molten metal onto a stereotype matrix.

flat color—spot color, use of any color, other than black, which does not attempt to simulate the full spectrum of nature.

Flexowriter—version of a typewriter used for cold-type composition.

flong—sheet of papier mache used to produce a stereotype matrix. Also used to designate the matrix so made.

flop negative—act of turning an engraver's negative face down before exposing it upon a metal plate in photoengraving, necessary to create mirror image required in a relief plate.

fluorographic—process to produce highlight halftones photographically.

flush head—short for flush-left head, a style in which each line begins near or at the left margin and aligns with that above and below it.

folio lines—those which give the title and page number of a book. Also called running heads. In newspaper usage, lines which carry name of paper, date, and page number.

font—subdivision of a series of type. It consists of all characters and spacing of one size of one series.

foreword—introduction to a book written by a person other than the author.

form—type and engravings, assembled within a chase, from which one page or signature is printed or stereotyped.

formal balance—layout pattern that balances elements of equal size in exact mathematical relation to a vertical axis.

format—shape, size, and general physical form of a publication.

former—scorcher (*which see*).

Fotorex—machine for producing cold type in display sizes.

Fotosetter—phototypesetting machine utilizing the principles of the Intertype.

foundry type—individual characters of hard metal used for handsetting.

Franklin, Benjamin—called the patron saint of American printers for his activity in the craft in early history of this country.

frisket—protective paper to shield areas of printing paper from ink or photographic paper from light.

fullface—normal design of a type face in regard to weight and width.

functionalism—philosophy of typography that requires that every printing element contribute to conveying information.

furniture—large spacing material placed around type area to lock it into a chase.

galley—shallow, three-sided container of metal or wood in which composition is stored before being placed into forms. Also the container on a linecaster into which the slugs drop after casting. Also short for galley proof.

galley proof—first impression printed from composition in order to detect errors.

ganged—several forms or plates combined for simultaneous printing on a single large sheet of paper.

geometric—layout pattern which divides the total area into smaller shapes in pleasant relation to each other.

ghosted—background which has been lightened by application of ink with an airbrush or of plastic shading sheets.

Giant Caster—typecasting machine that produces display type.

Golden Rectangle—approximately 3×5, considered by ancient artists as the most pleasant ratio for an area.

Gothic—type of the San Serif race in which strokes are usually but not always monotonal. Also called Block Letter, Grotesk, or Antique.

grain—predominant direction in which cylindrical cellulose fibers point in a sheet of paper.

graver—V-shaped steel cutting tool used by engravers.

gravure—commercial application of intaglio printing. Sheetfed gravure prints upon individual sheets; rotogravure (*which see*) prints from an endless roll of paper.

grippers—mechanical fingers that hold paper onto impression cylinder of a printing press.

groove—indention on bottom of a type character that separates the feet.

Grotesk—Gothic type.

ground—protective coating placed on a sheet of metal through which an artist scratches lines to be incised by acid.

guideline system—method of proofreading in which the error is circled and connected, by a line, to marginal instructions.

gum—colloidal vegetable substance used to increase the repulsion of ink by water in lithography.

Gutenberg Bible—42-line Bible or Mazarin Bible, believed to be first book printed from movable type, about 1450.

Gutenberg, Johann—inventor of movable type and letterpress printing as we know it.

gutter—that blank space on two facing pages that meet at the binding edge. Also used to refer to the inner margin of a single page, although correctly that is the gutter margin and consists of only half the gutter.

Hadego—machine for producing cold type in display sizes.

hairline—thinnest rule used by printers.

half-round—curved stereotype plate.

half-title—the first page of a book after the end papers.

halftone—printing plate which gives the illusion of gray tones by means of a dot pattern.

hanging indention—style for body and headline composition in which the first line is set full measure and all succeeding lines are indented an identical distance at the left.

hard copy—typewritten copy produced simultaneously with perforated tape to actuate typesetting machines.

Headliner—machine to produce display sizes of cold type.

height-to-paper—standardized measurement from feet to face of type and other printing elements.

hectograph—lithographic duplicating machine.

high-etch—dry offset, a combination of relief and planographic printing.

highlight halftone—drop-out or facsimile, printing plate in which the dots in certain areas have been removed by mechanical or photographic means.

horsing—reading proof by one man without assistance of copyholder.

hot metal—or hot type, linecaster slugs and foundry type as opposed to cold type (*which see*).

hue—that quality which makes colors as we recognize them. Also product of mixing two colors together.

ideogram—early form of writing in which a symbol meant an entire word or idea. Still used in Japan, China, and Korea.

illumination—decorations applied by hand to early printing. Also that style of handlettering in which letters are decorated, often with miniature pictures.

imposition—arrangement of several pages into a signature so they may be printed in one impression and, when folded, will follow in proper order.

impression—printing of ink on paper, especially by letterpress, but commonly used for all printing methods. Also the printed copy produced by type or a plate. Also the pressure of type or plates upon paper, as a kiss impression (*which see*). Also the appearance of the printed piece, as "a clear impression." Also the number of times a press has completed a printing cycle.

incunabula—early printing. Usually only that produced in the fifteenth century.

India paper—Bible paper.

informal—layout pattern in which approximate balance is achieved by free distribution of elements around an imaginary pivot at the optical center.

initial—first letter of a word or sentence set in type larger than body size for decoration or emphasis. Its size is indicated by the number of lines of body type it occupies, as a 3-line initial. (*See* rising initial, inset initial.)

Inline—form of Ornamented type in which a white line runs down the middle of the main stroke.

inset initial—large letter, used for decorative effect, dropped into an area that would otherwise be occupied by body type.

intaglio—method of printing in which the image is carried in incised lines.

intensity—strength and brilliance of a color.

intermediate color—that produced by mixing a primary color with a secondary one.

Intertype—keyboarded linecaster.

inverted pyramid—headline of two or three lines all centered, in which successive lines are shorter than the one above it. Usually abbreviated to pyramid.

Italic—letterform in which characters slant to the right and are more decorative than their Roman (perpendicular) counterparts. Also, incorrectly, used to refer to all letters that slant to the right although these are correctly called Obliques.

ivory—finish of paper produced by coating it with beeswax and then calendering.

jazz—connotative layout (*which see*).

jim-dash—short, centered line used between elements of a headline or between headline and story. Often designated by its length, as, most commonly, 3-em dash.

job shop—commercial printing plant.

justify—to fill a line of composition so it aligns at both margins.

Justowriter—typewriter that produces automatically justified lines of cold type.

kerning—also kern, that part of the face of a type character that projects beyond the body in Italic or Swash fonts.

key phrase—group of words repeated in each face and size of type in a specimen book.

key plate—usually the black plate, which carries strong definition in color printing.

kicker—short line in smaller, or accent, type above the main line of a head. Also called teaser, eyebrow, highline, and, erroneously, overline.

kiss impression—ideal meeting of type and paper so that ink is deposited completely and evenly without indenting the paper.

kraft—German for "strong," a sturdy paper commonly use for wrapping.

Kromecote—coated paper of extremely glossy finish.

Kromolite—method of producing drop-out halftones photographically through the use of filters and combining line and halftone negatives.

L's, cropper's—paper or plastic in the shape of a capital *L*, used to determine which portion of a photograph is most advantageous to use.

laid—finish of paper simulating texture of old handmade paper.

lampblack—intensely black pigment.

layout—arrangement of typographic units into a pattern. Also, in composing room, called make-up (*which see*). Also dummy (*which see*).

l.c.—lower case, the small letters, or minuscules, of a font.

l.c.a.—lowercase-alphabet length, the factor which determines the number of characters of type per pica, used in copyfitting.

lead—(pronounced leed), first or first few paragraphs in a newspaper or magazine story.

leader—(pronounced leeder), line of dots or hyphens used to connect elements of tabulation.

ledd—(always pronounced ledd, although often spelled lead), thin strip of metal, up to 4 points thick, used to create interlineal spacing. As a verb, to insert such spacing material. When not instructed otherwise, the printer will insert 2-point ledds.

ledger—paper with a smooth writing surface that withstands folding.

legibility—or visibility, that quality of type that effects the quickness of perception of a single word, line or compact group of lines. Often confused with readability (*which see*).

letterpress—relief printing.

letterspacing—addition of extra spacing within a word, either to create more pleasing appearance or emphasis, or to fill out a line to proper measure.

ligature—type characters consisting of two or more letters united as *fi*, *ffi*, and *æ*.

linecaster—machine that casts an entire line of type as opposed to those that cast individual characters. (*See* Linotype.)

line cut—photoengraving which prints only in lines and masses of black.

line gauge—pica rule, ruler with pica increments.

lining system—placement of letters upon the body so that all faces of the same point size will align on a common baseline. Most faces are designed in standard lining; those on art lining have a relatively high baseline to allow for longer descenders; those on title lining have low baselines because such fonts are made up of all capitals and no descenders must be provided for.

link—element that joins the two circular portions of the g.

Linofilm—phototypesetting system consisting of a keyboard, photographic unit, and composer.

linoleum block—relief plate resembling a wood block but cut from linoleum.

Linotype—first keyboarded linecaster and used so widely today that, with a lowercase *l*, it is used as a generic term. Keyboarded linecasters assemble matrices automatically when actuated by keys. In others, matrices are assembled by hand.

lithography—planographic printing process. (*See* offset.)

loading agent—mineral substance added to give gloss to paper.

lockup—process of fastening elements into a chase so they will remain firmly in place during printing or stereotyping.

logotype—or logo, a single matrix or type body containing two or more letters commonly used together as *the* or *and*. Often confused with ligature (*which see*). Also often used to refer to small ornaments cast from linecaster matrices. Also signatures or trademarks used in advertising. Also flag or name plate of a newspaper.

loop—semicircular portion of the *e*.

Ludlow—linecaster usually used for display type. Its product is T-shaped slugs which are further supported by underpinning.

machine finish—calendered, paper made very smooth by passing it between metal rollers during manufacture.

magenta—filter used in making color separations.

Mainz Psalter—early book printed by Gutenberg and considered by some to be the first printed from movable type.

majuscules—capital letters.

makeready—process of adjusting contact between printing elements and paper to assure perfect impression.

make-up—design of a newspaper or magazine page. Also, the physical process of assembling typographic units into pages or advertisements.

make-up man—printer who assembles typographic elements into a form.

manifold—onionskin, thin paper used especially for making carbon copies.

manuscript—ms. (sing.), mss. (pl.), technically a handwritten copy, but commonly designating any original copy, especially for a book, for the compositor.

matrix—mat, mold from which type, decorative materials, advertisements, or illustrations are cast. Linecaster matrices are brass; stereotype matrices are of cellulose fibers and adhesive. (*See* flong.)

matrix case—carrier of matrices in a Monotype.

matrix disc—carrier of negative images of characters in the Photon.

matte—textured finish on photographic paper.

Mazarin Bible—Gutenberg Bible (*which see*).

mean line—x-line, the line that marks the top of lowercase letters that do not have ascenders.

measure—length of a line of type.

mechanical—detailed dummy used as copy by, or instructions for, a plate-maker.

mechanical separations—copy for the platemaker prepared by an artist with separate sections for each color to be used in printing.

metal paste-up—method of preparing a printing form by pasting into position engravings of type and illustrative matter.

mezzotint—form of fine-art etching in which the entire surface is burred to act as many intaglio wells.

minuscules—lowercase, or small, letters.

Modern numbers—those numerals which align at the baseline.

Modern Roman—that letterform distinguished by thin, straight serifs and marked variation between thick and thin strokes.

modified silhouette—halftone engraving with one to three sides outlined.

modified vignette—halftone cut in which one or more sides are straight, the others blending from the gray of the picture into the white of the paper.

monitor—printer who services automatic typesetting machine.

monochromatic—harmony achieved by using tints and shades of only one color.

Monophoto—phototypesetting machine utilizing the principles of the Monotype.

Monotype—machine that casts individual pieces of type and assembles them into justified lines.

montage—single photograph produced by using several negatives or parts thereof.

mordant—any corroding substance used in etching printing plates.

morgue—collection of reference material for a newspaper or an artist.

mortise—opening cut in a printing plate for the insertion of type or other typographic material. An opening cut through lines of type for inserting other lines, illustrations, or ornaments. Formerly a mortise referred only to the area left open by cutting a rectangle out of a corner of an engraving. Today an internal mortise is one cut into the body of an engraving. Mortises may be, but rarely are, irregular in shape.

mosquitos—non-decorative elements such as trademarks, pictures of plants or founders, etc., that must be used on a letterhead.

ms. or mss.—manuscript.

Munsell system—method of designating colors by numerical gradation.

mutton—mutt, an em quad.

negative—photographic film on which tonal values are reversed so that appearing black on the original is white or transparent, and vice versa.

news line—portion of a composing room devoted to setting editorial matter. Especially linecasters setting such material.

newsprint—low-quality, weak paper commonly used to print newspapers.

nickeltype—electrotype (*which see*) faced in nickel instead of copper.

nicks—parallel grooves in the side of a piece of foundry type to identify it by font.

no-orphan—orientation layout system (*which see.*)

non-distribution—system of typesetting in which all used typographic matter is remelted instead of being distributed for reuse.

Novelties—Ornamented type.

nut—an en quad.

Oblique—letters, other than Romans, which slant to the right.

oblique axis—layout pattern in which type blocks are tilted off the perpendicular or set in a tilted parallelogram.

oblong—rectangle of 2×3 dimensions.

occult balance—dynamic layout (*which see*).

official envelope—Number 10, one which takes an $8\frac{1}{2} \times 11$ letterhead folded twice.

offset—offset lithography, printing process in which an image is lithographed or letterpressed onto a rubber blanket from where it is transferred to paper. Also, as off-set, the undesirable transfer of ink from one printed sheet to another.

Old English—Black Letter.

Old Style numbers—those in which the 3, 4, 5, 7, and 9 project below the baseline.

Old Style Roman—letterform distinguished by bracketed serifs, minimal difference between thick and thin strokes, and bowls that are on axes off the perpendicular.

one-up—printing one impression of a form at one time. By using duplicate plates, jobs may be printed two-up or even in greater numbers in one impression.

onionskin—manifold paper.

opacity—that quality of paper that prevents printing on one side of sheet from showing through to the other.

opaque—to paint out unwanted shadows or other detail in the platemaker's negative.

optical center—point 10 per cent above the mathematical center of a page or layout.

orientation layout—buddy system or no-orphan system, whereby every element in a layout aligns with at least one other element.

Ornamented—race of type in which the basic form is embellished or extremely altered.

Outline—Ornamented letter with only its outline defined.

overflap—protective cover of tissue and/or kraft over a piece of platemaker's copy.

overlay—transparent plastic flap over art work providing mechanical color separation.

overwire—spiral binding concealed by the cover.

Oxford rule—printing element that produces two parallel lines, one thick and one thin.

oxidation—process whereby ink dries.

Ozalid—photocopying machine used to produce cold-type proofs.

packing—layers of paper between the impression cylinder and the tympan upon which paper rests during printing. Manipulation of packing to assure a perfect printing surface is called makeready.

padding—simple method of binding paper by coating one edge of the sheets with flexible adhesive.

page proofs—sample impressions of a sheet of printing which are checked for errors. They may consist of one or several pages all on one sheet.

pagination—arranging type so it will print pages in proper sequence.

painting-up—method of preparing a one-color original to be used as copy for two-color plates.

paragraph openers—typographic elements to direct the reading eye to the start of a paragraph, usually without indenting.

paste-up—process of affixing elements into position for engraver's copy. Also, the copy so produced.

patrix—mold that casts right-reading, instead of mirror-image, type used for dry offset (*which see*).

pebble—finish of paper with tiny surface dimples.

perfecting press—rotary printing two sides of paper in one operation.

perfector press—flatbed utilizing perfecting principle.

photocomposition—typographic material produced and arranged photographically instead of by using metal type and engravings.

photoengraving—printing plate produced by photochemistry for relief printting.

photogelatin—collotype, a lithographic process using unscreened gelatin plates to make continuous-tone reproductions.

photography—writing with light, utilization of the action of light upon sensitive emulsions that change color or density, in order to produce pictures or printing plates.

photogravure—form of intaglio printing that does not use a screen but projects light between minute granules of resin.

Photon—phototypesetting machine.

Photostat—a photocopy.

phototypesetting—photographic production of composition by a keyboard.

pi—as a verb, to mix up type. As a noun, type so disarranged.

pica—lineal measurement of 12 points. Commonly but incorrectly called an em (*which see*). Also 12-point type.

piece fractions—those produced by combining two linecaster matrices.

pigment—substance which provides the color in ink.

planer—block of flat wood used to press type in a form into a perfectly flat printing surface.

planographic—lithographic.

plastic binding—method of loose-leaf binding.

platen—flat surface upon which paper rests when it comes in contact with printing surfaces. Also short for platen press.

plates—flat smooth pieces of metal which have been treated to create a printing surface. For offset, paper plates are often used.

ply—one of several pieces of paper pasted together to make Bristol board or similar stock which is then designated as 3-ply, etc.

point—unit of printer's measurement, .01384 inches, for practical purposes, $\frac{1}{72}$ inch. Also any punctuation mark.

porcelain—blotting paper to which a sheet of coated stock has been pasted.

pot—receptacle on a casting machine which stores molten metal.

precipitation—method of drying ink by causing certain of its components to solidify.

preface—formal statement by the author that precedes the text of a book. As opposed to a foreword, written by another person.

preliminaries—those portions of a book which precede the text itself.

primary colors—red, blue, and yellow.

primary letters—those lowercase characters which have no ascenders or descenders.

primary optical area—focal point, that point in or near the upper left corner where the reading eye first looks at a page or advertisement.

printers—men who prepare composition for, or actually perform, imprinting operations. Also machines which produce typewritten copy by electrical impulses, either independently or in conjunction with reperforating machines, as Teletype machines.

printer's devil—apprentice or helper in a printing shop, so named because early printers were believed to owe their craft to a pact with Satan.

printmaking—that part of the fine arts concerned with producing original works by printing methods.

prints—fine arts such as etchings, lithographs, etc., produced by various printing processes.

process color—a printing method that duplicates a full-color continuous-tone original copy by means of optically mixing primary colors.

progressive proofs—progs, proofs of each plate used for process color printing, singly and in combination with the others.

proofreader—printer charged with responsibility of verifying that type perfectly reproduces the copy or manuscript.

proofs—sample impressions of composition and engravings produced for inspection for errors. (*See* galley, repros, first revise, progs.) As a verb, to produce such an impression by "pulling."

ProType—manually operated machine for setting cold type.

prove—to pull a proof.

pyramid—placement of ads on a newspaper or magazine page.

pyramidal—layout pattern that arranges elements in a regular or inverted V shape.

quadrant make-up—layout pattern in which the page is divided in quarters, each designed independently of the others.

quadrat, or quad—blank printing unit to create spacing. (*See* em and en.)

quoins—toothed metal wedges used to hold printing elements tightly in chase.

railroad—to hurry copy through a composing room by eliminating or scanting proofreading.

rattle—stiffness of paper characteristic of bond.

readability—that quality which affords maximum ease and comfort in reading over a sustained period. (*See* legibility.)

reading rhythm—regular, comfortable motion of the reading eye.

rectangular—layout pattern in which the total area is subdivided into smaller units which have harmonious relation to each other.

reducer—solvent of the negative image on a photographic negative.

references—material at the end of a book which expands upon, but is not a part of, the basic text.

register—matching of impressions of color plates on a printed sheet. Loose register is that in which tight juxtaposition is not necessary. In hairline register two color areas meet precisely. In overlap register one color overprints the adjacent one by a small but definite margin.

register marks—devices, often a cross imposed upon a circle, printed on color work to facilitate moving plates into perfect register.

reglet—wood strips used for spacing. Sometimes, a 1-pica metal spacing strip.

reperforator—machine, actuated by electrical impulses, that perforates tape used for automatic typesetting.

replate—to rearrange elements in a newspaper page and prepare a new stereotype mat and plate, often while an earlier plate is still being printed.

reproduction proof—repro, that produced with great care, usually on glossy paper or acetate, then photographed to make printing plates.

reverse—printing plate which gives the effect of white letters on a black background.

rhythm—flowing movement of the reading eye through a layout.

right side—felt side of paper (*which see*).

ring binder—most common form of loose-leaf binding in which sheets are fastened by two or more rings through pre-punched holes.

ripple—finish of paper.

rising initial—one that aligns with smaller body type at the baseline. (*See* initial.)

roll a mat—to make a stereotype matrix by impressing a flong upon a printing form by means of a roller or by direct pressure.

Roman—family of type with serifs and with an appreciable difference between thick and thin stroke. Subdivided into Old Style and Modern (*which see*). Also, incorrectly, upright type as opposed to slanting, or Oblique.

ROP—run of paper, color printed in a newspaper without the use of special presses. Also, ads not in preferred position.

rotary press—letterpress in which paper, fed from a continuous roll, is printed as it passes between a cylindrical impression surface and a curved printing plate.

rotogravure—commercial intaglio printing on endless rolls of paper.

rough—dummy, in sketchy technique, which shows only masses, no detail.

routing—removing non-printing metal from a printing plate by grinding it away mechanically.

rule—type-high typographic element that prints a line or lines.

running head—name of a book and sometimes title of chapter at the head or foot of each page.

S-pattern—classic layout which produces superior reading rhythm. The reverse-S is a frequently used variation.

saddle stitch—saddle wire, method of binding by inserting staples or stitches along the fold of a page.

Sans Serif—race of type without serifs and of monotonal strokes.

scaling—determining dimensions of a picture which is enlarged or reduced from those of original art.

schedule—all the headlines used by a newspaper.

scorcher—equipment that forms a stereotype flong into a curve and drives out excess moisture prior to casting.

scratchboard—white paper coated with black ink which is scratched away to show the paper in white lines. Also the picture so produced.

screen—intersecting lines on a glass plate through which a projected continuous-tone original is broken into a dot pattern. The number of lines per lineal inch, as 55-line screen, indicates the fineness of the engraving. Also a tint block with a fine dot pattern.

scribed lines—those produced by scratching lines in the platemaker's negative instead of ruling them on original copy.

Script—race of type resembling handwriting in which letters are connected, as opposed to Cursive in which letters do not join.

Second Coming type—studhorse type, biggest and blackest headline, type reserved for use on epochal news stories.

secondary color—violet, orange, green, produced by mixing two primary colors.

self-cover—book in which the paper used for regular pages also makes the cover.

series—subdivision of a family of type consisting of all sizes of a particular letterform.

serifs—tiny finishing strokes at the end of main strokes of letters.

serigraphy—silkscreen printing, method of reproduction using stencils.

set—measurement, in points, of the capital M of a font. The collective set width of a font is measured as the lowercase alphabet length. Most commonly used to measure fonts used for automatic typesetting.

set-off—off-set (hyphenated to avoid confusion with offset printing), smudging caused by transfer of ink from one printed sheet to another.

sewed-case cover—binding process identical to a sewed soft cover (*which see*) except that its cover is stiffened with boards.

sewed soft cover—binding process in which saddle-sewn signatures are fastened to each other and to a soft cover.

shade—variation of a color by adding black.

shaded—form of Ornamented letter in which a white line runs near one edge of the strokes or in which the strokes are toned by a regular pattern of lines or dots.

shadow rule—line which appears gray because of the dot pattern within it.

shadowed—form of Ornamented letter in which a stroke or decorative element runs outside the letter proper.

sheetwise—printing one sheet of paper at a time.

shell cast—comparatively thin stereotype plate which is mounted on base to bring it to type-high, as opposed to type-high casting which is cast to the proper thickness.

shoulder—space on the body of a slug or foundry type which provides for descenders and to separate successive lines. Also that non-printing area surrounding the neck of type. Also a depressed ledge of metal that surrounds printing detail in an engraving.

show-through—visibility on one side of a sheet of printing done on the other side or another sheet.

side wire—side stitch, method of binding by inserting staples or stitches from the outside of folded sheets of paper, parallel to and near the fold.

signature—group of pages printed on one sheet of paper so they will fold into proper sequence.

silhouette—form of halftone in which the entire background is removed.

silverprint—photocopy used as a proof of cold type.

sizing—gluey substance added to paper to create a smooth writing surface and to make it resistant to moisture.

slant—variation of the basic letterform to create Italic or Oblique characters, slanting to the right. Those which tilt to the left are called backslant.

slipsheet—method of preventing set-off by inserting a blank sheet of paper between printed ones.

slug—line of composition produced on a linecaster. Also a spacing unit, usually 6 points but sometimes thicker. (*See* ledding.)

small capitals—s.c., letters in the form of capitals but in x-height.

sock—excessive pressure in imprinting.

solvent—liquid in which is dissolved or suspended the pigment of ink.

spaceband—steel device consisting of two sliding wedges which expand to equalize space between words on machine-composed slugs.

spacing—separation between words or letters in type. Wordspacing is that between words; letterspacing, between letters. Optical letterspacing is arranging type characters so the apparent areas of white space are more equally distributed than by mathematical means. Proportional spacing is the ability to assign, on a typewriter, varying space for thick and thin letters.

spine—backbone (*which see*).

spiral binding—fastening of pages by threading a continuous spiral of wire through pre-punched holes.

split fountain—technique for printing two colors at one time by dividing the ink fountain on a press.

spot color—flat color (*which see*).

spots—typographical decorative units.

spray—method of preventing set-off by spraying freshly printed sheets with a liquid which crystallizes to keep the succeeding sheet from coming in contact with the ink.

spur—serif-like projection from the short vertical stroke on some forms of the G.

Square Serif—race of type in which serifs are the same weight, or heavier than, the main strokes.

stage and re-etch—method of correcting a photoengraving by protecting certain areas (staging) and subjecting others to further action of acid.

stamping—printing by impressing type through metal foil and into the surface of the printed substance. Blind stamping uses no ink or foil.

steel engraving—printing plate made manually by cutting away non-printing areas on a metal plate, leaving only thin lines in relief.

stem—vertical stroke of a letter, especially those which also have a bowl or arms such as *b, d, p, q, k,* and *T*.

stereotype—process of casting a printing plate from a papier-mache mold. Also, the plate so produced.

stet—let it stand, proofreader's direction to ignore a change made inadvertently on the proof.

stick—composing stick (*which see*).

stock—the paper used for any printing job.

stock cover—book in which heavier paper is used for the cover.

stone—imposing stone, table, once of actual stone, now of metal, on which forms are assembled.

stoneman—printer who assembles typographic elements into advertisements and pages.

stone proof—beaten proof, rough impression of a printing form produced by placing paper over the inked form and impressing it with a flat block of wood which is pounded with a mallet.

straight matter—body composition as opposed to display, set in rectangular columns and without typographic variations. Editorial matter as opposed to advertising.

strip test—method of determining the direction of grain in paper.

stripping—peeling the thin emulsion off an engraver's negative and positioning it onto a flat or combining it with another piece as in making combination cuts.

Striprinter—a machine for setting cold type in display sizes.

stroboscopic—strobe, a bulb that produces an extremely brief but brilliant burst of light.

stylus—needle-like instrument used to cut plastic shading film. Also, the pyramidal piece of metal that burns dot patterns into a Scan-a-graver plate.

substance—weight of 1,000 sheets of paper in a basic size, that varies among categories of paper stock.

super-calendered—super, paper which has been given a high gloss by repeated pressure between metal rollers during manufacture.

syllabary—method of writing in which a character represents an entire syllable.

symmetrical—layout pattern consisting of two vertical halves which are mirror images of each other.

synthesis—process of creating all colors of the spectrum by printing only three primary colors.

T-harmony—complements and a third, harmony achieved by using two complementary colors plus one that is at right angles to a line drawn between the first pair on a color wheel.

tail—lower portion of the *g* and the projection on *Q*.

tape—perforated paper, in narrow rolls, which directs the action of automatic typesetters.

tempera—poster paint, opaque, water-soluble paint.

Tenaplate—plastic molding substance used to make electrotypes.

terminal—end of a letter stroke that has no serifs or finials.

tertiary colors—those produced by mixing two secondary colors.

Text—Black Letter, race of type based on the handwritten form of the Roman alphabet as developed in Germany. Also (not capitalized) editorial straight matter.

text type—body type.

thermography—process of applying resinous powder to fresh ink on a printed sheet, heating it to melt, then solidify in simulation of intaglio engraving.

thin space—copper spacing material much smaller than spaces or quads.

30-dash—mark that indicates the end of a story. Referring to the journalistic practice of ending a telegraphed story with -30-, probably a version of XXX.

Thompson Caster—machine for casting individual pieces of type.

thumbnails—small and very sketchy dummies. Also, half-column portraits used in newspapers, also called porkchops.

tied letters—ligature (*which see*).

tint—variation of a color produced by adding white.

tint block—screen, printing plate used to produce a color area that carries no detail, usually to be overprinted by a darker ink. When the tone of a tint block is lightened by a dot pattern, it is called a screen.

title lining—system which assures a common baseline for all title fonts in the same point size. Title letters are all caps and thus no room need be provided on the body for descenders.

title page—first full page of a book, bearing its name and that of the author and publisher.

toenail—quotation mark.

tone value—intensity of a color or a mass of type, as compared to black, white, and gray.

tongue cover—looseleaf binding in which binding posts are concealed by a flap folding over from the cover.

tooth—texture of paper particularly receptive to pencil or crayon.

totem pole—vertical axis layout (*which see*).

Transitional Roman—that variation of the race of type which combines the characteristics, in varying degree, of Old Style and Modern.

transposition—common typographic error in which letters or words are not correctly placed, as "hte" for "the," or "The Spangled Star Banner."

triad—harmony achieved by using three colors, equidistant from each other on the color wheel.

trimetallic—offset plate combining aluminum, copper, and steel or zinc.

TTS—Teletypesetter, device actuated by perforated tape, to operate keyboard of a linecaster.

two-tone paper—coated stock with different color on each of its two sides.

tympan—sturdy paper that covers the packing (*which see*) on a letterpress.

type-high—.918 inches, the distance from the foot to the face of a type character, linecaster slug or other printing material.

type metal—alloy of lead, tin and antimony.

Typesetter—(ATF), phototypesetting machine.

typographic errors—typos, mistakes made by the compositor.

typography—basic plan for the use of type, as contrasted to layout, which is the application of such a plan to a specific circumstance.

Typro—machine for producing cold type in display sizes.

u. & l.c.—upper and lowercase, capitals and small letters.

undercutting—action of acid as it cuts sideways, instead of only downward, in etching photoengravings.

underlay—underprinting, printing in a light color over which other elements are printed in darker ink. An underlay varies from a tint block in that there need be no definite relationship between the area of the former and that of the overprinting.

underlines—explanatory type matter that accompanies a picture.

underpinning—low metal slugs that support the overhanging portion of a Ludlow slug.

universal fractions—those designed to harmonize with all families in a type race.

upper case—capitals.

Vandyke—photocopy used as a proof of cold type.

Varityper—typewriter which produces different type styles with only minor adjustment. It can produce justified composition semi-automatically.

vehicle—liquid that carries the pigment in ink.

Velox—screened photographic print.

vertex—juncture of diagonal strokes in letters such as V and the lower ones in such letters as W and M.

vertical axis—layout pattern in which elements align at left or right with a perpendicular line, real or imaginary.

vignette—form of a halftone in which the tone of the engraving blends almost imperceptibly into the white of the paper.

warm—colors which seem to move forward in the reader's vision, usually reds, oranges and some yellows.

watermark—design pressed into paper while it is still wet during manufacture.

wave rule—printing element that produces a regularly undulating line.

web-fed—press that prints from a continuous roll of paper.

weight—variation of a basic letterform such as Light, Bold, etc., created by varying the width of the strokes. Also, weight of 500 sheets of basic-size paper. (*See* substance.)

wet printing—process of printing all process colors without waiting for any to dry.

white line—wood engraving (*which see*).

widow—short line of type. Some designers consider as widows only those lines shorter than a quarter of a full line.

width—variation of a letterform to create such forms as Condensed, Extended, etc.

wire loops—a method of loose-leaf binding.

wire side—wrong side, that side of paper which has rested on the wire screen during manufacture. As opposed to felt, or right, side (*which see*).

woodcut—printing plate made by carving relief masses into the grained side of a plank.

wood engraving—white line engraving, printing plate made by carving fine relief lines into the end grain of a plank.

wordspacing—that between words.

work-and-tumble—system similar to work-and-turn (*which see*) except that the sheet is turned so a new edge meets the grippers.

work-and-turn—w&t, a system of printing both sides of a printing piece on one side of a sheet, then turning it, so its gripper edge remains constant, and printing on the reverse side. Two sides are thus printed by one impression.

work-up—unwanted deposit of ink caused when pressure forces quads and spacing material upward to meet ink rollers and the paper.

wove—a finish of paper which resembles that of tight cloth.

writing—kind of paper with a smooth surface, sized to prevent ink from being absorbed into the fibers.

wrong font—typographic error in which a letter of another face is used.

X—Itlx, common abbreviation for Italics.

x-height—that of primary letters such as a, o, m, and x.

x-line—mean line, that which marks the top of primary letters.

Xerography—inkless printing method utilizing static electricity.

Zinc—metal most commonly used for photoengravings, also the engravings themselves.

Zip-a-Tone—plastic sheets imprinted with regular patterns to achieve tones in line cuts.

Index

Absorption, 259
  of light, 193
Accent face, 55
Accordion fold, 271
Acetate, 206, 225
Achromatic color, 193
Ad alley, 32
Agate, 36
Albumen plate, 222
Alphabet:
  Arabic, 14
  Caroline, 17
  Etruscan, 15
  Greek, 12, 15
  Hebrew, 14
  newly created, 19
  Phoenician, 11
Alphatype, 241
American Institute of Graphic Arts, 54
Andre, Johann, 221
Anheuser-Busch Brewing Company, 221
Aniline ink, 259
Apex, 37
Aquarelle, 235
Aquatint, 231
Aquatone, 235
Art lining, 39
Artype, 94, 241
Ascender, 37
Athens Daily Acropolis, 14
Author's alterations (AA), 83

Backbone, 129, 273
Back up, 280
Bank, 33

Barnum, P. T., 24
Baseline, 37
Basis size, 256
Baskerville, 54
Bauhaus, 23
Ben Day, 94, 159, 209
Beton, 25
Bewick, Thomas, 154, 229
Bible:
  Authorized Version, 16
  Gutenberg, 5
Bimetallic plate, 223
Binder, ink, 258
Binding posts, 274
Blackman, Barry, 160
Blake, William, 230
Bleed, 265
Blend, 280
Blind embossing, 261
Blueprint, 226
Bodoni, Giambatista, 27
Boustrophedon, 14
Boxes, sideless, 121
Brevier, 36
Brightype, 244
Bristol board, 251
Broken package, 256
Bronzing, 261
Brownprint, 226
Bruning, 244
Brushes, paint, 92
Buddy system, 114
Bulmer, 36
Burin, 229
Burnishing, 164
Burr, 230

Cairo, 24
Caledonia, 28, 54
Calendered, 248
California job case, 29, 32, 41
Calligraphy, 24, 126
Carbon tissue, 215
Cardboard, 251
Caslon, 30, 54
Casting box, 177
Chandler & Price, 145
Chapter headings, 135
Characters per pica, 67
Chase, 33
Cheltenham, 29
Chicago Tribune, 147
China, printing in, 3, 9, 143
Chroma, 193
Chromatics, 193
Cicero, 35
Circulating matrix, 44
Clephane, James O., 44
Clymer, George, 144
Coated paper, 248
Cold type, 40
Collage, 183
Collotype, 234
Colophon, 133
Color:
    combinations, 197
        analogous, 197
        complementary, 197
        complements and a third, 199
        monochromatic, 197
        split complements, 198
        T-harmony, 199
        triad, 198
    fake, 204
    flat, 204
    process, 200
        four-color, 203
        standard, 202
        three-color, 201
        two-color, 203
    ROP, 209
    separation, 200
    spot, 204
    uses of, 195
    wheel, 197
Combination plates, 169
Combs, binding, 274
Common diagonal, 187, 189
Complementary colors, 197
Complements and a third, 199
Composer, Linofilm, 239
Composing room, 32
Composing stick, 33

Composition, 42, 283
Compositor, 32, 42
Comprehensive, 98
Consistency of ink, 259
Cool color, 194
Copper engraving, 213
Copyholder, 75
Copyreading, 74
Core, halftone dot, 224
Corona, 36
Corps, 35
Coster, 3, 31
Cottrell and Sons, 149
Cover, book, 129
Cover stock, 251
Craftint, 159, 161
Craftype, 241
Crop marks, 184
Cropper's L's, 191
Cunieform, 12
Currency, printing of, 213
Currier & Ives, 192, 231
Curved electros, 181
Custer's Last Fight, 221
Cutler-Hammer, 166
Cutting, paper, 264, 268

DaBoll, Raymond F., 126
Daguerre, L. J. M., 155
Dandy roll, 248
Daumier, Honore, 221, 231
Daye, Stephen, 144
Day-Glow ink, 260
Decal, 224
Deckle, 251
Deep-etch plate, 223
DePol, John, 228
Descender, 37, 57
Designer, 32
Devanagari, 2
Diagonal, reading, 103
Diagonal axis layout, 113
Diamond, 36
Diazo, 244
Didot, 35, 247
Die cut, 268
Display type, 40
Distribution, 43
Distributor bar, 47
Ditto machine, 288
Doctor blade, 216
Dot etching, 223
Dot pattern, 162
Double-revolution press, 146
Doubletone, 161

Dragon's blood, 156
Dropout engraving, 167
Dry mats, 178
Dry offset, 224
Drypoint, 230
Dultgen process, 216
Dummy:
 comprehensive, 98
 mechanical, 100
 rough, 95
 thumbnail, 94
Duotone, 203
Duplex, 47
Duplicate plates, 176
Duplicators, 287
Durer, Albrecht, 230
Dwiggins, W. A., 119, 120
Dycril plate, 182

Eggshell, 249
Egyptian type, 24
Egyptian writing, 11
Electra, 54
Electrotype, 180
Electro-Typesetting (ETS), 52
Elgramma, 175
Elrod Caster, 49
Elyria (O.) *Chronicle-Telegram*, 72
Em, measurement of composition, 36
Em quad, 33
Embossing, 261
En quad, 33
End paper, 130, 274
English finish, 250
Engravings:
 blow-up, 168
 combination plates, 169
 copper, 213
 dot pattern, 162
 dropout, 167
 facsimile, 167
 halftone, 162
 highlight halftone, 167
 line, 156, 160
 lines of screen, 163, 168
 mechanical, 171
 modified silhouette, 164
 modified vignette, 166
 outline, 164
 reverse plate, 168
 silhouette, 164
 special screens, 171, 172
 square halftone, 164
 steel, 213
 vignette, 164

Envelopes, 278
Etchings:
 dot, 223
 drypoint, 230
 fine art, 213, 230
Evaporation, 259
Expanded layout, 113
Eye fatigue, 57

Facsimile engraving, 167
Fairchild engraver, 171
Fake color, 204
Felt side, 249
Fifty Books of the Year, 53
Figgins, Vincent, 24
Filler, 248
Film positive, 215
Filters, engravers', 201
Finial, 37
Flat, 158
Flat color, 204
Flat writing, 250
Flexowriter, 242
Flock, 234
Flong, 177
Flopping the negative, 157, 223
Flying paster, 151
Focal point, 103
Folding, paper, 270
Font, 28, 35
Footnote signs, 62
Form, 33
Formal balance, 107
Former, 179
Fortune magazine, 217
FotoRex, 241
Fotosetter, 237
Foundry type, 40
Fourdrinier, 247
Fournier, 35
Fractions, 62
Franklin, Benjamin, 17, 27
Frasconi, Antonio, 230
Frisket paper, 234
Functional layout, 89
Functionalism, 119
Furniture, 34
Fust & Schoeffer, 133

Galley, 33
Galley proof, 75
Ganging, 268, 281
Ged, William, 177
Gennoux, Claude, 177

Geometric layout, 109
Giant Caster, 51
Golden Proportion, Line of, 101
Golden Rectangle, 101
Golt, Elaine, 128
Goss Press, 147
Goss Printing Company, 147
Gothic type, 23, 28
Goudy, Frederic, 27
Goya, Francisco, 230
Grain:
  of paper, 253, 267
  test for, 253
Granjon, 54
Graphic arts:
  definition, 5
  economic volume, 6
Graphs, 125
Graver, 229
Gravure, sheet fed, 214
Greeley, Horace, 44
Grid, Linofilm, 239
Gropper, William, 231
Grotesk type, 23
Guideline system, 75, 82
Gum, 220
Gutenberg, Johann, 3, 22, 133, 143

Hadego, 241
Hadrian, 25
Hairline, 37
Half-round, 179
Halftone engraving, 162
Halo, 224
Handwriting, 16, 22, 25
Hard copy, 238
Harmony, typographic, 55
Harper & Row, Publishers, 133, 202-
  203 insert
Headline:
  schedule, 55
  unit count system, 73
Headliner, 241
Hectograph, 287
Heidelberg Press, 149
Height-to-paper, 36
Herman, Casper, 222
High-etch, 224
Highlight halftone, 167
Hieroglyphics, 2, 11
Hoe Press, 146
Hoe, Richard March, 146
Hogarth, William, 230
Hot metal, 40
Hue, 193

IBM typewriter, 243
Ideograms, 9
Imposition, 150, 279, 281
Informal balance, 107
Initials, 56, 58
  inset, 56
  rising, 56
Ink:
  aniline, 259
  gravure, 216
  textile, 260
Inline, 25
Inserts, 61
Intaglio, 212
Intensity, 193
Intertype, 47
Italic type, 22, 39

Jackets:
  book, 129
  record, 128
Janson, 54
Japan, printing in, 2
Job shop, 32
Justification, 42, 58
Justowriter, 242

Karnak, 24
Kelly, Kenneth, 196
Kemart, 167
Kern, 33, 240
Key-line overlay, 206
Key plate, 205
Kicker, 55
Klic, Karl, 214
Klischograph, 176
Knopf, Alfred, 133
Koenig, Friederich, 145
Korea, printing in, 9
Kraft, 252
Kromolite, 167

Laid finish, 249
Lanston, Tolbert, 49
Layout:
  functional, 89
  organic, 89
Layout patterns:
  Christmas tree, 110
  classic, 109
  connotative, 113
  diagonal axis, 113
  expanded, 113

Layout patterns (*Continued*)
geometric, 109
informal, 107
jazz, 113
oblique axis, 112
occult, 107
oriented, 114
rectangular, 109, 111
symmetrical, 107
totem pole, 110
vertical axis, 110, 112
Leaders, 61
Ledding (leading), 34, 58
Ledger, 250
Legibility, 52
Letterheads, 137
Letterspacing, 59
Life magazine, 149, 201
Ligatures, 37
Line cut, 156, 160
Lines of force, 105
Lines, of halftone screen, 163, 168
Lining system:
art, 39
standard, 38
title, 39
Linofilm, 239
linoleum block, 230
Linomatic Tape System (LTS), 52
Linotype, 19, 45, 46, 229
slugs, 48
Linotype News, 104
Loading agents, 248
Logotype, 37
London Illustrated News, 155
London Weekly News, 154
Look magazine, 149
Looseleaf binding, 274
Louis XV, 35
Lower case, 17
Ludlow, 48
Ludlow Typograph Company, 244

Machine finish, 248
Mainz Psalter, 5
Majuscules, 17
Makeready, 149
Makeup man, 32
Manutius, Aldus, 22, 133
Margins, book, 101
Martin, Esteban, 144
Maskomatic, 167
Matrix, 44
border, 122
circulating, 45

Matrix (*Continued*)
disc, 238
ruling, 238
slides, 121
Matte paper, 183
Maximilian Joseph, King, 220
McKee Press, 149
Meanline, 37
Measurement, for copyfitting, 69
Mechanical bindings, 274
Mechanical dummy, 100
Mechanical engraving, 171
Mechanical engraving machines, 171
Mechanical separation, 206
Memphis, 24
Mergenthaler Linotype Company, 67
Mergenthaler, Ottmar, 44, 229
Metal paste-up, 240
Metal type, 3, 9
Mezzotint, 230
Miehle press, 149
Milwaukee Journal, 209
Mimeograph, 288
Minion, 36
Minuscules, 17
Modern Library, 133
Modern Roman, 27
Money, paper, 2
Monochromatic colors, 197
Monophoto, 239
Monotype, 40, 49
Monotype-Thompson Caster, 51
Montage, 183
Morgue, 94
Mortising, 166, 184
Mosquitos, on letterheads, 138
Munsell, A. H., 196
Munsell color system, 196

Napier, D., 145
National Bureau of Standards, 196
Negative:
engraver's, 156
flopping, 157, 223
New Echotah (Ga.) *Phoenix,* 17
New-England Courant, 17
New York Herald, 147
New York Journal, 209
New York Times, 217
New York Tribune, 44
News line, 32
Newsprint, 248
Nickeltype, 181
Niepce, Joseph, 155
Non-color, 199

Non-distribution, 50
No-orphan system, 114
Novelties, 25
Numbering, 270
Numbers, Arabic, 27

Oblique axis layout, 112
Obliques, 28
Oblong, regular, 101
Occult balance, 107
Office corrections, 83
Offset stock, 250
Old English type, 21
Oldstyle, 27
One-up, 281
Opacity, 252
Opaquing, 167
Optical spacing, 60, 118
Optimum line length, 56
Organic layout, 89
Oriental printing, 2, 9, 143
Oriented layout, 114
Origami, 270
Ornamentation, 119
Ornamented letters, 26
Ornamented type, 25
Ornaments, 121, 123
    Caravan, 120
    Troyer, 120
Outline engraving, 164
Outline letters, 25
Overflap, 183
Overlay, 205
    key-line, 206
Overwire, 275
Oxford rule, 121
Oxford University Press, 133
Oxidation, 258
Ozalid, 244

Pablos, Juan, 144
Packaging, 286
Padding, 272
Paige compositor, 44
Paint, 182
Painting up, 206
Paper master, 289
Paperback books, 137
Papyrus, 246
Paragraph:
    indention, 60
    starters, 60, 106
Paste-up, 225
    metal, 240

Patent Office, U. S., 30
Patrices, 224
Perfect binding, 272
Perfecting press, 147
Perfector press, 147
Perforating, 270
Photocopying, 99
Photogelatin, 234
Photography, 155
Photogravure, 231
Photolathe, 175
Photolettering, 241
Photon, 238
Pi, 43
Picasso, Pablo, 235
Pigment, 258
Planographic printing, 222
Plate:
    albumen, 222
    bimetallic, 223
    deep-etch, 223
    presensitized, 223, 289
    surface, 222
    trimetallic, 223
Platen press, 145
Plastic binding, 274
Point system:
    American, 34
    French, 35
Portfolio, 263
Presensitized plates, 223, 289
Press:
    Colt's Armory, 145
    cylinder, 145
    double-revolution, 146
    Goss, 147
    Heidelberg, 149
    Hoe, 146
    McKee, 149
    Miehle, 149
    perfecting, 147
    perfector, 147
    platen, 145
    rotary, 146
    stop-cylinder, 146
    Washington, 145
    web fed, 147
Primary color, 193
Primary letter, 37
Primary optical area, 103
Primer, 54
Print magazine, 173
Printer, 32
Printing, spread of, 3
Printing House, Craftsmen, International
    Clubs of, 133

Printmaking, 31
Prints, 235
Prisma, 25
Process color, 200
Progressive proof, 202
Proofreader's marks, 76
Proofreading:
  book system, 75, 82
  guideline system, 75 , 82
Proofs:
  beaten, 75
  dirty, 75
  first revise, 75
  galley, 75
  page, 75
  progressive, 202
  reproduction, 225
  stone, 75
Proportional spacing, 242
ProType, 241
Punctuation, 17

Quads, 33
Query author, 82
Quoins, 33

Race, type, 27
Radio Corporation of America, 261
Ramses, 24
Random House, 133
Readability, 52, 64
Reading rhythm, 57
Ream, 256
Rebus, 10
Record album jackets, 128
Rectangular layout, 109, 111
Reducer, 224
Reflection, of light, 193
Right-reading positive, 223
Register, 150, 205
  mark, 203
Reglet, 34
Reid, Whitelaw, 44, 229
Rembrandt, 230
Remington, Frederic, 209
Replating, 179
Reproduction proof, 225
Reverse plate, 168
Rhythm, 104
Right side, 249
Ring binder, 274
Rivera, Diego, 231
Roberts, Nicholas Louis, 247
Rocker, 230

Roman type, 21, 27
ROP color, 209
Rotary press, 146
Rotogravure, 214
Roto paper, 249
Rough dummy, 95
Routing, 167
Rubber plates, 182
Rubel, Anton, 222
Ruggles, Stephen P., 145
Rules, printing, 121
Ruling matrices, 238
Running head, 132
Ruzicka, Rudolf, 54, 119

Saddle stitching, 272
Saddle wiring, 272
Sans Serif type, 23
Saphir, 25
Sauer, Christopher, Jr., 144
Scan-a-Graver, 171
Scan-a-Sizer, 175
Scarab, 24
Schoolbook, 54
Scorcher, 179
Scoring, 269
Scotch, 28
Scraper, 231
Screen:
  halftone, 164
  as tint block, 208
  tints, 169
Scribing, 238
Script, 25
Secondary color, 193
Selective precipitation, 259
Self-cover, 275
Senefelder, Alois, 218, 231
Sequoyah, 18
Series, 28
Serifs, 29, 37
Serigraphy, 232
Setting-off, 152
Sewed case binding, 273
Sewed soft cover, 273
Shade, 193
Shaded letters, 25
Shading sheet, 158
Shading wheel, 288
Shadowed letters, 25
Sheetwise, 279
Shell cast, 177
Shrinkage, stereotype, 179
Side stitching, 273
Side wiring, 273

Signature, 264
Silhouette halftone, 164
Silk-screen, 232, 259
Silverprint, 226
Sizes, type, 28, 36, 39
Slant, 28
Slipsheet, 152
Solvent, 258
Sorensen, Inge, 160
Spaceband, 44, 59
Spacing, 57
Special screens, 171, 172
Spine, 129, 273
Spiral binding, 274
Split complements, 198
Split fountain, 280
Spoilage, 286
Spot color, 204
Square halftone, 164
Square Serif type, 25
Stage and re-etch, 164, 202
Stamping, 274
Stamps-Conhaim-Whitehead, 168, 169
Standard lining system, 38
Standard process colors, 202
Stanhope, Earl of, 144
Stock cover, 275
Steel engraving, 213
Stereotype, 146, 177
Stone, 33
Stone man, 32
Stop-cylinder press, 146
Stop-out varnish, 213
StripPrinter, 241
Strip test for grain, 253
Substance, paper, 256
sulphate, 252
Supercalender, 248
Surface plate, 222
Swash, 37, 39
Swipe file, 94
Syllabary, 18
Symbol writing, 10
Symmetrical layout, 107

T-Harmony, 199
Tabulation, 50, 61, 125
Teletypesetter (TTS), 51
Teletypewriter, 51
Tenaplate, 180
Tertiary color, 193
Texas, University of, Press, 133
Text paper, 249
Text type, 21

Textile inks, 260
Texture, 53
Thermography, 261
Thumbnail dummy, 94
Times of London, 145
Tinned, 180
Tint, 193
Tint block, 208
   silhouetted, 208
Tipping-in, 270
Title lining, 39
Title page, 130, 134
Tone, 193
Tongue cover, 274
Tooling, 167
Totem pole layout, 110
Toulouse-Lautrec, 220
Trajan, 21
Transitional Roman, 27
Triad, primary, 197
Trimetallic plate, 223
Troyer ornaments, 120
Ts'ai Lun, 246
Twain, Mark, 44
Two-tone paper, 253
Type:
   in irregular areas, 63, 124
   nomenclature of, 33, 37
   Oblique, 28
   Perpendicular, 28
   screened, 159
   series, 28
   sizes, 28, 36, 39
   specifier, 32
Type faces:
   Antique, 24
   Black Letter, 21
   Cursive, 25
   Egyptian, 24
   Gothic, 23, 28
   Grotesk, 23
   Italic, 22, 39
   Old English, 21
   Ornamented, 25
   Roman, 21, 27
   Sans Serif, 23
   Script, 25
   Square Serif, 24
   Text, 21
Type high, 36
Type metal, 45
Typesetter, ATF, 244
Typewriter type, 66
Typographic design, 101
Typographical errors, 84

Typro, 241

Umbra, 25
Undercutting, 157
Underpinning, 49
Unit count system, 73
Unitype, 43
Universal Press, 145
Updike, Daniel B., 7

Value, 193
Vandyke, 226
Varityper, 243
Vehicle, 258
Velox, 170, 226
Vellum, 249
Vertex, 37
Vertical axis layout, 110, 112
Victorian era, 23
Vignette, 164
Viking Press, 133

Warm color, 194
Washington Press, 145
Watercolor wash, 232
Watermarks, 248
Web, paper, 150
Web fed press, 147

Weight, 28
    paper, 255
Western Newspaper Union, 178
Whistler, James, 230
Whitcomb, Jon, 195
White line engraving, 154
Widow line, 33, 60
Wirephoto, 201
Wire loops, 275
Wire side, 249
Wood blocks, 143
Woodcut, 229
Wood engraving, 229
Word, characters per, 70
Work-and-tumble, 280
Work-and-turn, 280
World Publishing, 133
Wove finish, 249
WPA Federal Arts Project, 232
Wraparound plates, 182
Writing papers, 250

X-height, 37
X-line, 37
Xerography, 261

Zinc etching, 156
Zip-a-Tone, 94, 158

EDMUND C. ARNOLD, editor of *Linotype News*, has been closely involved with the graphic arts since he edited his first weekly at the age of 17, some thirty years ago. During World War II, he edited service magazines and newspapers, worked on the *Stars and Stripes*, and was decorated for service as a combat correspondent.

An associate editor of *The Quill* and *Canadian Weekly Editor*, Mr. Arnold writes weekly columns for *Publisher's Auxiliary* and is an active consultant on newspaper design and advertising to publishers throughout the world.

Since 1960, he has been professor and chairman of the graphic arts department of the School of Journalism at Syracuse University. He is also the author of PROFITABLE NEWSPAPER ADVERTISING and FUNCTIONAL NEWSPAPER DESIGN, winner of a Special George Polk Award for Distinguished Contribution to Journalism, 1957.

This book is set in 11-point Caledonia, duplexed with Italic, on a 13-point slug. Caledonia, a Transitional Roman, was designed by William Addison Dwiggins and is one of the most widely used American book faces.

Chapter headings are in 30-point and 14-point Bulmer. Chapter numbers are in 36-point Delphian. The index is set in Caledonia 8-on-9 and the glossary in Caledonia 10-on-11. It was composed by Brown Bros.; printed by Murray Printing Co.; and bound by Haddon Craftsmen.

HARPER & ROW, PUBLISHERS, INCORPORATED